Food, craft, and status in medieval Winchester

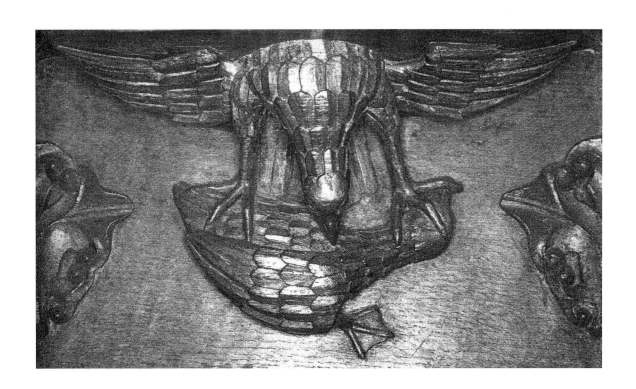

Food, craft, and status in medieval Winchester

The plant and animal remains
from the suburbs and city defences

Edited by
D Serjeantson and H Rees

With major contributions by

J Bourdillon, K M Clark, J P Coy, F J Green,
H Rees, D Serjeantson, and P Smith

Other contributions by
M Gomersall, K E Qualmann, G D Scobie, and K D Thomas

Winchester Museums
2009

Published in 2009 by Winchester Museums
Copyright 2009 Winchester City Council

British Library Cataloguing in Publication Data
A catalogue record for this book is available from the British Library
ISBN 978-0-86135-018-6

Produced for Winchester Museums by
Archetype IT Ltd, 12 Place Balmigère,
112200 Camplong d'Aude, France
www.archetype-it.com
email: info@archetype-it.com

Printed by TJ International Ltd, Padstow

Front cover: Based on the months from the Winchester Psalter: November, killing the pig (design by Mark Barden)
Frontispiece. Falcon, probably a gyrfalcon, with a teal. Misericord of the late 14th century, in Winchester College
Chapel (Photograph by M Laird; reproduced by permission of the Warden and Scholars of Winchester College)

Contents

List of figures

List of tables

List of appendix tables

List of contributors

J Bourdillon — formerly of the Faunal Remains Unit, Department of Archaeology, University of Southampton

K M Clark — formerly of the Centre for Human Ecology & Environment, Department of Archaeology, University of Southampton. Now freelance faunal specialist

J P Coy — formerly Head of the Faunal Remains Unit, Department of Archaeology, University of Southampton

M Gomersall — formerly Archives Officer with Winchester Museums

F J Green — formerly Environmental Archaeology Assistant with Winchester Museums, now Archaeologist, New Forest National Park Authority

K E Qualmann — formerly Head of Winchester Museums

H Rees — Curator of Archaeology, Winchester Museums

G D Scobie — Heritage Information Officer, Winchester Museums

D Serjeantson — formerly of the Faunal Remains Unit, now the Laboratory for Social Zooarchaeology, Department of Archaeology, University of Southampton

P Smith — formerly of the Faunal Remains Unit, Department of Archaeology, University of Southampton, now Education Officer with English Heritage Eastern Region, Cambridge

K D Thomas — Professor of Human Palaeoecology, Institute of Archaeology, University College London

Acknowledgements

The sites were excavated in many and varied conditions between 1972 and 1986, by past and present staff of Winchester Museums. Notable amongst the excavators were Marion Barter, Kathy Gordeuk, Ian Horsey, David McNickle, Patrick Ottaway, Gerry Koch, Jacqui Qualmann, Ken Qualmann, and Graham Scobie.

The excavations were largely funded by the Department of the Environment, but the support and cooperation of Winchester City Council, Hampshire County Council, and numerous private developers is also gratefully acknowledged.

The finds team was led by Charlotte Matthews and, later, by Gillian Dunn, with Sandy Mounsey. The editors express warm gratitude to them for their painstaking work at both the excavation and assessment stages of the project. In addition to author credits within the text, we would like to thank Malcolm Gomersall, Graham Scobie, and John Zant, whose much longer and painstaking work on the stratigraphic analysis has been reproduced in summary where relevant.

All the authors with the exception of Kate Clark were funded by English Heritage whilst carrying out the studies which contributed to this book, and the entire post-excavation project (of which this volume is part) was managed under the auspices of Winchester City Council. The editors would like to acknowledge the two organisations and their staff, especially Brian Kerr (EH), Ken Qualmann and, latterly, Richard Whinney (both of WCC), who kept up the momentum of the project while zooarchaeologists have come and gone.

The editors also thank the late Nick Bradford, John Crook, and Dave Webb for the photographs and Marshall Laird for permission to use his photograph of the misericord from Winchester College Chapel as a frontispiece illustration. Thanks are also due to Penny Copeland and Mark Barden for their line drawings.

Dale Serjeantson warmly thanks the following people for stimulating discussions on the provision and consumption of food in medieval England and Europe: Umberto Albarella, Chris Dyer, Barbara Harvey, Alison Locker, Naomi Sykes, and Chris Woolgar. She is also grateful to the people who have read and commented on different chapters at various times, in particular Simon Davis and Umberto Albarella.

Last but by no means least, Frank Green would like to thank John Bradfield, Megan Meyer and also the volunteers, especially Florence Hyde, who assisted with soil sample processing and retrieval.

Summary

This volume is part of an integrated series of studies of Winchester's archaeology. It provides a record and analysis of medieval environmental evidence from the less studied extra-mural areas of Winchester and assesses what these new discoveries add to the understanding of the city's past. The report includes the most comprehensive study of animal remains from a medieval English town published up to this time. The study is based on excavations from the 1970s and early 1980s, which, by examining sites on the defences and in the historic suburbs, enlarged the scope of previous extensive investigations within the city walls.

The volume consists of seven chapters, of which the first forms an overall introduction, covering the nature of the sample and how it was retrieved; the methodologies employed during analysis; and the influence of site and context on the interpretation of the dataset. The locations of the sites themselves and an outline of the structural sequences within them are linked to the changing history and archaeology of the medieval city as a whole. A small sample of molluscan remains from the western suburb is also discussed.

Chapter 2 deals with plant remains from all phases of all of the sites. The contents of four large charred grain deposits are presented in detail, and examined within the framework of the results from an extensive soil sampling programme. The implications, both for actual cultivation and use of plants in medieval Winchester, and for their survival in the archaeological record are assessed. Faunal assemblages are examined in a further three chapters which between them cover the period from the 10th to the 17th century AD, with the late Saxon and high medieval assemblages being particularly important. Inferences concerning inter- and intra-site variability are addressed through description of the remains as groups by context, feature, and phase: species-by-species discussion brings together observations concerning animal husbandry as a whole. A sixth chapter discusses a specific topic – the pathologies of the Winchester sheep and the implications.

Finally, all of the evidence is reassembled and synthesised in a seventh chapter which considers Winchester's medieval economy and society – the food, craft, and status of the title – through time and in relation to other towns and settlements, drawing on the documentary record. Throughout the volume, as here, description and discussion are backed up by the presentation of quantified data, in the form of tables and charts, both within the text and as appendices. In addition, the question of how far individual assemblages might represent a whole time period, site, area, or settlement is a constant theme.

Thus, this volume will be essential reading for all those concerned with the animals, plants, and environment of a medieval town, as well as being of value to urban archaeologists and to those with an interest in the history and archaeology of Hampshire. It sheds new light on the management of the animal and plant resources in and around one of England's foremost cities, as well as providing glimpses of everyday life in Winchester through its keeping, buying, consuming, and disposal of the familiar fowls and fish, plants and animals, over a period of almost a thousand years.

Résumé

Ce volume fait partie d'une série intégrante d'études de l'archéologie de Winchester. Il fournit un registre et une analyse des indices environnementaux médiévaux provenant des quartiers extra-muraux de Winchester et il évalue ce qu'apportent ces nouvelles découvertes à notre compréhension du passé de la ville. Incluse dans le rapport se trouve l'étude la plus complète des vestiges animaux provenant d'une ville médiévale publiée jusqu'à ce jour. L'étude est basée sur des fouilles des années 1970 et du début des années 1980, lesquelles, en examinant des sites situés sur les défenses et dans les faubourgs historiques, ont étendu la portée d'enquêtes antérieures approfondies à l'intérieur des murs de la ville.

Ce volume contient sept chapitres, dont le premier est une introduction générale, couvrant la nature de l'échantillon et la manière dont il a été récupéré; les méthodologies employées pendant l'analyse ; et l'influence du site et du contexte sur l'interprétation de l'ensemble des données. L'emplacement des sites eux-mêmes et une esquisse des séquences structurelles à l'intérieur des sites sont liés à l'évolution de l'histoire et de l'archéologie dans la cité médiévale dans son ensemble. Un petit échantillon de restes de mollusques provenant du faubourg ouest fait également l'objet d'une discussion.

Le chapitre 2 s'occupe des vestiges de plantes provenant de toutes les phases de tous les sites. Les contenus de quatre grands dépôts de grain carbonisé sont présentés de manière détaillée, et sont examinés dans le cadre des résultats d'un programme approfondi d'échantillonnage des sols. Les implications sont évaluées, à la fois pour la culture à proprement parler et pour l'utilisation des plantes dans le Winchester médiéval, et pour leur survie dans le registre archéologique. Des assemblages de faunes sont examinés dans les trois chapitres suivants, lesquels couvrent entre eux la période entre le 10ème et le 17ème siècle, les assemblages de la fin de la période saxonne et ceux du haut moyen-âge étant tout particulièrement importants. Les conclusions concernant la variabilité inter- et intra-site sont abordées par le biais de la description des vestiges regroupés selon le contexte et la phase ; une discussion espèce par espèce rassemble les observations concernant l'élevage dans son ensemble. Un sixième chapitre traite d'un sujet précis – les pathologies des moutons de Winchester et ce qu'elles impliquent.

Finalement, tous les indices sont regroupés et une synthèse est présentée dans un septième chapitre qui prend en considération l'économie médiévale et la société de Winchester – la nourriture, l'artisanat et le statut du titre – à travers le temps et par rapport à d'autres villes et peuplements, en utilisant le registre documentaire. Dans tout le volume, comme ici, la description et la discussion sont appuyées par la présentation de données quantifiées, sous la forme de tableaux et de chartes, à la fois dans le texte et dans les annexes. En outre, la question du degré auquel les assemblages individuels pourraient représenter une période entière de temps, un site, une région, ou un peuplement est un thème constant.

La lecture de ce volume sera donc essentielle pour tous ceux dont le travail porte sur les animaux, les plantes et l'environnement d'une ville médiévale, et sera également importante pour les archéologues urbains ainsi que tous ceux qui s'intéressent à l'histoire et à l'archéologie du Hampshire. Il porte un nouveau regard sur la gestion des ressources animales et végétales dans l'une des plus importantes cités de toute l'Angleterre ainsi qu'aux alentours, et il fournit également un aperçu de la vie quotidienne à Winchester à travers l'élevage, la vente, la consommation et la mise au rebut des volailles et des poissons familiers, ainsi que des plantes et des animaux, pendant une période de près d'un millénaire.

Zusammenfassung

Dieser Band ist Teil einer Serie von integrierten archäologischen Studien in Winchester. Es wird ein Inventar von mittelalterlichen Umweltfunden und deren Analyse erstellt, die aus den weniger erforschten Gebieten ausserhalb der Stadtmauern stammen, und es wird beurteilt, was diese neuen Ermittlungen zum Verständnis der Vergangenheit der Stadt beisteuern. Der Bericht enthält die umfangreichste Studie von tierischen Überresten, die bisher von einer mittelalterlichen englischen Stadt veröffentlicht wurden. Diese Untersuchung basiert auf Ausgrabungen aus den 70er und 80er Jahren, die vor allem Fundorte in den Verteidigungsanlagen und den historischen Stadträndern untersuchte, und somit das bisherige Untersuchungsareal innerhalb der Stadtmauern erheblich erweitern konnte.

Der Band besteht aus sieben Kapiteln, das Erste ist eine allgemeine Einleitung, die sich mit den Fundtypen, den Ausgrabungsmethoden und den analytischen Methoden befasst, und den Einfluss von Fundort und Umfeld auf die Interpretation der Fundsätze erwägt. Die räumliche Verteilung der Fundorte, und der Schichtenablauf werden mit der Geschichtsentwicklung und Archäologie dieser mittelalterlichen Stadt verknüpft. Ausserdem wird ein kleiner Fundsatz von Molluska aus dem westlichen Stadtrand diskutiert.

Das zweite Kapitel behandelt die Pflanzenreste aus allen Phasen und Fundorten. Der Inhalt von vier verkohlen Getreidefunden werden im Detail dargestellt und im Rahmen eines weitreichenden Programms von Bodenanalysen untersucht. Diese ermöglichen Aussagen über die Kultivierung und den Gebrauch von Pflanzen im mittelalterlichen Winchester, und deren Erhaltung im archäologischem Datensatz wird beurteilt. Die Untersuchung von tierischen Fundsätzen sind Thema von drei weiteren Kapiteln, in denen die Periode vom 10. bis 17. Jahrhundert n. Chr. erfasst wird, wobei die spätsächsischen und hochmittelalterlichen Funde von besonderer Bedeutung sind. Auf Problemstellungen bezüglich der räumlichen Fundstreuung innerhalb eines Areals und zwischen verschiedenen Fundorten wird eingegangen, indem die Überreste aufgrund ihres Umfelds, Eigenschaften und Phasen gruppiert werden. Artenspezifische Beobachtungen werden in einer Diskussion über die allgemeine Tierhaltung zusammengebracht. Im sechsten Kapitel wird ein besonderes Thema diskutiert – die Pathologien der Winchester Schafe und deren Interpretation.

Zum Schluss werden im siebten Kapitel alle Beweismaterialien zusammengefügt und man wendet sich dem Geschäftsleben im mittelalterlichen Winchester zu – Esswaren, Handwerk und Eigentumsrechte. Aufgrund von schriftlichen Quellen wird die chronologische Entwicklung, als auch der Vergleich zu anderen Städten und Siedlungen beurteilt. In diesem Band werden Darstellung und Diskussion durchgehend durch quantitative Daten unterstützt, in Form von Tabellen und Diagrammen, sowohl im Text als auch im Anhang. Die Frage inwieweit individuelle Fundsammlungen eine gesamte Zeitperiode, Orte, Gebiete oder Siedlungen repräsentieren können, wird als Thema durchgehend angesprochen.

Dieser Band kann allen empfohlen werden, die sich mit Tieren, Pflanzen und der Umwelt einer mittelalterlichen Stadt befassen, er ist auch wertvoll für Stadtarchäologen und Geschichtsinteressierte der Grafschaft Hampshire. Er gibt Aufschluss über die Handhabung von Tier- und Pflanzenfunden in und um Englands führende Städte und liefert einen Einblick in das Alltagsleben in Winchester über einen Zeitraum von fast eintausend Jahren, anhand von Beispielen von Tierhaltung, Handel und Verkehr, als auch die Abfallbeseitigung von alltäglichen Geflügel, Fisch, Pflanzen und Tieren.

1 Introduction

Background *by K E Qualmann*

This volume is part of an integrated series of studies on aspects of archaeological investigations carried out in the suburbs and on the defences of Winchester, mainly since 1972. In the previous year, the large-scale programme of city centre excavations directed by Martin Biddle for the Winchester Excavations Committee had been completed, and the Committee's Research Unit was concentrating its efforts on the publication of findings from these earlier investigations.

The continuing destruction of the buried remains of the city's past was, however, recognised to be a serious problem, and a Rescue Archaeologist – one of the first such posts in the country – was appointed on the establishment of Winchester City Museums, but seconded to the Research Unit Director. This arrangement enabled a full-time response to sites threatened by development to be maintained within the framework of an informed evaluation of on-going research.

Despite core support from Winchester City Council, substantial excavation grants from the Department of the Environment, Ancient Monuments Inspectorate, and help-in-kind from Hampshire County Council, mainly on road schemes, it soon became clear that resources were not available to respond to every development threat. Watching briefs were maintained on most sites, but controlled excavation had to be much more selective. After 1973, a policy for the selection of sites for excavation was developed. This was strongly influenced by the plans then being put forward for a partial ring-road, threatening important sites to the north and west of the city's defences, as well as housing schemes that would affect the eastern suburb and the Hyde area. At the same time as these potential threats to archaeology in the suburbs, conservation was the watchword in the city centre, and in this urban core such new development that did receive planning consent was quite small in scale.

Practical considerations were thus a major factor in the creation of a policy that stressed suburban excavation during the 1973–1980 period in Winchester. So too was the academic need to 'balance the sample' of previous work, which had focused largely on key sites within the area of the city walls. Equally, it was felt that certain types of new information might more cost-effectively be gained from the extra-mural areas at this stage in the archaeological understanding of the city. Martin Biddle summarised the results of this policy: whereas 80 per cent of the 1961–71 programme was undertaken within the city walls, more than 90 per cent of excavation between 1974 and 1980 was carried out in the suburbs (Biddle 1983, 103).

Changes in the organisation of local government, implemented in April 1974, further modified the base from which Winchester archaeology operated. The new District Council agreed to provide an archaeological service for its largely rural area of 159,000 acres (64,345 hectares), in addition to that already provided for the city at its core. A survey of the potential of Winchester District led to the establishment of a Sites and Monuments Record (SMR) for the area, investigation of key sites threatened by development, and a continuing commitment to the management of the archaeological resources of the district.

Initial publication proposals reflected the pattern of this work, with volumes planned to gather together new information on each of the extra-mural areas of the city, or from district projects. Neither of the two publication series already established for Winchester seemed a particularly appropriate vehicle for these new reports. *Winchester Excavations 1949–1960* was clearly designed to describe the work of a particular era, though a continuation of the title to cover later work was, at one stage, proposed. Similarly, *Winchester Studies* took as its basis Martin Biddle's excavations of 1961–71. The thorough research planned as part of this project, and its finite time scale, also made major new additions difficult to accommodate.

A great deal of preliminary work on this new series of reports was carried out in the 1970s and early 1980s, with substantial funding from the Department of the Environment, Ancient Monuments Inspectorate. In 1986, their successor body, English Heritage, commissioned an assessment and review of Winchester publication programmes. The result was a complete revision of previous proposals and the adoption of a more thematically-based project.

In 1989, nine publication proposals, in addition to the nearly completed 'western suburb' project, were submitted to English Heritage and approved. A tenth, on late Roman pottery from Winchester, was deferred for a final decision at a later date. Early in 1990, English Heritage recommended that the prehistoric sections of the 'western suburb' draft text should be formed into a separate publication. This work included most of the recent evidence for the Oram's Arbour Iron Age enclosure on the western side of Winchester. The remainder of the 'western suburb' sections were to be integrated with the other nine proposed publications (including this one) as appropriate.

During the 1980s, substantial new development took place within the town centre as a result of a changed political and economic climate, with the guiding principles set out in the draft Winchester Area Local Plan. New policies were established in an attempt to coordinate the response to the threatened destruction of archaeological remains. In practical terms, excavation in advance of development was made possible initially as the result of Manpower Service Commission Community Projects and later with the support of developer funding.

As the 1986–89 English Heritage assessment progressed, it was clear that some of this more recent fieldwork contributed significantly to the interpretation of the earlier government-funded 'core' sites. It was therefore proposed to include such information, amounting to about 15 per cent of the total project, in the new publication programme.

The scope of the work represented by the proposed titles varied quite significantly, from substantial volumes that integrated results from a number of sites, to short articles describing much more limited fieldwork projects. There were also substantial differences in the post-excavation research designs adopted for each. The broadly thematic approach meant that some excavation sites would be partially reported in more than one publication and that, as here, some classes of finds would be published independently from the excavation sites from which they were recovered.

Developments and restructuring of the programme since the early 1990s have allowed for a decision on the fate of the pottery reports: these are now all collected into one volume (forthcoming). It was also realised that the thematic basis of the proposed volumes meant that complete sequences for multi-period sites would be split up between them. It has therefore been proposed that archive summaries be published, but because most of this information is now available on the Winchester Urban Archaeological Database, this work has since taken a low priority. At the time of writing (2008), P6, P9, and P11 have been published (Rees *et al* 2008; Gomersall and Whinney 2007; Qualmann *et al* 2004) and P4 is in press (Maltby in press). A proposal to recombine P1 and P3 into one volume covering all aspects of Winchester's Roman suburbs is also under consideration.

In summary, the publications are as follows:

P1   The cemeteries of Roman Winchester
P2   The town defences of Winchester
P3   The suburbs of Roman Winchester
P4   Feeding a Roman Town: environmental evidence from excavations in Winchester, 1972–1985 (Maltby in press)
P5   All this of pot and potter: one and a half thousand years of Winchester pottery, excavations 1971–1986
P6   Artefacts and society in Roman and medieval Winchester: small finds from the suburbs and defences, 1971–1986 (Rees et al 2008)
P7   The Saxon and medieval suburbs of Winchester
P8   Hyde Abbey, Winchester
P9   The Hospital of St John the Baptist, Winchester (Gomersall and Whinney 2007)
P10   Food, craft, and status in Saxon and medieval Winchester: the plant and animal remains from the suburbs and city defences (this volume)
P11   Oram's Arbour: the Iron Age enclosure at Winchester (Qualmann et al 2004)
P12   Archaeological archive summaries

Introduction to this volume *by D Serjeantson*

This volume in the Winchester publications series describes the biological data – specifically the plant and animal bone remains – from the excavations in the medieval suburbs. The material dates from the 9th to the 18th and early 19th centuries. Most is from the western, northern, and eastern suburbs of the city, and a rather smaller quantity of material is included from some sites close to or just within the city defences. One seed assemblage from well within the western part of the town is also discussed. The excavations from which the seeds and bones were recovered (Table 1.1; Appendix 1) will be published in a separate study, but the relevant features and contexts are described below. This book does not deal with objects of bone and antler; they are described in the volume in the Winchester publication series on the Roman and medieval finds (Rees *et al* 2008).

The excavations took place from 1972 onwards, and the plant and animal remains were identified and analysed between the late 1970s and 1994. Five reports are brought together here, one of the plant remains and the balance of the animal remains. The reports were written between 1979 and 1995 and since then all of the authors have moved on. The chapters have not been updated, except to up-date publication references. However, the overview in Chapter 7 takes into account work up to 2001.

A number of assemblages of plant and animal remains from medieval urban sites in England have been published since the different chapters were completed, of which the most significant are those on Lincoln (Dobney *et al* 1996), Norwich: Castle Mall (Albarella *et al* 1997) and York (Bond & O'Connor 1999). New historical studies of the medieval economy and husbandry have also appeared. The discussion and conclusions of the various authors of this book would no doubt be modified if the reports were to be rewritten today; but even if some discussion is now out of date, publication is worthwhile so that the data can be made public.

Introduction to the Saxon and medieval suburbs of Winchester *by G D Scobie, H Rees, and F J Green*

Winchester is located at a point where two opposing spurs of chalk downland constrict the valley of the River Itchen. This narrowing forms the southern-most point at which the River Itchen can easily be forded and from pre-Roman times onwards the ford acted as a focus of local and regional communication. The western spur of chalk downland, St Paul's Hill, slopes gently eastwards down to the valley floor and northwards into the Fulflood Valley, through which a minor stream flows. To the south, the land drops more steeply into Sparkford Combe. On the lower slopes, the chalk is fissured by periglacial features filled with an orange-brown clay with flints. These are in turn sealed by a capping of orange-brown silty loam similar to

Table 1.1 Summary of sites with plant and animal remains discussed in this volume
(the site code and area excavated is also shown)

Site	Code	Area	Ch2	Ch3	Ch4	Ch5
Chester Road	CHR 76–80	eastern suburb			x	x
Crowder Terrace	CT 74–77	western suburb	x	x		
Hyde Abbey	HA 72	northern suburb	x			
	HA 74	northern suburb	x			
Henly's Garage	HG 84/85	city defences	x		x	x
27 Jewry Street	27 JS 84	city defences			x	
New Road	NR 74–77	western suburb	x	x		
St John's Street	SJS 76	eastern suburb				x
	SJS 81/82	eastern suburb				x
Sussex Street	SXS 76	western suburb	x	x		
	SXS 79	western suburb	x	x		
Trafalgar House	TH 74–77	within the walls	x			
Victoria Road	VR 72–80	northern suburb	x		x	x

brickearth. The higher slopes have been truncated to expose chalk bedrock, and, as a result, these areas are better drained.

Excavated sites in the western suburb were situated on this chalk slope, as were sites on the northern and southern city defences and the Trafalgar House site, the only intra-mural site that produced evidence considered in this volume. Sites in the northern suburb were at the base of the clay-capped Fulflood Valley running east–west towards the Itchen Valley to the north east of the town (Fig 1.1). There has been up to now little archaeological investigation of the southern suburb.

The top of the eastern spur, St Giles Hill, is relatively level and ends as a steep bluff to the east, now accentuated by a railway cutting. To the south, the hill drops steeply into Chilcomb Vale, while to the north, it slopes more gently to Winnall Moor. Higher up, the surface deposits are similar to those of the western spur. However, at the base of the steeper slopes, where the excavated sites of the eastern suburb and the eastern defences were located, they consist of hill wash. During the Roman period, the drainage pattern of the river through the eastern part of the town was altered to enable more space to be used for occupation (see, for example, Zant 1993, 78) and the natural soil at the eastern defences sites is the highly compact chalk-derived hill wash that formed the east bank of the River Itchen in the pre-Roman period.

All of the excavated sites were on chalk substrata, which partially accounts for the very good preservation encountered amongst some animal bone assemblages. Because of the presence in the northern suburb of the Fulflood stream, heavier clay soils were encountered at sites such as Hyde Abbey and Victoria Road. These, whilst not specifically waterlogged, preserved a wider range of plant materials, and also small vertebrate remains such as fish bones, in miner-

alised or only partially aerobic conditions, compared with the strata at sites such as Crowder Terrace and Sussex Street which are on the better drained soils. The modern water table was not encountered on any of the sites, although, of course, the local hydrology need not have been the same in antiquity as it is today.

The topography and general character of the Saxon and medieval town, its defences, and its suburbs have been described by Biddle (1976) and Keene (1985). The framework of the post-Roman city incorporated several inherited elements, the most important of which are the Iron Age Oram's Arbour defences, the Roman town defences and gates, and the long-distance approach routes. That portion of the Oram's Arbour defences that was located in the western suburb was retained in the early Roman period and remained a significant feature in the landscape for a considerable time afterwards. The New Road site produced evidence that this feature was not fully silted-up until the 12th century. About this time, a new ditch, defining the boundaries of the northern and western suburbs was dug. This boundary reused part of the line of the Iron Age defences (Keene 1985, 48, 67) but did not cross any of the excavated sites. The environment is indicated by the molluscs (see below) from a sequence of samples from the upper fills of Oram's Arbour ditch and from a medieval property boundary ditch which cut it.

Although the positions of the gates were quite similar in the Roman and post-Roman periods, the late Saxon street system within the defences shows little in common with the Roman pattern other than the approach to the ford (the High Street). By contrast, most of the principal streets in the western and eastern suburbs followed the lines of the Roman long distance approach routes. In the northern suburb, the Roman roads from Cirencester and Silchester were lost as they approached the city's north gate, but Hyde Street, the

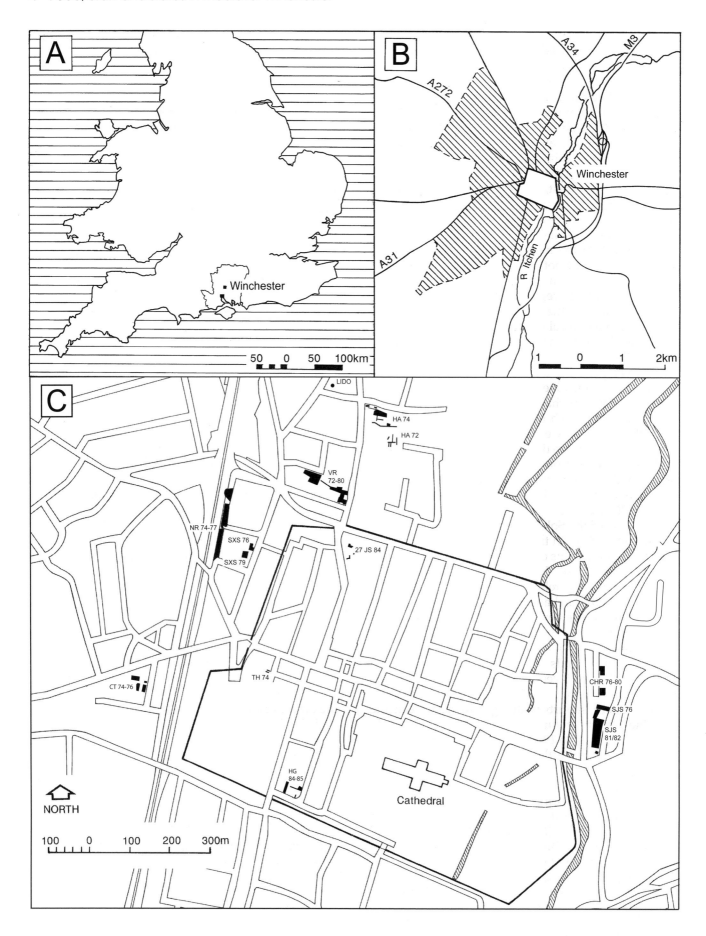

Figure 1.1   Map of Winchester showing the excavation sites referred to in the text (key to site codes in Table 1.1)
(Drawing by M Barden)

principal street of the northern suburb, was in position by the 10th century (Biddle 1976, 261).

It has been suggested that the suburban population was concentrated along the principal approach routes to the city (*ibid*, 263) and it seems likely that, in general, occupation was less intensive in the suburbs than within the walls. The western suburb is believed to have been older, and more intensively occupied than the northern suburb, the development of which was bound-up with that of Hyde Abbey (*ibid*, 265–6).

To a certain extent, the archaeological evidence could be seen to corroborate this. In the western suburb, large-scale excavation revealed a quantity of very well-preserved late Saxon deposits especially at Sussex Street. In the northern suburb excavation on a similarly large (if not larger) scale at Victoria Road showed the late Saxon deposits to be badly truncated but perhaps also to represent less intensive occupation. Occupation of the western suburb seems to have continued in medieval times on a similar scale to that of the late Saxon period, but its heyday was probably over by the middle of the 14th century. Victoria Road witnessed a period of decline in early medieval times followed by a massive increase in building activity somewhat later, perhaps at the end of the 12th or beginning of the 13th century. At some time during the 15th century, however, the medieval buildings at Victoria Road fell into disuse and were not replaced.

Little is known from documentary sources of the origins of the eastern suburb, but it is believed to have been demarcated by a boundary ditch by *c* AD 1208–09 (*ibid*, 264). In medieval times, the eastern suburb formed part of the Soke of the Bishop of Winchester (Keene 1985, 267). On the top of St Giles Hill was the site of the Fair, with its own independent street system (Biddle 1976, 286–8; Keene 1985, 1091–1132). Both truncation and the relatively smaller scale of excavation make the archaeology of the late Saxon and early medieval eastern suburb difficult to interpret. However, at least some of the sites there were occupied by buildings well into the post-medieval period and the quantity of finds of the later medieval period and the 15th to 16th centuries is witness to continued intensive occupation.

The western suburb is thought to have been the wealthiest of the suburbs, at least during the early Middle Ages (Biddle 1976, 265). There is some archaeological evidence for this amongst the group of sites considered in the current series of publications; all three of the best-crafted and unusual 'small' finds were recovered from sites in the western suburb – a late Saxon knife (Rees *et al* 2008, 317, catalogue no 2238), a late Saxon reliquary (Hinton *et al* 1981), and a medieval stylus (Biddle and Brown 1990, 731). However, in general, the excavated material culture of each suburb (including some discussed in this volume) holds much in common with that of the others during the late Saxon period, perhaps showing slightly more evidence of specialisation and diversification in medieval times, as made clear by other publications in the series and work in progress (Rees *et al* 2008; Gomersall & Scobie in prep – P7).

Molluscan evidence for the environment of the western suburb *by K D Thomas*

Post-Roman fill of Oram's Arbour ditch, New Road

Oram's Abour ditch was on ground that sloped to the east and to the north. A series of samples at alternate 10cm intervals were taken by Carol Keepax of the Ancient Monuments Laboratory. These are numbered with a 'CK' prefix. A long column sample was taken through the whole fill of the Iron Age ditch (CK1–CK18) (Table 1.2). The post-Roman part of the fill (from sample CK15 upwards) indicates open country around the ditch, but there is evidence for ploughing, or at least some disturbance of the soil leading to drier conditions – as suggested by the increased frequencies of *Vallonia excentrica*. The influence of human activity in this period may also be suggested in the increasing frequencies of *Trichia striolata*, generally regarded as a synanthropic species.

New Road boundary ditch

A second series of samples was taken through the fill of a late 12th- to early 13th-century property boundary ditch at New Road. The ditch was partly recut in the middle of the 13th century. Samples CK19–CK22 fall into the first phase and CK23–CK27 into the recut phase (see Table 1.2).

The first phase of the fill shows a progressive increase in the frequencies of shade preferring species from bottom to top. Open country species are never really abundant in this part of the ditch fill. Probably the area around the ditch at this time was covered by fairly dense vegetation which afforded plenty of shade. The nature of this cover is not clear; it could have been scrub but more likely was just wasteland overgrown with tall plants.

This is in contrast to the interpretation of the assemblages recovered from the recut ditch, which indicate open conditions with little vegetation cover. The shade-preferring component of the fauna is very weakly represented. The site was probably cleared at the time that the ditch was recut. The assemblages are probably indicative of bare soil under the plough and associated cultivation of crops. Towards the top of the ditch fill, the snail assemblages tend to contain higher frequencies of shade-requiring species; this may be more indicative of the vegetation growing in the ditch than of shaded conditions around it.

The archaeology of the sites discussed
by M Gomersall, F J Green, K E Qualmann, and H Rees

Retrieval

The period since 1972 has witnessed the evolution of archaeological techniques in Winchester (as elsewhere) and practices carried out in 1972 had com-

Table 1.2   Mollusca from Oram's Arbour enclosure ditch (CK15–CK18) and New Road boundary ditch (CK19–CK27)

	Oram's Arbour ditch				New Road ditch				New Road ditch (recut)				
	CK15	CK16	CK17	CK18	CK19	CK20	CK21	CK22	CK23	CK24	CK25	CK26	CK27
Pomatias elegans (Müller)	–	–	–	–	1	–	–	–	–	–	–	–	–
Carychium tridentatum (Risso)	1	–	–	–	1	–	–	–	–	–	–	–	–
Carychium sp.	–	–	–	–	–	2	–	–	–	–	–	–	–
Cochlicopa lubrica (Müller)	–	–	–	5	–	–	4	4	6	10	–	+	–
Cochlicopa sp.	7	3	6	9	–	–	–	9	9	8	2	–	2
Vertigo pygmaea (Draparnaud)	1	16	6	–	–	–	1	–	–	1	10	1	2
Pupilla muscorum (Linnaeus)	7	3	13	9	–	1	–	4	16	2	12	1	1
Vallonia costata (Müller)	12	72	–	27	1	3	6	11	27	28	26	6	9
Vallonia excentrica (Sterki)	61	–	32	37	2	3	1	4	31	10	7	2	2
Ena obscura (Müller)	1	–	–	–	–	–	–	–	–	–	–	–	–
Punctum pygmaeum (Draparnaud)	–	–	1	–	–	–	1	–	–	–	–	–	–
Discus rotundatus (Müller)	–	–	1	9	3	37	59	51	1	24	4	10	7
Vitrea contracta (Westerlund)	–	1	2	15	–	4	11	8	–	2	4	–	–
Nesovitrea hammonis (Ström)	5	–	–	–	–	1	1	–	2	1	–	–	–
Aegopinella pura (Alder)	–	–	–	–	–	–	–	–	–	–	–	–	2
Aegopinella nitidula (Draparnaud)	–	–	–	4	1	16	9	15	3	13	5	2	5
Oxychilus cellarius (Müller)	–	–	–	6	–	4	–	–	–	–	–	1	–
Oxychilus alliarius (Müller)	–	–	1	–	–	–	–	–	–	–	–	–	–
Oxychilus sp.	–	–	–	–	4	–	–	–	–	3	–	–	2
Limacidae	11	–	–	5	–	2	4	–	1	1	–	–	1
Cecilioides acicula (Müller)	16	52	171	163	5	6	24	18	30	29	80	63	18
Cochlodina laminata (Montagu)	–	–	–	–	–	–	–	–	–	–	–	–	1
Clausilia bidentata (Ström)	–	–	–	1	–	–	–	1	–	–	–	+	–
Cernuella virgata (Da Costa)	–	–	–	–	–	–	–	–	–	24	–	1	1
Helicella itala (Linnaeus)	11	5	3	4	–	–	–	–	3	–	1	1	1
Trichia striolata (C Pfeiffer)	10	3	10	64	15	31	33	25	32	57	45	13	37
Trichia hispida (Linnaeus)	55	38	13	21	5	6	4	9	26	33	25	2	5
Cepaea sp.	+	–	+	+	1	+	+	+	–	–	–	–	2
Helix aspersa (Müller)	+	–	1	3	2	4	2	7	2	7	+	+	4
Totals*	**182**	**141**	**89**	**219**	**36**	**114**	**136**	**148**	**159**	**224**	**141**	**40**	**84**

(* totals exclude *Cecilioides acicula*)

pletely changed by the 1980s. There were a number of problems in allocating time and resources to all the various investigation opportunities that became available during the period. This early problem has not disappeared; rather, it has grown worse as the dramatic rise in rescue archaeology throughout the country has been reflected here.

A number of the sites that produced environmental evidence reported in this volume were excavated under rescue conditions, especially after 1975. It should be stressed at the outset that, within a broad framework of 'best practice', the quality of the data recovered sometimes varies from site to site in a way that is difficult to quantify. Nevertheless, it will be clear from subse-quent pages that, where excavation under controlled conditions was possible, the principle of careful hand recovery of animal bones was adhered to in the vast majority of cases. Moreover, the soil sampling policy (which is described in more detail below), although it could not always be followed entirely consistently, has produced a useful complement of information on the botanical remains and bones of smaller animals. This programme of sieving has especially repaid the labour involved for pits in the eastern and northern suburbs where fish bone survived exceptionally well. The findings from these areas contrast strongly with those from pits where sampling was less extensive, in which the range of species recovered was small and partial. The utility of the samples has also been demonstrated in pits that had few fish bones, such as those at Chester Road in the 13th–14th centuries (Phase 53). These contained some of the smaller bones such as sheep phalanges, which are hard to recognise with the naked eye, and confirm that these anatomical elements are missing from the skeletal parts recovered because they were overlooked.

Sampling and Processing

Prior to 1974, soil samples were taken in order to augment the archaeological interpretation of particular deposits and also to recover environmental and economic data. It was also realised that significant information could be retrieved from well-preserved waterlogged deposits. A system of sampling for biological materials was devised by the Winchester Excavations Committee, directed by Martin Biddle. Soil samples were removed on a judgmental basis, and collections of readily identifiable botanical items such as nuts and fruit stones were also recovered by the excavators. Before 1974 these items were retained in separate organic finds sequences in a similar way to 'small' or other 'recorded' finds.

Processing of material from these earlier excavations by one of the present writers (FJG) was undertaken at the same time as the suburban excavations of the 1970s and 1980s were being carried out. This allowed the policy for sampling to be reorganised to include an enlarged range of deposit types, especially those that had the potential to inform the understanding of the wider environment and the economy of the suburban sites.

The sample sizes from the earlier period of excavation in Winchester varied depending on the volume of the context excavated and the preservation conditions encountered. In practice, the average and normal soil sample size was approximately five litres. In an attempt to ensure a degree of consistency, so that comparisons could be made between the predominantly intra-mural excavations prior to 1974 and those from the suburbs discussed here, a sample volume of five litres was chosen.

The proviso was that deposits of greater than 300mm thickness, or those that were in excess of 1m in surface area were to be sampled further on a routine basis. Thus, for every 100mm of depth and 100mm² of surface area, or both, it was recommended that further samples were to be taken by the excavators. The aim was to recover enough botanical material to allow reliable identification through aggregating the results from the individual samples. This was to ensure maximum retrieval of the range of species and at the same time to allow worthwhile assessment of any variation in density of botanical components within a single deposit in an attempt to begin to understand site formation process.

Further, the sampling programme allowed for removal of 100 per cent of specific deposits, for example large charred grain accumulations, again

using five litres as the basic sample unit. The objective was that analysis of the distribution of plant material through deposits would lead to a better understanding of the processes that had originally contributed to their formation. (Green 1979a, 17–38). Even in the early 1970s it was already clear that the principal range of cereal species was relatively well understood for the major periods in southern Hampshire and that more detailed questions of the evidence could and should be explored.

At the time that this process was implemented, it was then standard practice, especially on the larger prehistoric and Roman sites then being excavated, to remove very large individual soil samples, frequently to be processed in variations of the 'Siraf' seed machine. The formative work at Winchester experimented with such devices (Green 1979a, 307–09). This rapidly demonstrated the limitations of using such mechanical recovery devices to process the heavy clay-based and alluvial soils frequently encountered capping the chalk bedrock at Winchester (Green 1979a, 54).The five litre sample units were an ideal size for rapid laboratory processing. This involved 100ml of 100 vols solution of hydrogen peroxide per 2500ml of water, and 2500ml of sample.

Flots were collected in a 250-micron sieve and the resulting plant assemblages identified using a low-powered binocular microscope. Bones in both the flots and the residues trapped in the 1mm-mesh sieves were also sorted for analysis. The volumes of soil processed, the methods employed throughout each stage of processing, and the weights of the various organic and non-organic components of the processed sample were recorded on index cards, which now form part of the site archives.

Provenance

Few deeply stratified post-Roman deposits were encountered on the sites that produced environmental evidence discussed in detail in this volume. Almost all the material came from deep negative features, the vast bulk of which were pits. This is well-illustrated by the fact that over three-quarters of the hand-recovered animal bone from the western suburb was from pits whilst ditches, general layers, and structural features accounted for only around one fifth of the assemblage.

Whereas all the bone from the western suburb sites was quantified to archive level, the bone from the northern and eastern suburbs and the city defences was subject to assessment before some assemblages were selected for detailed study. Again, over three quarters of the material selected was from pits, and only just over and just under 10 per cent respectively from other negative features (ditches and cellars or quarries) and general layers. It may be of interest that no bone at all was selected from structural features, such as wall foundations, floor layers, postholes, and demolition deposits – because such assemblages were generally small and scrappy.

Phasing

It has been the policy of the Winchester Museums Archaeology Section to regard the fieldwork stage of any project as incomplete until the stratigraphic analysis has been carried out. This has been achieved in a fashion similar to that described by Biddle (1990, 14–18), by grouping contexts and/or features that can be shown to be stratigraphically contemporary. These groups or 'provisional phases' are the blocks from which is built the understanding of the development of the site through time and on which the wider interpretations of the site are based. Each of these phases is allocated a number, in the same way as contexts and features are during excavation.

This system has been of value in dealing with bulk finds such as the animal bones discussed in this volume, as it provides a means of grouping contexts, and thus enlarging the size of the sample to be studied, in a way that has an independent basis in the stratigraphic evidence. Phase numbers are therefore used freely in the following chapters to refer to parts of sites and groups of contexts. However, it has not always been necessary to describe or enumerate individual phases at publication level when discussing the sites themselves (Gomersall & Scobie in prep – P7) and, in these cases, the reader is referred to the site archives for detailed information.

Scope of the project

As has been outlined above, there are real differences in topography, settlement, and chronology between suburbs, and the grouping of individual excavations according to the area in which they were located is not merely a convenience for the purposes of publication. The sites belonging to the city defences sites are a disparate group, since the excavated areas often produced evidence of activity just within the walls of the city and it is these areas rather than deposits directly related to the defences themselves from which the best groups of finds were recovered. In addition, the sites were dispersed around the circuit of the defences to the north, east, and south. Thus, although the term has been retained in this volume, the sites can just as usefully be viewed individually.

Material from only one intra-mural site has been included in this volume, that at Trafalgar House. The work on the botanical remains was carried out by 1979, and since the site produced a large deposit of charred grain, it was felt that its inclusion would provide a useful addition to the sample to be studied.

The summary of sites in Appendix 1 includes only those that produced environmental evidence discussed in detail in this volume, but it should be reiterated that material recovered from many more excavations, watching briefs, and observations has not been deemed to warrant full publication. The method of assessment and selection of phases and contexts for detailed study is discussed further below, along with the more detailed interpretations of the individual

contexts and phases studied (Chapters 2–5). The sizes of the areas opened up for excavation at each site are given in Appendix 1, but it should be emphasised that archaeologically significant deposits were not necessarily encountered in every trench, and that it was not always possible to record those that were under controlled conditions. References to tenement boundaries throughout this volume follow Keene (1985).

The northern suburb: Hyde Abbey and Victoria Road

No bone groups were studied from Hyde Abbey, but the site produced some good botanical data. Evidence from these sites for late Saxon and early medieval occupation of the northern suburb is fairly limited. On the eastern side of Hyde Street and to the north of the Fulflood stream, sites later within Hyde Abbey (here, HA 72 and HA 74) were little used; only in Trench XII at Hyde Abbey (HA 74) were positive signs of occupation of this date recorded. At Victoria Road (VR 72–80), though, situated to the south of the Fulflood and the west of the street, evidence was recovered of properties fronting both Hyde Street (Trenches X–XV) and Swan Lane (Trenches I–VI; in medieval times, Beggare Lane). In Swan Lane, only the property boundary ditches survived later truncation, but in Hyde Street, ditches, pits, a timber building, and associated structures were recorded.

The building and the boundary ditches fronting Hyde Street at VR went out of use at some time in the 11th century at the latest, and were not replaced. Pits continued to be dug on the site after this, but in declining numbers until the mid- to late 13th century, when both the Swan Lane and Hyde Street frontages witnessed large scale building development.

Meanwhile, the construction of Hyde Abbey was sufficiently far advanced by 1110 to allow the move from the New Minster to take place (*cf* Carpenter Turner 1992, 16–17). The precise line of the monastic precinct is unknown, while documentary evidence suggests that it may not have been static (P8), and as a result its relationship to properties in Hyde Street is uncertain. Some of the Hyde Abbey trenches were located in or next to the south-western quarter of the abbey precinct. Excavations in 1972 (HA 72, Trenches I–IV), sampled an area on the eastern side of the inner courtyard, where traces of buildings, one of timber, and two possibly partly of masonry were recorded, together with a cobbled surface. These could be interpreted as ancilliary buildings ranged around the eastern edge of the courtyard.

Trench XII of the HA 74 excavations examined a small area well to the north and west, adjacent to the eastern side of Hyde Street and its junction with King Alfred Place. Here, a property boundary ditch of three phases located 2m to the east of the street was succeeded by a boundary wall in the mid-13th century. A timber building also stood on the site in the medieval period. This trench alongside Hyde Street was too small to elucidate fully the spatial relationships between the sites where the properties stood, the western edge of the abbey precinct, and the eastern edge of the street. The ditch recorded in HA 74, Trench XII, may represent the earliest demarcation of the abbey boundary and the timber building the abbey's earliest occupation. However, it is possible also that both predate it. What may have been the northern wall of the south-western quarter of the precinct was, however, recorded in HA 74, Trench XIII.

From the 13th century, the Hyde Street frontage at Victoria Road (X–XV) witnessed the construction and modification of several buildings, the use of external hearths and ancilliary structures, and the digging and infilling of pits in profusion. Around the middle of the 15th century, with the demolition of those buildings then standing on the site, activity declined until the 19th century. These developments were mirrored in Swan Lane (VR 72–80, Trenches I–VI); a timber building associated possibly with cultivation of a heavily rooted crop, was in use there from the mid- to late 13th century up to the mid-15th century, and a large feature to the east perhaps represented a cellar, cut and filled within the same time-span.

On the site of Hyde Abbey, the Dissolution of 1539 is marked by evidence for a subsequent period of gardening or horticulture in most of the excavated trenches. On one site, which did not produce any material discussed in this volume, this phase was followed by the construction of another building in the 16th century. The Bethel family, to whom the site had passed after the dissolution, is recorded as responsible for the erection of a fine town house in the south-western corner of the abbey precinct, with a series of courtyards and walled gardens extending to the river meadows. This building and the one that succeeded it have been interpreted as part of this complex.

Although the Bethel family house was mostly demolished in the late 18th century (one wing still stands today), the late 17th, 18th, and 19th centuries saw a gradual renewal of occupation in the Hyde Abbey area. In the late 18th century, a prison for minor offenders known as the Bridewell was built on the former site of the abbey church. This was demolished at some time in the later 19th century to make way for the construction of the brick-built terraced housing that characterises much of the northern suburb in the present day.

The eastern suburb: Chester Road and St John's Street

In Chester Road (CHR 76–80) and St John's Street (SJS 76–82), pit digging had begun probably by the 10th century, and there were structures, possibly buildings associated. Whether late Saxon occupation was as dense here as in the western suburb (below) is uncertain, as not all of the trenches (CHR, I and III and SJS, I and IV) could be excavated fully to natural (see Appendix 1).

In the medieval period the property partly excavated as Trench I at Chester Road would have fronted the medieval lane which ran from Water Lane to St John's Church. At this time, a masonry building associated

with a yard stood on the site. To the south was a very large cut feature, possibly a construction pit for a well. The building remained in use until the 16th century, but the later history of the site is unknown, as 19th-century house construction had razed the stratigraphy to medieval levels.

Trench I at St John's Street sampled an area to the rear of properties on the street. Here was a site of pit digging in the 12th and early 13th centuries, but by the late 13th century, a timber building accommodating a substantial oven had been constructed. This was the first of a series of buildings and associated pits, presumably ancillary to a house on the street frontage, which occupied the site until the end of the 16th century. In the 17th and 18th centuries, the area was again turned over to pits. Subsequently, the site was host to 19th-century terraced housing that was demolished to make way for redevelopment in 1976.

Little activity of the 12th to 14th centuries was recorded in SJS, Trench IV, but in the later medieval period, a vaulted undercroft was built on the site. Subsequently this was modified by the insertion of a thick clay floor and flint rubble masonry in the north and south walls. No evidence for the form of any superstructure was recovered, but a small part of a timber-framed building abutted the undercroft to the north. The 17th and 18th centuries saw the construction of a chalk-lined well and a series of further buildings, one cellared. A late 19th-century brick built house stood on the site until 1968, when its demolition led to the discovery of the more or less intact medieval undercroft. The undercroft survived until 1982 when, after recording, the vault was deemed unstable and was deliberately collapsed.

It will be deduced from the foregoing that evidence of 14th- and 15th-century decline is much less marked on these sites in the eastern suburb than on those of the northern (above) and western (below) suburbs. Quite what the reasons for this might be is currently unclear. The proximity of the St Giles Hill Fair is one possibility, but this too had dwindled almost to nothing by the early 16th century (Keene 1985, 1031). It may be that a good living was still to be made in the service of the cathedral and college fairly nearby (*ibid*, 147), or even that the dominance of London in matters of trade had led to a revival in use of the old Roman route that passed close to the sites on its way to Staines and the capital.

The western suburb: New Road, Sussex Street, and Crowder Terrace

The Roman cemetery in the old Iron Age enclosure ditch, the Oram's Arbour ditch (Qualmann *et al.* 2004) at New Road (NR 74–77, now Station Road) was sealed by silting layers containing coins dated up to AD 402, suggesting that burial did not continue there much beyond the end of the 4th century. At Sussex Street (SXS 76; SXS 79) the ditch seems to have been totally filled up before the end of the Roman period (above), but at New Road it was still a significant feature (1.2m–

1.6m in depth) during late Saxon times. In that period, the whole area investigated at Sussex Street (at least where archaeological deposits had not been totally destroyed by recent development: see Appendix 1) was covered with a layer of redeposited chalk and clay. The proximity of the site to the western wall of the town, and the scale and extent of this deposit has led to its interpretation as upcast from the digging of the city defences of the late 9th century.

Evidence of intensive occupation of the late Saxon and early medieval periods, in the form of pits both small and large, property boundary features, timber structures, and a hearth, was found overlying the upcast deposit at Sussex Street. New Road, and Crowder Terrace (CT 74–77), too, were sites of pit-digging by the late 9th or early 10th centuries, and evidence for property demarcation there dated to the end of the 10th century at the latest.

The area sampled as SXS 76–79 produced evidence of medieval properties fronting Sussex Street (then, La Parokkes), whilst NR 74–77 probably lay to the rear of properties on Sussex Street and Upper High Street (then, Atheling Street). In the 12th to 14th centuries, an undercrofted building stood on the area recorded as SXS 79 Trench XVII. Evidence for a further masonry-built structure was recorded in the standing section above the Oram's Arbour ditch (Trench XIV). Elsewhere on the site, occupation continued on a scale similar to what had gone before. At New Road, the Oram's Arbour ditch was finally filled up in the 12th century, whilst pits continued to be dug, and property boundaries modified, throughout the medieval period. Part of the site was also used for cultivation, possibly of a root crop.

In medieval times, the site at Crowder Terrace was located on tenements on the south side of Romsey Road (then, Wode Street). In the 12th to 14th centuries, it was occupied by a number of deep latrines and wells, and a hearth or oven with associated structures. To the south, and demarcated by an east–west boundary, was an area used for human burial, interpreted as part of Winchester's Jewish cemetery (Keene 1985, 1034).

At some time during the 14th century, the building on Trench XVII at Sussex Street was demolished and not replaced. This evidence of decline is matched in all of the other excavated areas: the western suburb sites were little used from the 15th century until the coming of the railway and urban renewal saw the erection of 19th century housing over much of the area.

The city defences: Henly's Garage and 27 Jewry Street

The excavations which sampled areas on the city defences were at Magdalene Almhouses and 10 Colebrook Street (MA 80 and 10CS 86) on the eastern arm of the circuit, at North Walls, Jewry Street, Crown Hotel, and 27 Jewry Street (NHW 79, JCH 84, and 27JS 84) to the north, and at Henly's Garage and St Swithun's Street (HG 84/85 and SSS 74) to the south. The site at 27JS lay to the south of the line of the defences, but was included in this publication programme as it was immediately adjacent to JCH. Only Henly's Garage and 27 Jewry Street produced evidence reported in detail in this volume.

There were some signs of defensive activity of the late Saxon period on the city defences excavations, but not amongst the sites with samples reported here. Fragments of the post-Roman street system were recorded on the eastern and the northern defences, including the forerunner of modern Jewry Street at 27 Jewry Street (27JS 84), for which there is one bone group in this volume. An unnamed east–west street connecting Jewry Street and Staple Gardens was also present at 27JS from the late Saxon period onwards.

The best-preserved late Saxon deposits were from 27JS, where a timber building stood at the corner of the east–west street and Jewry Street. This had gone out of use by the end of the 10th century, and the site was briefly turned over to pits before the street was reinstated. At Henly's Garage, a series of working surfaces was recorded in section. The debris recovered from associated pits and found in samples taken from the section showed that these were the site of intensive iron smithing in the late Saxon and early medieval periods.

Medieval buildings and associated pits and wells were recorded at 27JS, but only pits and wells were identified at HG. Throughout the late 15th, 16th, and 17th centuries, buildings recorded at all of the sites fell into decay, or were deliberately demolished, and the areas investigated were given over to garden soils (where they had not been truncated). The line of Jewry Street recorded at JCH went out of use, probably as a result of turnpike improvements carried out around 1800 (Keene 1985, 38) and at this time, redevelopment began to gather pace in the street. By the later 19th century, the foundations of the thriving town we see today had been laid.

Within the walls: Trafalgar House

Four pits and a possible rectangular timber structure of late Saxon date were identified in the area of Trench VII at Trafalgar House (TH 74), but only limited excavation and recording were possible. A later, undated, grain deposit was sampled. This may represent part of an early medieval grain storage structure, or merely be the remains of a pit.

Introduction to the plant and animal remains
by D Serjeantson

As the account of the excavations above has made clear, the plant and animal remains discussed in this book are from a wide range of contexts. The number of animal bone groups from each period is summarised in Table 1.3. The number from each period declined over time, for reasons that are discussed below. The late Saxon material is discussed by Jennie Coy and Jennifer Bourdillon in Chapters 3 and 4 respectively, and later medieval material is considered by Jennie

Table 1.3 Summary table showing distribution of animal bone groups by period and totals (NISP)

Period	Date	Ch3	Ch4	Ch5	Total
late Saxon	9th–10th C	9	10		**19**
early medieval (Saxo-Norman)	late 10th–12th C	12		4	**16**
high medieval	13th–14th C	3		12	**15**
late medieval	late 14th–16th C			5	**5**
post-medieval	17th C			1	**1**
n bones		49,985	7,821	22,064	**79,870**

Coy, Dale Serjeantson, and Pippa Smith in Chapters 3 and 5. Chapter 5 also includes some 16th-century material and one 17th-century group. The plant remains (Chapter 2) also include one assemblage dated to the 18th century.

Bones from towns: the special problems

The study of animal and plant remains from towns presents many opportunities to the archaeologists and historians whose interests lie in diet, status, the agricultural economy, craft processes, and the organisation of town life in the past. For much, though not all, of the time in which people have lived in towns, they have used the written record, but animal and plant remains, as part of the wider group of material remains, supplement or complement these sources. There are, however, problems which arise in the interpretation of the animal bones from towns – difficulties that have long been recognised (Serjeantson 1989a; O'Connor 1992). 'The most difficult sites in which to understand economic changes are the urban sites or central places where every assemblage will not be representative of that settlement's classification' (Gerrard 1987). Analysis of the assemblages from suburban Winchester studied here have demonstrated that *no* single assemblage can be taken as fully representative of the town or even of that part of the town, and each of the authors who have contributed to this book has had this in mind.

What is an assemblage?

There is an assumption, sometimes unstated, that even quite small samples of bones reflect randomly the animal food remains discarded, allowing for loss due to destruction and attrition. This is not the case with animal remains from complex sites, especially towns in the later stages of their growth and development. As Jennifer Bourdillon points out, the pits from mid-Saxon Hamwic are remarkably homogenous; the contents of the pits associated with the late Saxon houses at Flaxengate, Lincoln, too, were regarded as a direct reflection of the diet (O'Connor 1982). By the 10th or 11th centuries, however, the complexity of the social organisation of the town increased, and this homogeneity is no longer found. The material from the medieval suburbs discussed in Chapters 3 and 5 shows this very clearly. Neither a single assemblage/group, nor all the material from a single period or single pit will necessarily reveal the 'average' animal component of the diet. Where context-groups are amalgamated, there is no way yet of knowing if the diet of the town has been randomised. The assemblages or groups considered here are from single phases as defined above. They include material from a group of contemporary linked features, and this is the largest unit that can appropriately be used. Even in the phase groups, pits and other deposits may contain material from more sources than a single household.

Assessment and selection of material for analysis

Since the explosion of rescue excavations in towns in the 1970s and early 1980s, of which Winchester was one of the major campaigns, it has become increasingly clear that it is of key importance on urban excavations to select for study only those bones which are capable of being used reliably to answer the questions posed (Serjeantson 1989a; O'Connor 1989).

It cannot be stressed too strongly that animal bones from contexts which appear to have accumulated over a long period, or from features which contain a component of earlier material as well as that contemporary with the fill of the feature, have very limited value for answering questions about changes in size or age structure over time, or indeed many of the other questions which have been posed here. The bones themselves may suggest whether an assemblage is closely dated but, other than in exceptional circumstances, the date and level of contamination is much more reliably indicated by the pottery and other small finds. This, though self evident to specialists working with animal bones, is not always appreciated by other archaeologists. The proportion of bones analysed out of those excavated diminishes from the late Saxon period onwards for this reason. Winchester shares with cities such as York, London, and Lincoln (Dobney *et al* 1996, 15) particular problems with potential for residuality because – in the suburbs as well as the centre – there has been activity from the Roman period onwards. The fact that most of the problems here have been resolved successfully has been entirely due to cooperation between the animal bone specialists and those working on the post-excavation project at Winchester.

In the early 1980s, it was the practice to record all excavated material. The animal remains from the western suburb, described by Jennie Coy in Chapter 3, were recorded in the 1980s and include more material from small contexts and from contexts that contained possible residual material (see below) than in the other reports. The balance of the material from the suburbs was assessed in 1989 by Mark Maltby and Jennifer Bourdillon (nd), following guidelines later published by English Heritage (1992), after the pottery and small finds had been studied in enough detail for the implications of any mixing or residuality to be fully taken into account. They, in conjunction with the finds team at Winchester, quantified the bones and made a judgement on the integrity and quality of each phase group. The assessment included a brief description of the sites and phases not analysed. As well as the justification of inclusion or omission of groups, it also indicated the quantity and quality of material in store: the approximate numbers of bones, the species present, and bone condition.

While preliminary assessment of material has proved its value, the act of assessment by a specialist carries a minor problem on large sites. At Winchester, at the time of the assessment, bones of smaller species were separated from those of the larger mammals when they were counted, and were then bagged separately. The advantage of this method was that it protected the smaller bones from damage in handling, thus making later recording quicker. It had the disadvantage that bags from a context could become separated, and the most serious consequence for Winchester was that the bird bones from Victoria Road, Phase 763, and the fish bones from Phase 975 have been misplaced, and consequently have not been analysed.

Identification and recording of animal bones

All bones were identified at the Faunal Remains Unit, University of Southampton. The elements selected for identification are similar between the three authors, though more parts of the skeleton of sheep and goats were distinguished by Coy and Bourdillon, than by Serjeantson and Smith. In addition, Bourdillon identified rib heads to species, while the other workers did not. Quantification using number of fragments (NISP) is however broadly comparable. The bones listed before 1991 were recorded following the Ancient Monuments Laboratory's computer based methods (Jones *et al* 1981) on Comart disks. Those from the northern and eastern suburbs and the city defences were recorded directly in dBase files. The computer files and paper records are held by Winchester Museums with the site archives. Bone measurements were recorded by each worker following Driesch (1976). They are also listed in the archives and have additionally been included in the Animal Bone Metrical Archive Project database at the University of Southampton,

which can be accessed at *http://ads.ahds.ac.uk/ catalogue/specColl/abmap/*. The bones themselves are in the museum stores.

The plant remains and animal bones discussed in this book are only a portion of those which have been recovered over the 40 years of excavations in Winchester. The material from the excavations in the city centre has not yet been published, with the exception of Lower Brook Street. When the plant and animal remains from the medieval deposits within the city proper have been published, they will provide crucial complementary evidence for variations in diet and status within the city.

Overall aims

Each of the authors of the chapters on animal bones has therefore written with three principal objectives, explicitly or implicitly stated.

The first has been the investigation of the origins of the deposits studied. This is of importance both to the archaeological interpretation of the area and as a prerequisite to the study of the more general topics, and has been crucial to the interpretation of the plants as well as the animal remains. The individual groups of bones from each phase have been briefly described: in Chapters 4 and 5, the description of individual groups precedes the general discussion, and in Chapter 3 follows it. Serjeantson and Smith also used the animal bones in an attempt to investigate the organisation of space on the outskirts of the town, examining such aspects as whether the dumps of material were locally generated or brought from a distance, and whether they are domestic waste or from craft processes.

A second aim of each author has been to consider the changes which took place in the animal food component of the diet of the occupants of urban Winchester, including the range of species consumed, the changing proportions over time and the quality of the meat.

A third aim has been to consider changes in animal husbandry and management of the animal population of Winchester and its hinterland. This is manifested in a change in the proportion of species, age at death, and sex ratio of the main domestic species – cattle, sheep, pig, domestic fowl, and goose. Whether all animals were brought to the town for sale or whether any were raised in the town has also been considered by each author.

There are variations in the status or wealth indicated by the bone and plant assemblages: in the overview of food, craft, and status in Chapter 7, consideration is given as to whether the variations are related to the area of the town or to change over time. Where it has been possible to demonstrate that the bones do indeed reflect the diet of the inhabitants of the suburb, the authors have examined whether the species eaten, or the age of the animals eaten, reflect a high or low status diet. Here the hypothesis is that animals which have been imported from a distance; animals which are scarce or protected (such as red deer); and those which were selected for slaughter at an age that suggests that they were raised for meat rather than a secondary product – are from wealthier and grander households than assemblages with a narrower range of species, and remains of older animals. When all the finds from within the city have been published, it will be possible to investigate whether the city as a whole changed in relative status compared to other medieval towns over the same period.

2 Late Saxon, medieval, and post-medieval plant remains *by F J Green*

Introduction

The botanical evidence to be discussed here was recovered as long ago as the 1970s. The methods of sampling and retrieval of the botanical materials are summarised in Chapter 1 and have been previously discussed by the author (Green 1979a). Full data collection under the author's supervision was undertaken on the Sussex Street (SXS), Crowder Terrace (CT), New Road (NR), Victoria Road (VR) and Hyde Abbey (HA) sites. Full data collection had also occurred on the Trafalgar House (TH) site prior to the author's involvement with excavations in Winchester. The data collection from other sites conformed generally to the standards set by the author, though some aspects of sampling may have not been quite so thorough.

Assessment

For the purposes of the present report and for a number of very good reasons, the botanical materials were subject to assessment. The author was concerned that significant advances had occurred since the evidence was originally collected and what seemed like useful or meaningful information some twenty years ago, when there was a general lack of comparable data, could in some cases be viewed today as being not so informative. However, inclusion of the extensive sampling imposed on many of the sites, allows a meaningful assessment of what constituted background-noise – residuality and more recent contamination: these formative processes were therefore essential. However, it was thought necessary to re-assess the level of detail necessary in other respects. This report therefore includes references both to material from the principal sites from which botanical remains were recovered and some other sites in the suburbs and from within the walls; from which remains of other significant species were recorded, but otherwise not found on the main sites discussed here.

Assessment of the material revealed that some sites, which were well-sampled, failed to produce significant assemblages of preserved plant remains: 27 Jewry Street, Henly's Garage, The Lido, St Bartholomew's School, Chester Road, and St John's Street. Within the northern suburb, the Hyde Abbey excavations of 1972 and 1974 were sampled but again the evidence was disappointing. The medieval deposits failed generally to produce preserved plant remains in significant quantities. However, a deposit of charred grain in a ditch was recovered from this site and the 18th-century fill of a garderobe pit contained abundant botanical material. The extensive samples from the Victoria Road site were assessed and it was determined that the bulk of the evidence was more indicative of background-noise. It seemed to result from highly mixed deposits, possibly containing significant accumulations of residual material. It was therefore decided that only material from well-sealed, specific contexts, in particular charred grain deposits, were worthy of detailed discussion. However, some individual botanical finds from some of these sites are referred to below.

The preservation of botanical materials varied across the sites and was confined to charred and mineralised plant remains. Waterlogged deposits were absent from the suburban sites and anoxic preservation conditions were not encountered. Victoria Road was one of the first sites from which mineralised plant remains were recovered; they were also encountered in Southampton at the same time. The condition was shown to be the result of calcium phosphate replacement of the original organic material (Green 1979b, 279–84).

Methods

The identifications of plant materials from the sites at Crowder Terrace and Trafalgar House were made by the author prior to 1979. The identification of material from the 1979 Sussex Street excavations was undertaken by Rupert Houseley under the author's supervision. The other plant remains discussed here were identified by the author in 1994. The bulk of the work was part of the author's research towards an MPhil thesis (Green 1979a), from which much of this report has been extracted. The plant remains were identified using the author's reference collection now deposited with English Heritage (Centre for Archaeology, Fort Cumberland). The material has been ordered according to Clapham, Tutin, and Warburg 1962.

It should be noted that the data presented here in the bar diagrams and the discussion of these reflects all the available data from Sussex Street, New Road, Crowder Terrace, and Victoria Road and not simply those contexts selected for detailed discussion. At the outset, when the work on individual sites was progressing, it was assumed that each site would be written up as a separate report. Subsequently publication plans have changed on a number of occasions and therefore the information is being presented here as an overview of the evidence from these sites. The evidence has not been discussed in detail by individual site phase but by period. It is recognised that for some purposes this method of discussion makes it difficult to re-evaluate the botanical evidence through time from a specific site.

The statistical analysis used to assess the assemblages were those employed in the late 1970s. Unfortunately

Table 2.1   Percentage composition of bulk grain deposits

	Sussex Street	Trafalgar House	Hyde Abbey	Victoria Road
Triticum aestivum L.	12	6	26	83
Hordeum vulgare L.	60	6	5	1
Avena sativa L.	3	0	31	3
Secale cereale L.	0	69	0	<1.0
Brassica sp.	2	0	0	1
Vicia and *Pisum* sp.	1	1	4	1
Other contaminants (ruderals)	22	18	1	4
Rachis and glumes	0	0	0	6
Total contaminants	**40**	**31**	**37**	**17**
Total non-cereal contaminants	**25**	**19**	**6**	**6**
Sample size (ml)	500	500	200	200

at that time it was not possible to undertake the type of numerical analysis so easily achieved today through the use of computers. The primary data has never been entered into any computer database. It has not been possible, therefore, to look at the density of plant components to soil excavated, or for that matter to re-examine questions of residuality, contamination, or, more important, site formation processes across the sites. These are all aspects that could in the future form the basis of further worthwhile analysis, since all the information required exists in archive form. Detailed analysis of the abrasion of charred cereals can provide an indication of potential residuality as advocated by the author and others (Murphy & Wiltshire 1994, 1–6) but this was not attempted here.

A major difficulty encountered in providing this overview is that not all the sites produced contemporary contexts, therefore it is not always possible to be certain that the evidence from a particular site and period can be used to extrapolate across the sites as a whole. Gener-alisations resulting from the analysis of material from a particular site may therefore have little if any real validity. The lateral variation that can occur due to anthropo-genic, economic, geographical, and other factors within an urban environment cannot be underestimated.

Results

Botanical material discussed here came from sites principally in the city's western and northern suburbs, since the excavations in the eastern suburb failed to yield useful samples. Botanical evidence for the 9th–11th centuries was recovered mainly from Sussex Street, Victoria Road, and Hyde Abbey in the western and northern suburbs. Material from the southern defences was recovered from Henly's Garage. For the later medieval period, evidence was recovered from Victoria Road, Hyde Abbey, other small sites in the northern suburb, and Crowder Terrace. Evidence for the 14th–15th centuries came predominantly from

the northern suburb; from Victoria Road and Hyde Abbey; the Victoria Road site alone provided some 3050 samples. From the various sites four bulk deposits of charred grain were recovered (Table 2.1) which are discussed separately below.

Cereals

In Figure 2.1, the density of seeds per 10 litres of soil is shown for wheat, barley, and oats. The relative pro-portions of the different cereals from each period can be observed. It can be seen that the sites produced rel-atively high quantities of charred cereal remains.

Wheat and barley

Wheat was recovered most frequently, based on presence and dominance analysis of the sequence at Victoria Road (Fig 2.2). Most was a free threshing bread type wheat (*Triticum aestivum/compactum/durum*). It was recovered from features in combination with other cereals, of which barley (*Hordeum vulgare*) was often found in very similar quantities. The barley recovered was usually a hulled six-row form. Measurements are shown in Tables 2.2 and 2.3. Due to poor preservation of barley grains in many of these deposits, it was often impossible to provide a precise identification. Both barley and wheat were occasionally found in large accumulations, as in the fill of the mid- to late 9th-century pit (F10) at Sussex Street, where barley formed some 60 per cent of the total deposit (Table 2.1). A large wheat deposit was also recovered from Victoria Road, 14th- to 15th-century pit F968, where wheat accounted for 83 per cent of the material. Examination of the relative presence and dominance of cereal species of all sites combined suggests very few differences in their distribution on sites, either in the number of features containing the individual or the total quantities present. The large charred grain deposits are an exception.

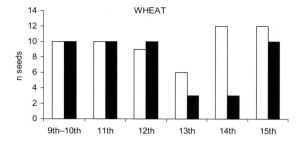

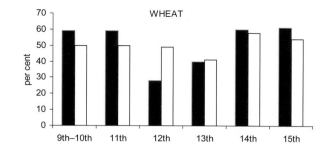

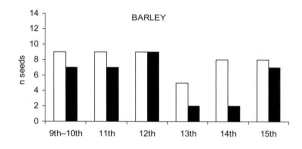

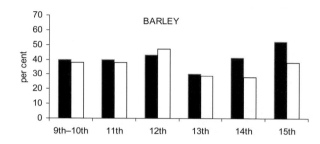

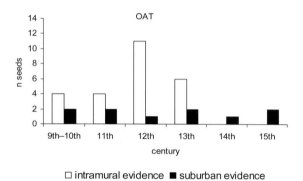

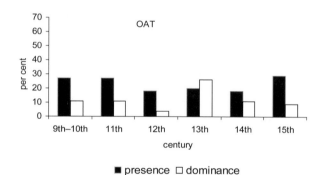

□ intramural evidence ■ suburban evidence

■ presence □ dominance

Figure 2.1 Winchester: all sites. Density of cereal seeds to soil over time: wheat, barley, and oat seeds per 10,000 ml soil

Figure 2.2 Winchester: all sites. Dominance and presence of wheat, barley, and oats through time

Table 2.2   Size of carbonised grains of barley (*Hordeum vulgare* L.), median caryopsis: Sussex Street: 9th–11th century

	Length (L)	Breadth (B)	Thickness (T)	L/B	T/B
Maximum	7.2	3.7	3.2		
Minimum	5.0	2.0	1.3		
Mean	6.3	2.8	2.4	225	86
Standard deviation	0.7	0.47	0.49		
Coefficient of variation %	12.0	17.0	20.0		

Population 30

Key: L/B length/breadth ratio; T/B thickness/breadth ratio

Caution has to be exercised in the interpretation of the relative abundance of the cereals. Whilst the author has previously (1982) made assumptions, it is difficult to be certain if the apparent decline in density of cereals (Fig 2.1) was entirely site or suburb specific. This evidence can only be tested against data collected on a systematic basis rather than from those sites sampled judgmentally: this was possible only for the northern suburb, where there were samples from each century. Changes in the percentage of wheat, barley, oat, and rye at Victoria Road are shown in Figure 2.3.

It is difficult to interpret cereal use from these deposits and therefore the following discussion has to be viewed with caution given our current lack of knowledge and the possibility of creating a circular argument. If barley, as seems likely in the early medieval period, was used

Table 2.3 Size of carbonised grains of barley (*Hordeum* sp.), Trafalgar House: medieval

	Length (L)	Breadth (B)	Thickness (T)	L/B	T/B
Maximum	7.1	4.0	3.7		
Minimum	4.0	2.2	1.7		
Mean	5.6	3.2	2.6	175	81
Standard deviation	1.0	0.49	0.52		
Coefficient of variation %	17.0	15.0	20.0		

Population 18

Key: L/B length/breadth ratio; T/B thickness/breadth ratio

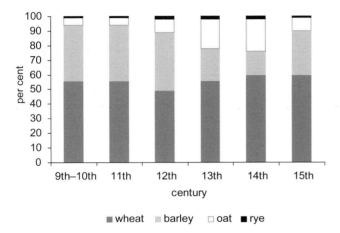

Figure 2.3 Victoria Road: ratio of cereals (wheat, barley, oat, and rye) through time

Table 2.4 Size of seeds of oat (*Avena sativa* L.), Sussex Street: 10th–11th century

	Length (L)	Breadth (B)	Thickness (T)
Maximum	7.8	2.1	2.0
Minimum	6.5	1.7	1.4
Mean	7.1	2.0	1.8
Standard deviation	38.0	12.0	22.0

Population 7

for brewing and wheat for baking, then theoretically most of the wheat would have been ground into flour, leaving little evidence. Barley as a whole grain is more easily damaged by fire during the malting process. Therefore, it has to be asked why this species does not contribute a larger proportion of the grain recovered. In general, throughout the period under discussion, barley is only rarely recovered in larger concentrations than wheat. Increasingly, through time, wheat seems to be recovered from a wider range of contexts and is more consistently distributed across sites.

Oats

Oats (*Avena* sp.) was the next cereal species most commonly encountered after barley and wheat. Unfortunately, due to the absence of lemma bases, it has not been possible in most cases to identify the oats to species and indicate if they were cultivated rather than wild forms. The large size of many of the grains (Table 2.4) strongly suggests that most of this material is probably *Avena sativa*. The large charred grain deposit recovered from the ditch at Hyde Abbey (F320), discussed below, clearly consisted of *Avena sativa*. Apart from these large charred accumulations, there is a general lack of evidence for oats from these Winchester sites of medieval date. Whether this is due to their unimportance in the economy or results from

differential food processing cannot be established from the available information. Documentary evidence from the medieval period (Titow, pers comm) indicates that oats were a major cash crop on the Bishop of Winchester's estates in Hampshire. Oats were commonly fed to livestock or crushed and eaten as porridge or gruel or used for beer so might well leave little archaeological evidence.

Rye

Rye (*Secale cereale*) was very rarely encountered on these sites. The general indication is that this species was of little importance as a cereal consumed or used within domestic contexts in Winchester's medieval suburbs, though possible differential use to wheat and barley might leave it under represented, ie inclusion only as a whole cereal in bread. The evidence suggests that rye was generally a weedy species of other crops rather than a principal cultivated crop and this has been argued by others (Helbaek 1971, 296; Lange 1975, 120). However, there is an exception to this in Winchester: a large deposit of charred rye was recovered from a 9th- to 11th-century feature (F20) at Trafalgar House, for which the measurements are shown in Table 2.5.

Curiously, rye is a species that is frequently encountered on sites in the neighbouring settlement at Romsey in the late Saxon and early medieval periods. The Romsey evidence (Green & Lockyear 1994) might reflect a dietary preference for rye. The presence of this species might also reflect the wider use of rye straw for thatching in Romsey, a settlement with a generally rural rather than urban character in the late Saxon and early medieval period. Perhaps Romsey's inhabitants

Table 2.5   Size of carbonised grains of rye (*Secale cereale* L.), Trafalgar House: medieval

	Length (L)	Breadth (B)	Thickness (T)	L/B	T/B
Maximum	6.0	2.7	2.7		
Minimum	4.0	1.4	1.3		
Mean	4.9	1.9	1.8	258	95
Standard deviation	0.5	0.3	0.3		
Coefficient of variation %	10.0	13.0	17.0		

Population 30

Key: L/B length/breadth ratio; T/B thickness/breadth ratio

were exploiting marginal land for the cultivation of rye. Such land, characterised by thin and sandy soil types, is found to the west of Romsey, where this species has been recovered associated with other dated plant remains at Bowmans Farm (Green 1996, 118).

It might be expected that the Winchester suburbs ought to produce evidence perhaps reflecting rural activities. This does not appear to be the case and the evidence might suggest that the Winchester suburbs were generally less rural in character and wealthier than developing settlements such as Romsey. Thus the medieval inhabitants of the Winchester suburbs were perhaps less dependant on rye for any purpose, including its usage as a thatching material.

Other cereal fragments

Other non-caryopses fragments of cereals were rarely recovered from these sites. Bread wheat rachis fragments were recorded from Sussex Street, pit F6 and the culm nodes of unidentified cereal species were recovered from the Victoria Road sites. The general lack of such fragments suggests that cereal straw was rarely burnt in situ on these sites. It is also possible that burnt cereal straw might simply have been entirely converted to ash. The lack of well-preserved waterlogged deposits from these sites makes further interpretation difficult, but analogy with evidence from intra-mural sites (Green forthcoming) indicates that waterlogged straw was more frequently recovered from pits where decomposition had not taken place. The entire lack of crop processing residues is perhaps what might be expected from a medieval urban settlement and it can be suggested that these activities, with the exception of some slight evidence from the Victoria Road site, were confined to rural areas with perhaps only sporadic activity in the northern suburb.

Charred grain deposits

When this work was begun, only three large accumulations of Saxon and medieval cereals had been recovered in southern England: one from Hamwic which has been examined by M Monk; one from Lydford, Devon excavated by Peter Addyman and subsequently analysed by the present author (Green

1979a, 200–08); and the third, a deposit from Trafalgar House, which was located in early 1974. Subsequent to the initial analysis, the range of information that can be deduced from large charred cereal assemblages has been more widely discussed by others (Hillman 1984, 1–42; Jones 1984, 43–61). The evidence from the Winchester sites has also been discussed elsewhere (Green 1982, 43; Green 1984, 103–07).

It was initially anticipated that extensive sampling of sites would ultimately result in locating a number of large charred accumulations of cereal grains. Since the original campaign of excavations, only one additional large deposit of charred grain is known with certainty to have been located from Winchester. It was located on the more recent Brooks excavation. There is, however, evidence from excavations at Newbury, Romsey, Southampton and elsewhere in the Wessex region (*cf* Green 1994, 85) that is continuing to provide data, from which it is to be hoped in the future that it will be possible to address more specific questions about cereal crop husbandry. Such material, preserved as a result of a major catastrophe, can provide a wide range of information about medieval crops. Such information is not available from the relatively small quantities of other charred cereal remains recovered from these sites, that are possibly representative of a very wide range of domestic activities and are typical of finds normally recovered from most sites.

Large grain deposits were defined as samples that produced over 200ml of grain per 5000ml of soil examined. In practice, this was the lower limit of acceptance. The four samples discussed (Table 2.1) here contained between 4000–4500ml of grain per 5000ml of sample. They are from Sussex Street, Trafalgar House, Hyde Abbey, and Victoria Road. The ratio of seed to other constituents clearly depended on whether the grain had been dumped and formed a discrete deep layer before any further mixing with other rubbish, as possibly the case at Trafalgar House, or had been swept up and deposited in a feature, as the evidence suggests from the Hyde Abbey ditch, Victoria Road, and Sussex Street deposits. In these latter cases there is always the possibility that charred material resulting from other activities may have become incorporated along with the grain from the major accident, for example residual material contained within the soil used to back fill the pit or feature.

It was considered that the analysis of large grain deposits might provide information on the following

Table 2.6 Size of carbonised grains of brome grass (*Bromus secalinus / mollis*), Sussex Street: 10th–11th century

	Length (L)	Breadth (B)	Thickness (T)	L/B	T/B
Maximum	6.2	2.2	1.3		
Minimum	4.7	1.0	0.9		
Mean	5.5	1.6	1.1	344	69
Standard deviation	0.45	0.41	0.11		
Coefficient of variation %	8.0	27.0	10.0		

Population 30

Key: L/B length/breadth ratio; T/B thickness/breadth ratio

aspects: the health of the crop; the crop's composition; the soil type where the crop was grown, as indicated by weed species; whether the crop was spring or autumn sown, based on weeds within the crop; how the crop had been processed after harvesting; whether it was winnowed or sieved; and possible rotation of crops, based on the seeds of other economic species occurring as contaminants. Finally it was considered that it might be possible to link this information with documentary knowledge of crops, in particular from the later medieval period.

Late Saxon Sussex Street (pit F10)

The Sussex Street sample came from the secondary fill of a pit (F10) dating from the mid- to late 9th century. The charred grain consisted of 60 per cent barley. Other cereals within the sample accounted for 75 per cent of the contaminants. At least 25 per cent of the seeds recovered were from non-cereal contaminants. Of these corn cockle (*Agrostemma githago*) accounted for 4 per cent of the deposit, and brome grass (*Bromus secalinus / mollis*), accounted for 10 per cent. Corn cockle and brome grass are invariably associated with autumn sown cereals. The large quantity of brome grass within the sample (measurements in Table 2.6) should be considered as a chaff element, since normally this species could have been removed by winnowing without significant loss of grain. It is possible that this particular crop had not been winnowed or sieved. Perhaps of greatest interest is the fact that a large part of the grain along with weed seeds had sprouted prior to burning. The sprout fragments of the cereals were of a consistent length, though shorter than recorded for corn cockle (Green 1979a, 342).

This accumulation may have resulted from an accident during malting, though deliberate burning of poorly stored wet grain that had sprouted may also be a possibility. The charred cereal and other plant remains from this deposit suggests possibly a winter-sown crop and that crop husbandry was poor.

Late Saxon Trafalgar House

The Trafalgar House sample, which is probably of ninth-eleventh century date, consisted nearly entirely of rye, as noted above. The non-cereal contamina-tion amounted to some 19 per cent by seed count, of which 6 per cent consisted of brome grass, 3 per cent of brassica, and 2 per cent of corn cockle. There are here clearly some similarities between the percentages of weed seeds within the Sussex Street barley sample and the Trafalgar House rye sample though this par-ticular sample contained slightly more corn cockle. The overall contaminant count for each sample is very similar, 40 per cent of the Sussex Street sample consisted, by seed count, of contaminants, whereas the Trafalgar House sample is somewhat cleaner, possibly reflecting the health of the harvest field.

12th- to 13th-century Hyde Abbey

The charred cereal sample from Hyde Abbey was recovered from a north–south boundary ditch associ-ated with 12th- to 13th-century pottery. This sample is of a completely different nature: it represents a mixture of cereals and some legumes. The general nature of preservation indicates that the sample had probably been wet and that burning had been intense and rapid. Both observations are consistent with a burnt pottage or partly cooked meal that was allowed to boil dry and burn. However, the sheer quantities of grain recovered may argue against this idea, unless the sample resulted from the preparation of food for a large community. It is conceivable that the mixed nature of the sample results from the mixing of species stored separately prior to burning. This argument is strengthened by the presence of lentils (*Lens culinaris*) in the sample. Lentil is a species that generally cannot easily be cultivated even in southern England, suggesting it most likely represents an imported food species.

The quantity of weed seeds recovered from this sample was small. This argues that the crop cleaning processes had been thorough. The deposit lacks species such as wild radish (*Raphanus raphanistrum*), corn cockle, and brome grass, all of which are typically found within autumn sown crops. Equally, there is a lack of the species that might be expected from a spring sown one.

14th- to 15th-century Victoria Road

The Victoria Road charred cereal deposit was recovered from a pit (F968) dated to the 14th–15th century. This sample contained 94 per cent cereal (on fragment count), of which 83 per cent was a bread-type wheat (*Triticum aestivum / compactum / durum*), with about 6 per cent of the sample consisting of wheat rachis and chaff elements. This sample is particularly interesting since it contained a mixture of bread wheat (*Triticum aestivum*) and club wheat (*Triticum compactum*) as based primarily on the identification of rachis fragments as confirmed by Hillman (pers comm). The presence of weed seeds such as corn cockle possibly indicate that the crop was spring rather than autumn sown, though this is by no means conclusive. The other weed species present are those that have small seeds such as fat hen (*Chenopodium album*), meadowsweet (*Spiraea ulmaria / Filipendula ulmaria*), dock (*Rumex crispus*), yarrow (*Achillea mille-folium),* and mayweed (*Anthemis cotula*).

The quantity of these weed seeds could indicate that the crop was not sieved to remove the smaller contaminants. However, this is unlikely since examination of the non-seed component indicates that all elements of the wheat plant were present: straw, straw culm nodes, rachis fragments and glumes. Also, a large proportion of unquantifiable chaff fragments preserved only as silica skeletons were recovered. It is thus possible to infer that the sample represented a harvested crop that had not undergone any processing whatsoever. Conversely, it would be possible to interpret the cereal assemblage as representing the chaff element and tail corn from a crop, which contained small percentages of weed seeds. The problem with this sample is that it is very difficult to quantify the silica skeletons present and ascertain whether there were more glumes and rachis fragments than cereal caryopses in the sample. Given this limitation, and by making comparison with other crop samples from Winchester, it is possible, even taking into account the inability to assess the true charred chaff element, that the crop only contained about 17 per cent contamination of which some 6 per cent consisted of chaff. The weed contaminants of this crop were consistently lower than in the other samples discussed here, suggesting that the cereal elements represent a crop rather than crop waste.

Discussion

Unfortunately large charred grain deposits from Winchester are few in number and they reflect a wide time span such that no patterns are observable at this time. The contaminants in large charred grain samples can potentially provide some information on crop rotation. Some are species of economic significance and many may represent a residual weed flora indicating crops previously grown in the fields. It is also known that weed species were frequently introduced into crops via seed corn (cf. Jones & Halstead 1995) often from considerable distances (Ochinsky 1971, 325) and the Winchester evidence may simply reflect seed corn contamination unrelated to the immediate locality and previous crop cycle.

The main contaminants of the Sussex Street barley sample were bread wheat and oats *Avena sativa*. The presence of over 10 per cent of wheat in this and other such samples (Green 1979a, 236) may indicate that wheat preceded barley in rotations. The likelihood that this represents a mixed field crop can, on the basis of documentary evidence, be discounted as the percentage of wheat is too low an admixture to be significant. The main contaminants of the Trafalgar House sample were near equal quantities of wheat and barley, both of which might have preceded the rye crop. The Hyde Abbey sample is difficult to interpret, consisting as it does of nearly equal parts of oat and wheat. This is not helped by the fact that, as stated above, a further one third of the deposit consisted of cereals that could not be further identified.

The Victoria Road sample, which appears to consist of two types of free threshing wheat (see above), with two distinctive rachis types with no obvious intermediary forms, may be compared to the documentary evidence from the Bishop of Winchester's estates. Titow (pers comm) noted that two types of wheat were recorded, one of which was inferior to the other. It is not known from the documentary evidence precisely what makes one type of wheat inferior. Bread wheat (Usher 1974, 585–6) has a higher gluten content than spelt wheat (*Triticum spelta*) and this is specifically important for raising the dough during bread making. It is possible that the documentary sources involving mixtures of wheat could relate to mixtures of bread wheat (*Triticum aestivum)* and spelt (*Triticum turgidum*), though no spelt was recorded and identifications were confirmed at the time by Hillman (pers comm). From this limited evidence it can be inferred that late Saxon and medieval crops were generally subjected to efficient crop cleaning methods, if not husbandry. There was a range of tools designed for such purposes, as discussed by Addyman (1976, 319).

Wheat abundance

Clearly, explanations have to be provided as to why wheat is more frequently preserved by charring than barley, or why oats are always a poor third to these other species with the virtual absence of rye. The latter species at best never accounts for more than 8 per cent of charred cereals. Questions have to be asked whether or not these patterns reflect actual usage and if they do why are these variations visible through time on these suburban sites. It seems that discard of charred grains reflects consistent accidents of charring, presumably in the main, in domestic contexts. These involve whole rather than crushed or rolled grains, and the processes must have been ubiquitously performed by the inhabitants of the suburbs. Thus, the observable differences between the absolute quantities of the different cereals must firstly reflect the different uses to which they were put – the different chances for their survival, the cultural preferences and suitability of different cereal types for malting, bread making, animal feeds, and other purposes.

It has to be borne in mind that all the different

cereals have traditionally, in the past, been used for both brewing and baking. Therefore whilst barley was not so frequently used for bread making, rye and oats certainly were. Oats and wheat were also traditionally used for beer, as is still commonplace in much of Europe at the present time. Other crops such as beans and peas were used at Winchester College for brewing and to some extent baking (Beveridge 1939).

Except for the large grain deposit from Sussex Street F10, it is noticeable that very little of the barley recorded from these sites shows any sign of sprouting, which would be expected if the grain was used for brewing. It is therefore possible to suggest that in general the charred barley did not originate from accidents associated with malting and brewing. Whilst the barley can invariably be identified to species, caryopses are rarely contained within surviving palae and lemma. In fact, the bulk of the evidence indicates that these elements had probably been removed by milling especially where the radicle tip had also been removed. In other cases, this may simply reflect the chaff burning off the grain. Barley may therefore have been used in much the same way as wheat. This could account for the similar occurrence to wheat. This also suggests that barley did not originate from straw used as floor coverings that were subsequently burnt, since such material would probably have included unthreshed grain along with rachis and other diagnostic components.

Origin of the charred grain

It is more difficult to explain the processes that might have led to the charring of this material. The evidence from the Winchester suburban sites, the consistent small quantities of charred cereals from pits and other features is unlike the charred plant remains from small town sites in the region. Those from Andover and Romsey (Green 1991, 363–7) in many cases have been demonstrated to have originated from single episodes involving major catastrophes, as has been confirmed by radiocarbon dating (Green & Lockyear 1992, 57–70).

A range of possible activities presumably of a domestic and culinary nature has to be considered that might have resulted in the accumulations of charred grain. Other sources might assist interpretation. Clues can be gleaned from medieval cookery and recipe books and the lists of purchases by large or corporate institutions (Beveridge 1939). Such documentary sources have limited value, when it is the information about the everyday activities of ordinary people that is required; since this may be poorly, if at all, reflected in the diet and food preparation methods associated with records that survive for the wealthier classes. It is clearly the commonest foods prepared that must have resulted in the charred assemblages. In this respect, even in modern times, bakers have traditionally tested the heat of their ovens by throwing in whole cereal grains. Such a practice itself may well have contributed in part

to the assemblages of charred grain recovered from these sites.

The charred cereal material may result from waste and spillage during food preparation, floor sweepings, and food waste discarded onto open fires. The bulk of such material would have been turned entirely into ash, and is not normally recoverable by most crude sieving and flotation techniques. The surviving material must therefore only reflect a very small proportion of the cereals that were originally discarded and burnt. The evidence suggests that little care was given, or that food was prepared in such large quantities that the wastage was of minimal concern to those involved. Assuming that most households might well both bake and brew and that all foods had to be produced within the domestic context from the raw materials, it is still difficult to perceive by modern culinary standards how so much wastage could consistently occur, material which has then subsequently been burnt.

One distinct possibility is that small quantities of grain were dried in a domestic context prior to 'home grinding'. Specific ordinances proscribed this practice (Biddle & Smith 1990, 882–3) and for such ordinances to be required suggests widespread domestic grinding of cereals. The evidence of querns discussed by Biddle and Smith (*ibid*) and in Rees *et al* (2008) suggest that they were fairly commonplace in Winchester in the 11th and possibly the 12th century. However, within the walls there would appear to be an increase in mortars on sites in the 13th and 14th centuries and this is also reflected in finds of mortars in the suburbs. It may well be that the use of mortars reflects changing methods of food preparation, or a means of circumventing the ordinances in respect of milling.

Whilst it is tempting to conclude that the observed grain-soil density decline in the 13th and 14th centuries (Fig 2.1) might reflect greater control exercised by the lord or principal tenant, for centralised milling, with less use of domestic hand mills and grain drying in a domestic context; other economic factors have also to be considered. Of these, from the 14th century, there would certainly have been some impact on the suburbs from the Black Death. With an increasing wage economy it was quite simply easier to purchase flour and processed cereals in the open market.

Apart from brewing and bread making, most households would probably have consumed large quantities of cereals either in stews, soups, or pottages, or as baked puddings much in the same way as rice is prepared as a sweet pudding today. Cereals not yet ground would therefore have been widely kept for such purposes, perhaps only deliberately being discarded when mouldy, through damp storage, or contaminated by insects. Whilst traditionally such material would have been fed to livestock, pigs or chickens, it is possible that in the Winchester suburban context this was not always or generally practicable, and that being discarded on a domestic or specifically a kitchen hearth was an easier and ultimate solution. Such waste products used as fuel might have been seen as of more immediate benefit, since wet food preparation waste has its uses to damp and create slower burning fires overnight or between phases of food preparation.

Change over time

The observable decline in the density of grain in the soil (Fig 2.1) must reflect some changes in social activities. Whether such social activities have any relationship with economic ones and which of these takes precedence is problematical and no easy answers can be provided. It is only possible to record that actual garbage disposal of these components does change, even though rubbish pits are still and possibly are even an increasingly frequent feature of excavated sites during the later medieval period. Thus, whether these results can be correlated with historical evidence for the medieval period has yet to be established. It can, however, be suggested that the decline in the occurrence of all species in the 14th century may well represent the known poor harvests in the early part of that century coupled with the effects of the Black Death.

It seems perhaps too simplistic a model to account for the observed charred cereal distribution, given all the difficulties of establishing the mechanics of domestic utilisation and discard. If the decline remained constant then it could perhaps be argued that this reflects social changes in the usage of these cereals and their storage and discard. However, the increase in the 15th century matches the pre-14th-century figures. It is possible to postulate that if the suburban population of the city declined and properties become vacant in the city centre, the surviving suburban families might have been able to move closer to the city centre. The properties they formerly occupied might in turn have become available to other, perhaps poorer, families migrating from rural areas. These families may have had somewhat different social and culinary preferences, perhaps involving different cereal utilisation, and perhaps less consumption of cereals involving whole grains. Their methods of refuse disposal might also be different. It can be postulated that following this, with an improved economy, rising prices, and the absorption of the rural population into the city over two or three generations, any cultural differences in cereal consumption would have tended to disappear and the original patterns strongly influenced by the city would perhaps become re-established.

In one respect the charred cereal distribution from these sites does match documentary evidence. The lack of rye from these sites cannot be ignored. This species, though recorded as having been grown on many of the Hampshire estates of the Bishop of Winchester, appears to be a species only cultivated for short periods on specific manors (Titow, pers comm). The quantities recovered from the suburban sites in Winchester are possibly indicative of the general lack of rye cultivation and utilisation during the later medieval period in central southern England (Green 1994, 84–6).

Other Plant Remains

Remains from daub

The only significant quantity of daub recovered from any of the sites that contained charred plant remains originated from the same context (F10) as the layer that produced the large charred barley accumulation on the Sussex Street site. Plant remains were only recovered from those areas of the daub that had been reduced fired. Oxidised portions of the daub simply contained voids with fragmentary silica residues of the original organic material.

The botanical material recovered from the late Saxon daub was very similar in composition to that recovered from more recent unfired daub (Green 1979a, 258). Both wheat and barley straw constituted the major botanical components. The weed species recorded included corn cockle (*Agrostemma githago*), redshank (*Polygonum persicaria),* and corn marigold (*Chrysanthemum segetum*). These species are commonly associated with arable crops and fields and possibly originate as crop contaminants rather than material perhaps introduced from the source of the clay. Significantly, redshank was recovered from the fired clay waste of the Winchester Cathedral bell moulds (Green 1979a, 340). In that case, it has been concluded the bulk of the botanical constituents originated from horse dung. It is possible in the case of the daub that redshank originated from the clay / mud source. This species is commonly found growing on muddy otherwise bare soil patches in spring sown crops and similar bare and disturbed areas of pasture. Clearly straw was the main botanical constituent of the daub. However, the presence of redshank may suggest that one or both of the cereal crops represented may have been grown on heavier clay or in damp soil conditions. Deep clay with flint soil types capping the chalk bed-rock are characteristic of the Victoria Road (VR) area of the city, perhaps even indicating a local origin within the northern suburb of the city.

Whilst corn marigold (*Chrysanthemum segetum*) may often be regarded as a weed of sandy soils, it is a species commonly found within cereal and other preserved plant accumulations from Winchester. In this respect and given the absence of sandy soils in cultivation at this period in the area, this species clearly had a more ubiquitous origin than more recent plant studies and data might suggest.

Hyde Abbey garderobe

The plant remains from the fill of the garderobe (Trench XIV) on the Hyde Abbey site were originally believed possibly to be associated with the Prior's lodging or guest hall of the monastic establishment. However, they have subsequently been redated to the 18th or early 19th centuries. The botanical evidence was entirely preserved by mineralisation (calcium phosphate replacement); it consisted of the seeds of false and fleshy fruits. Elderberry (*Sambucus nigra*) was the main botanical constituent, followed by blackberry (*Rubus fruticosus*), raspberry (*Rubus ideaus*), grape (*Vitis vinifera*), and fig (*Ficus carica*). *Prunus* species seem to be lacking from this assemblage. There is a virtual absence of cereal bran fragments which are normally to be found in cess and garderobe pits of the medieval period, and this absence may be indicative of the consumption of highly processed white bread. A virtually identical deposit has recently been recorded by the author; it was recovered from the latrine of a former private school in Romsey dating to the late 19th century. The deposit was characterised by large quantities of raspberry seeds and some bran, possibly suggesting that a significant component of the diet was raspberry jam sandwiches.

Other economic crops

Pulses

The earliest medieval phases on these sites seem to lack any significant evidence of pulse crops. Pulses from sites in Winchester are most likely to be found either preserved by phosphatic mineralisation or have been recognised from waterlogged deposits where hilum fragments have been recorded. Such material has been recovered from well-preserved waterlogged deposits on medieval intra-mural sites (Green forthcoming). Sites such as Castle Yard within the city, whilst situated well above the modern or ancient water table, have also produced plant materials preserved anaerobically beneath the later castle mound. No such deposits were located on any of the suburban sites discussed here. Contexts from the 13th century onwards, from Victoria Road, Crowder Terrace, Henly's Garage, and Hyde Abbey produced legumes such as pea (*Pisum sativum*) and bean (*Vicia faba*), albeit in small quantities and preserved in the main by charring or mineralisation. Other legumes do appear more widely in these contexts and include *Vicia* and *Lathyrus* species. These latter are most likely merely contaminants of other crops, rather than cultivars in their own right, since it would have been difficult to separate out ruderal legumes from the main cereal or legume crop. Lentil, as mentioned above, has only been recovered from a restricted range of contexts in Winchester and only on the Hyde Abbey site in the suburbs.

Fibre Crops

Significantly, evidence of flax (*Linum usititissimum*) was recovered from only one site, the excavations at the Lido in the northern suburb: it was found in a 12th- to 13th-century deposit, F39. Hemp (*Cannabis sativa*), a species present on Saxon waterlogged sites within the walls such as at New Minster, was absent from the suburban sites. Other arable crops were poorly represented, once again probably due to the absence of waterlogged preservation conditions, though the presence of herb species must not be underestimated.

Part of the medieval economy involved the cultivation of plants and fruits in urban back gardens (Keene 1985, 152). Leeks, parsley, onions, beans, peas, vetches, sage, and hyssop are all recorded in the 15th century. Small garden areas were used for the production of specialist crops clearly being grown for profit. Opium poppy (*Papaver somniferum*), was recovered in quantities from the Crowder Terrace site. It may have been deliberately cultivated for medicinal or more likely culinary purposes. The material was mineralised and it is therefore highly likely the poppy seeds originated from human faecal material (Green 1979b, 279–84).

Orchard crops

Orchard crops or fruit species that could have been collected as part of a hedgerow or garden harvest were generally absent from the late Saxon phases, with the exception of elderberry (*Sambucus nigra*) that seems to be ubiquitous. It is very difficult to interpret evidence of this species. The seeds naturally survive for long periods prior to decay and are frequently moved by insect activity, often to great depth below land surfaces, into older archaeological deposits. This was specifically observed on the Hyde Abbey site by the author, where ants were moving blackberry and elderberry seeds down into 18th-century loosely compacted archaeological deposits. Furthermore, even concentrations of greater than 200 plus seeds per 5000ml of sample processed may not reflect any specific anthropogenic activity. Thus for the purposes of this discussion this species is not considered as providing any reliable information. It was probably always present, especially on vacant or poorly maintained properties, and was probably tolerated, as it is so often today, in hedgerows and the margins of allotments, since its flowers and fruit have a number of culinary uses.

The general absence of other fruit species cannot only be attributed to the lack of waterlogged deposits; it must also be because few of the features that were available for sampling had a primary or even a secondary function as cess or garderobe pits. Thus, the earlier features contain a thin scatter of blackberry, some poorly preserved specimens of *Prunus*, rarely identifiable to species, and apple (*Malus sylvestris*) – and most of the early medieval evidence comes from the western suburb, an area that had gone into decline by the later medieval period. For the later medieval period, the evidence comes from the northern suburb. Thus pits on the Victoria Road site provided evidence of an increasing range and quantity of fruit species through time. These species were preserved by mineralisation.

Prunus species make up the bulk of the evidence. Due to the frequent absence of the endocarp identification could rarely be precise. However, cherry (*Prunus avium*) was recovered from Crowder Terrace and bullace (*Prunus insititia*) from Victoria Road. Blackberry was also recovered from deposits of this period, but raspberry was absent.

There was a general absence of exotic or imported

species from sites prior to the 15th century. From the later medieval contexts, grape and fig were found, in particular at Victoria Road, but also at the northern suburb site at St Barthomew's School. It is possible that these species were imported. Fig in particular does not set seed in the British Isles in any way that would be archaeologically recognisable (Williams 1977, 20). It can be suggested that individuals lower down the social scale, were probably consuming more of both these species in the 15th century than previously. Both these species were recovered from the 18th- or early 19th-century garderobe fill at Hyde Abbey.

It is also possible that the increasing practice of digging deep cess or latrine pits during the 14th and 15th centuries in the Winchester suburbs has led to the skewed impression that fig and grape became more widely consumed in the later medieval period. The increased presence of mineralised remains of fruit species does suggest an increasing use of pits for the disposal of human waste. This may reflect an increased density of population, possibly increased land values. Maybe smaller yards and garden areas where it would be less acceptable to tolerate surface middens lead to more pits being excavated. Fundamental changes in the methods of refuse disposal may also be an increasing characteristic of change from a semi-or suburban economy with mechanisms for disposal via manuring to an increasingly urban one, where households had no other means of waste disposal involving land they may have farmed or had access to outside the city or its suburbs.

The absence of pits on most Hampshire rural village sites is a noticeable characteristic and is also a feature of the smaller urban centres such as at Romsey (Green & Lockyear 1992). Refuse disposal on rural sites seems to have been via surface middens cleared and used as manure on adjacent town fields and backland areas well into the post-medieval period. Even where cesspits exist on these other sites they seem to have been regularly cleaned and contain little evidence of organic residues until the late 18th century, not dissimilar to the evidence from the Hyde Abbey garderobe discussed above.

Hops

Evidence of hops (*Humulus lupulus*) was recorded on both the Hyde Abbey and Victoria Road sites, albeit as single finds. It is known from documentary sources that this species was cultivated in the northern suburb and the regular spacing of bedding trenches at the New Road site (western suburb) is perhaps a more tangible piece of evidence for cultivation of the species than the meagre finds from excavations. Most of the documentary information for hops suggests post-medieval cultivation when the suburbs had become depopulated.

Nut crops

Evidence of hazelnuts (*Corylus avellana*) was widespread on all the sites examined. The entire evidence

was preserved by charring, and therefore this species is no doubt significantly under-represented, especially if comparison is made with the anaerobically preserved street deposits found beneath the castle mound at Castle Yard (Green 1979a, 111 and fiche tables 51–60).

Evidence of industrial processes

The Victoria Road site consistently produced evidence of charred oak cupules. Such fragments are not at all common on archaeological sites and their interpretation is problematical. It can be suggested that this evidence may originate from charcoal brought into the city for domestic fuel in the later medieval period. It is perhaps significant that the oak cupule fragments were invariably associated with wood charcoal deposits that contained few if any other identifiable seed or extra floral botanical items. Cupules attached to small round wood will clearly become charred by the charcoal production process and could thus be imported into the city. There is, however, no specific indication from this evidence that charcoal was being produced in the suburbs, though this cannot be ruled out.

There is always the possibility that the oak cupule fragments originated with oak bark and chippings used in the tanning industry. Unpublished evidence recovered from Tanner Street in the city centre indicates that oak chippings were widely used, rather than oak bark, resulting in high levels of polyphenols still being present within the waterlogged deposits, with implications for long-term botanical preservation. The tanning industry was clearly located close to reliable and constant sources of water that were not readily available in the northern and much of the western suburb. The evidence from Victoria Road is simply too sparse to be meaningfully interpreted and, significantly, no evidence was recovered that would unequivocally support the documentary sources for the cultivation of madder, teasels, or flax in the suburbs (*cf* Keene 1985, 152). Also, information about the documented cloth finishing trades is virtually absent from the archaeological record (*cf* Rees *et al* 2008).

Weeds and the ecology of the suburbs

The ruderal species recovered from Sussex Street, Victoria Road and Crowder Terrace are not remarkable and give little additional information about economy or ecology of the individual sites. Ruderals of specific habitat such as chalk downland or typical of waterlogged areas were not recovered. Having said this some sites did produce weed floras containing species rarely recorded from intra-mural sites. Corn gromwell (*Lithpospermum arvense*) was specifically recorded on the Sussex Street site, in particular from F10. The pit was also associated with the large charred cereal deposit and the daub sample discussed above. This species could possibly either have originated as a site-specific weed, or it could represent seed regularly imported to the site as a crop contaminant. It may be over-represented in relation to other species as it has a greater chance of survival (Jones 1978, 197–8).

Another species that regularly occurred on the Sussex Street site and was also recorded on the Victoria Road site was cow parsley (*Anthriscus sylvestris*). This species was exclusively preserved by mineralisation. It is a species specifically associated with areas enclosed by hedges or fences away from the predation of sheep and rabbits. Cow parsley is to be widely seen on modern country roadside verges in early May when in flower, and whilst ubiquitous and by far the most common of umbelliferous species in southern England today, and probably in the past, its occurrence in seed form on archaeological sites is anything but common. It is unlikely that this species had any specific use, particularly to livestock since by the time it sets mature seed the rest of the plant has little nutritive value, though when dried it is suitable for kindling, or floor covering material.

The evidence for species related to specific habitats or environments increases throughout the medieval period. This relates as already stated to increasing numbers of pits containing mineralised or partly anaerobically preserved material. Mint (*Mentha* sp.) was recovered from Victoria Road from 14th- and 15th-century deposits. This may possibly reflect local damp conditions, since this is a species frequently found adjacent on damp ground or near streams. It is always possible that mint may have been a culinary herb and deliberately cultivated in back gardens. Unfortunately due to poor preservation the specimens could not be identified to species. Other species that may be indicative of damp ground included a range of *Cyperaceae*, possibly associated again with damp or acid grassland. Hemlock (*Conium maculatum*) was recovered from a number of 14th- and 15th-century contexts. It is a highly poisonous species, frequently found in damp and wet places, woodland margins, and hedgerows, possibly indicative of local environments. This species might have been brought to the sites in mixed vegetation for bedding or flooring materials, as suggested for cow parsley. Greater celandine (*Chelidonium majus*) was also recorded from the Victoria Road site. This prolific seeding species was always an important medicinal herb in the past, containing a number of poisonous alkaloids, traditionally used to cure warts and eye infections. Its grey-green or slightly glaucus foliage being quite ornamental, it is frequently tolerated in gardens even if not used for any specific purpose.

General discussion

The lateral variation and the lack of deposits of particular periods on many of these suburban sites in Winchester makes it difficult to interpret economic and social change over time in the city. As has been demonstrated, not all sites were equally densely occupied at all periods and the social status of the site's inhabitants was not the same through time, or across these sites. As has been seen, the variation between the sites is as much a function of preservation as it is of past economy, or wealth of the individuals inhabiting them. Preservation has clearly biased and skewed the evidence to such a degree that it is difficult to be certain of comparing like with like, not only on an inter-site basis but also between sites and through time.

Having said that, many of the botanical finds are a direct reflection of cultural activities, for example the material recovered from garderobe or latrine pits. However, without further detailed cultural and historical information on these sites, it is impossible to be more specific about the economy of individuals and the social implications of differential refuse disposal mechanisms. Different groups or individuals may have discarded their refuse in a variety of ways that is not apparent from the botanical material currently available. The evidence from these sites on the periphery of Winchester suggests that major industrial activities using plant products were not taking place or have left little or no specific evidence in the archaeological record. Since the bulk of charred cereal grain deposits, so far recovered, have been located within the suburbs, the evidence suggests that the storage and sale of such crops perhaps took place in these specific areas. This is possibly consistent with the documentary evidence (*cf* Biddle 1976, 265; Keene 1985, 152) for the western suburb of the city.

Overall, the plant materials from the suburbs of Winchester provided a complete contrast to the earlier recovered evidence from excavations undertaken under the direction of Martin Biddle and the Winchester Research Unit. These earlier excavations were predominantly on low-lying waterlogged sites or where anaerobic conditions existed in the city centre, also at Wolvesey Palace and Winchester Castle. The two sets of data are complementary, involving as they do very different preservation conditions and sites of very different spatial and social patterning and it is for these reasons that at present it is virtually impossible to integrate the two data sets. The need to undertake the detailed sampling and retrieval programmes on the suburban sites, where essentially only charred and mineralised plant remains were preserved, has been demonstrated here. Furthermore, this highlights the need to undertake further detailed research, as and when such opportunities arise, for the recovery of data sets of mineralised and charred plant materials from city centre sites. The analysis of specific features that contain material preserved in the same way may provide the basis for obtaining such information. All the pits examined from sites in Winchester produce a consistent charred cereal component. It may therefore be that pits may represent the best group of features for time depth studies of cereals and some other charred crop plants from Winchester.

Comparison of the archaeological evidence with that available from documentary sources for the city (Keene 1985, 151–5), provides further information about plant species cultivated and utilised in medieval Winchester. The absence of evidence for the herb, vegetable, and dye plant species recorded in documentary sources from Winchester's suburbs is in sharp contrast to the evidence from the city centre and also the evidence from other English medieval cities and clearly reflects the preservation conditions encountered on the Winchester suburban sites.

This report has indicated the range of research and analysis that has been and is still possible from the material retrieved from the Winchester suburbs. The validity of this work is self-evident and the detailed analysis of urban charred plant assemblages provides an insight into site-formation processes and change through time. Waterlogged or anaerobically preserved plant materials may be more plentiful and better preserved, but are no easier to interpret, posing as they do different problems related to site formation processes. The charred and mineralised archaeological plant material from the suburban sites in Winchester is still one of the most extensive, consistently recovered archaeological assemblages from southern England and it is hoped this discussion provides a greater insight into some aspects of plant usage and life within Winchester's medieval suburbs.

3 Late Saxon and medieval animal bone from the western suburb *by J P Coy*

Introduction

Materials and methods

The animal bones from the late Saxon and medieval western suburb were excavated between 1974 and 1979. Material was mainly recovered by hand, but at these sites in the western suburb a very comprehensive series of samples was also taken and wet-sieved to 1mm mesh.The analysis and computer recording (see Chapter 1) of the bones from the earlier phases was completed by the author in 1983, and a full report and archive prepared (Coy 1984). An attempt has been made throughout the working of this material to make the results comparable with those of other sites in Wessex studied in Southampton by the Faunal Remains Unit (FRU) during the 1980s. Bones and teeth were identified to species where possible; otherwise fragments were assigned to size classes, large ungulate or small ungulate. The bones from 13th-century and later contexts were studied somewhat differently, aiming to answer specific questions about the relationship between the different areas in the western suburb during this period and about the functions of some of the individual features. The usual context divisions of pit, ditch, and other contexts were observed, but bones from 13th-century and later contexts were not individually computer coded. Fragments were put into categories in the same way as for the earlier material, so that the statistics for this phase are comparable with those for earlier phases. This chapter is based on the report completed in 1984, with some updating of references. A full archive and the preliminary report is held with the bones by the Winchester Museums.

Arrangement of the chapter

Domestic ungulates are discussed first: relative proportions of the main species; parts of the body present; butchery and carcass utilisation; and finally the individual species. Other larger mammals – domestic and wild, birds, and fish are then described. The microfauna and amphibians are discussed separately. Most of the bones were recovered by hand, but samples were taken (see Chapter 1), and tables show finds from the sieved samples separately. The final part of the chapter provides an account for the main phases and features analysed.

Dating

The animal bones have been dated by association with the pottery. It was possible on the basis of associa-tions of differing pottery types in large pit groups, to suggest the existence of six ceramic phases covering the 9th to 14th centuries. Originally this dating was used to divide the stratigraphic sequence into six broad periods overarching all of the sites, Final Phases 10–15: but subsequent work suggested that this system was too inflexible a way of presenting such information. However, as a general indication of the passing of time the ceramic phases still hold good ,with the probable exception of Phase 14. This is discussed further in a companion volume to this one (P5).

It has proved more difficult to date each individual phase, as there is very little independent dating evidence from the western suburb, and, indeed, from the suburbs as a whole. By analogy with the pottery recovered within the defended area of the city, it is tentatively suggested that the earliest late Saxon phases (10 and 11) belong to the mid-9th to 10th centuries, the third (12) to the mid-10th to 11th centuries, and the fourth (13) to the later 11th and 12th centuries ('Saxo-Norman'). The latest material (14 and 15) is of medieval date (the now defunct Phase 14 has been retained in the tables).

The dating of each phase is summarised as follows:

Phase 10	late Saxon	mid-9th – 10th centuries
Phase 11	late Saxon	early – mid-10th centuries
Phase 12	late Saxon	mid- /late 10th – 11th centuries
Phase 13	Saxo-Norman	late 11th – mid- /late 12th centuries
Phase 14	medieval	late 12th – 13th centuries
Phase 15	medieval	late 12th – mid-14th centuries

Area and contexts studied

The overall totals for the animal bone fragments studied both from normal excavation and from sieving are given in Table 3.1, by site and by phase. This overall total of over 40,000 bones includes nearly 10,000 very small fragments from sieved samples, which are shown separately in Table 3.2. These contained most of the fish, nearly 2000 amphibian bones, and a small number of bones of rarer species of mammal and of bird. The bulk of the material represents the bones of common domestic ungulates. For common domesticates the anatomical elements are given in Appendix Tables A3.2–3.28 for all the material in Phases 10–14 and for the significant contexts of Phase 15. The anatomical elements of other mammals and all birds are detailed in Appendix Tables A3.29–3.46.

Table 3.1 Western suburb: overall totals for animal bone fragments

Phase	Context type and date	Crowder Terrace (CT)	New Road (NR)	Sussex Street (SXS)	Total
10A	Late Saxon pits		1322	6702	**8024**
10B	Late Saxon other			775	**775**
10C	Late Saxon ditch		293		**293**
11A	Late Saxon pits	54	889	6247	**7190**
11B	Late Saxon other		187	338	**525**
11C	Late Saxon ditch		183		**183**
12A	Late Saxon pits			1591	**1591**
12B	Late Saxon other			17	**17**
12C	Late Saxon ditch	213			**213**
13A	Saxo-Norman pits		61	5015	**5076**
13B	Saxo-Norman other	2033	23	293	**2349**
13C	Saxo-Norman ditch		282		**282**
14C	12th/14th-century ditch			212	**212**
14B	12th/14th-century other			210	**210**
15C	12th/14th-century ditch			54	**54**
15A	12th-/14th-century pits	6768		1367	**8135**
15B	12th-/14th-century other	63	36	1529	**1628**
15C	12th-/14th-century ditches	299	2279	996	**3574**
Total		**9430**	**5555**	**25346**	**40380**

The western suburb sites analysed include Sussex Street (SXS), New Road (NR), and Crowder Terrace (CT). A section of the Oram's Arbour enclosure ditch (referred to in the figures and tables as the 'OA ditch') was excavated at New Road. Some small collections are omitted from the discussion and some of the tables. About 32,000 of the 40,000 bones are from pits. Four large collections each contained over 5,000 bones: two from late Saxon pit groups from Sussex Street, one from early medieval (Saxo-Norman) pits in Sussex Street; and the fourth from the medieval period pits at Crowder Terrace.

Bones from pits, ditches, and other features have as far as possible been analysed separately, as earlier work has shown that for animal bones important information may be lost by lumping together material of different origins. Comparisons between phases and sites were strengthened by separating the results from different types of context and so comparing like with like. Since this study, faunal analysis techniques have become more sophisticated with the level of deposition in pits, for example, also being taken into account in comparisons (Maltby 1985). Results from all deposit types, however, complement one another. Who knows which gives a 'truer' picture of life?

Context differences

The condition of the bones is discussed below for each major group analysed, but some aspects are summarised here. As is usual in any animal bone analysis, the more the sample is split up into its constituent parts the more complicated the factors are seen to be. The proportion of bones which could be identified to anatomy but could be identified only as large or small ungulate is shown in Table 3.3. Column A shows the total number of bones identified as horse, cattle, and cattle-size (c-size) and column B shows the percentage. Columns C and D show the same for sheep, goat, pig, and sheep-size (s-size). Table 3.4 shows the number of fragments which could not be identified even to anatomical element and were recorded only as large (cattle-size) or small (sheep-size) ungulate fragments.

Some pits contained primary deposited material, which is suggested by the presence of joining bones. This does not guarantee, however, that these were wholly primary deposits, that only one process was involved in the deposition, or that post-deposition movement had not taken place. To assume otherwise would be naive in the light of the findings from the detailed analysis that was carried out on one pit at

Table 3.2   Microfauna, fish, and small fragments of large species from sieved samples

Phase	1 UNX	2 UNM	3 UNB	4 FISH	5 FROG	6 TOAD	7 AMPH	8 SHREW	9 WVOLE	10 BVOLE	11 STVOLE	12 MOUSE	13 BRAT	14 UNMM	Total
10A		598	43	3438	1101	15	179	6	26					3	**5409**
10B		125	4	76	2										**207**
10C		17	1				1								**19**
11A		345	32	333	31	5	64							7	**817**
11B		22	5	19											**46**
11C		1	1				1								**3**
12A	10	50	16	6	28	11	208	1						1	**331**
13A	141	381	98	755	4		51	1			1	4		38	**1474**
13B		3	8	15		1									**27**
14A			1	20											**21**
14C			1												**1**
15A			27	158	58	56	91			1			1	2	**394**
15B		72	5	680	14		13							1	**785**
15C			47	18	1		5								**71**
Total	151	1614	289	5518	1239	88	613	8	26	1	1	4	1	52	**9605**

Key:

1	UNX unidentified very small fragments
2	UNM unidentified fragments, obviously mammal
3	UNB unidentified bird
4	FISH fish identified to species and unidentified (UNF)
5	FROG frog, probably common frog (*Rana temporaria*)
6	TOAD toad, probably common toad (*Bufo bufo*)
7	AMPH frog or toad
8	SHREW common shrew (*Sorex araneus*)
9	WVOLE water vole (*Arvicola terrestris*)
10	BVOLE bank vole (*Clethrionomys glareolus*)
11	STVOLE short-tailed vole (*Microtus agrestis*)
12	MOUSE house mouse (*Mus musculus*)
13	BRAT black rat (*Rattus rattus*)
14	UNMM unidentified small mammal

Hamwic (Colley *et al* 1988, 105). Some of the deposits showed a mixture of depositional processes, including the discarding of whole carcasses.

Some of the assemblages from the Saxo-Norman fill of the Crowder Terrace ditch included bones of a residual character. The contemporary fill of the New Road ditch and the later medieval ditch fills at both Crowder Terrace and New Road shared some of the same characteristics: all contain a high proportion of fragments which were unidentifiable to species. The last are mostly long-bone splinters and other small fragments which could only be put into the categories of large or small ungulate. The high proportion of unidentified bones is expected for bones which have been severely fragmented. The cause is possibly trampling. The different treatment of bones meted out by different excavators also needs to be taken into account. What is surprising is that the medieval pits and well at Crowder Terrace also contained a high percentage of unidentifiable bones (Tables 3.3 and 3.4). The percentage of loose teeth (Fig 3.1) follows a similar pattern to the fragments, being much higher in ditches than in pits except, again, in the medieval Crowder Terrace pits and well. The percentage of loose teeth tends to rise as material breaks up, either through complex depositional history or through poor preservation in the soil, but poor preservation is not a characteristic of these deposits. There is a very high percentage of dog gnawing on material from most of the western suburb; the percentage of bones from late Saxon and Saxo-Norman periods on which canid gnawing was recognised is shown in Figure 3.2.

The normal processes of butchery, domestic food

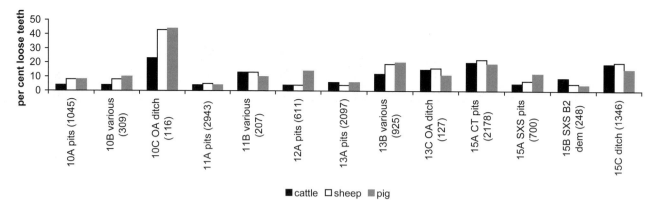

Figure 3.1   Western suburb: percentage of loose teeth in identified remains of cattle, sheep, and pig (sample size in brackets: key to site codes in Table A3.1: see text for definitions of phases: 'dem' demolition layer)

Table 3.3   **Percentage of fragments identified to anatomy in different context types**

| Phase | Context type | large ungulate | | small ungulate | | both |
		n	%	n	%	%
10A	pits	1165	18	1168	34	26
10B	various	270	17	330	21	19
10C	OA ditch NR F371	130	34	129	31	32
11A	pits	2770	21	3351	21	21
11B	various	253	41	211	28	35
11C	OA ditch NR F371	94	21	85	27	24
12A	pits	454	19	766	19	19
12C	ditch CT F74	69	48	151	34	39
13A	pits	1432	20	1938	18	19
13B	various	760	48	1520	45	46
13C	OA ditch NR F371	124	61	153	37	48
14A	pits	58	22	123	18	19
14B	various	63	24	136	41	36
15A	CT pits	1338	55	2465	44	48
15A	CT well	830	51	1434	48	49
15A	SXS pits	496	39	662	26	32
15B	SXS B2 dem	289	21	267	18	19
15C	CT ditch F74	147	57	142	51	54
15C	SXS F126 and F401	385	41	421	35	37
15C	NR OA ditch recut F391	524	50	1012	50	50
	all pits	8543	30	11907	30	30
	all ditch fills	1473	46	2093	43	44
	Total	**11651**	**33**	**16464**	**33**	**37**

n large ungulate total of cattle, horse, and large ungulate; n small ungulate total of sheep, goat, pig, and small ungulate (key to site codes in Table A3.1); OA Oram's Arbour; B2 dem demolition of Building 714.2

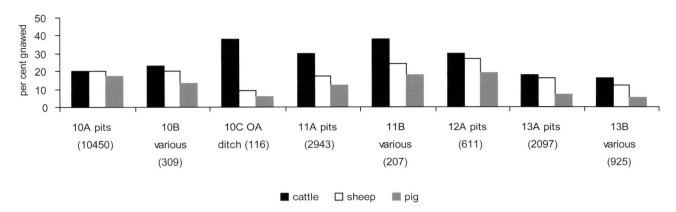

Figure 3.2   Percentage of gnawing on identified bones from selected groups (sample size in brackets: key to site codes in Table A3.1)

Table 3.4   Number and percentage of bones identifiable only to size class

Phase	Context type	cattle- + sheep-size		
		n	%	Total
10A	pits	1275	55	2320
10B	various	290	48	599
10C	OA ditch NR F371	130	53	246
11A	pits	3159	52	6102
11B	various	255	55	462
11C	OA ditch NR F371			
12A	pits	596	49	1207
12C	ditch CT F74			
13A	pits	1244	37	3341
13B	various	1341	59	2266
13C	OA ditch NR F371	149	54	276
14B	various	95	48	197
15A	CT pits	2417	64	3782
15A	CT well	1440	64	2253
15A	SXS pits	510	45	1146
15B	SXS B2 dem	238	49	486
15C	CT ditch	171	61	281
15C	SXS F126 and F401	362	46	794
15C	NR OA ditch recut F391	961	64	1509
15C	NR gullies	221	51	432
	pits only	10641	53	20151
	ditch only	1994	56	3538
	all features	14854	54	27699

Key to site codes in Table A3.1

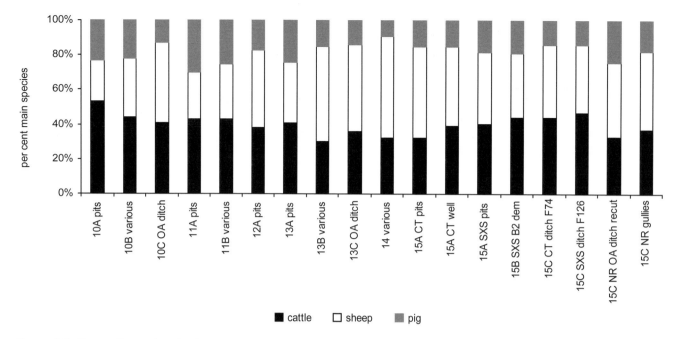

Figure 3.3   *Proportions of main domestic species (sample sizes as in Fig 3.1:key to site codes in Table A3.1)*

preparation, cooking, and in some cases several stages of waste disposal, including dog-gnawing, can render bones too fragmentary to be identifiable to species, though they may be identifiable to anatomical element, and it is most likely that the fills of the Crowder Terrace pits and well are fragmented from these causes. The high proportion of bones unidentifiable to species in these contexts is not necessarily an indication of residuality.

Domestic ungulates

General discussion

About 30,000 of the bones examined were from the common domestic ungulates: cattle, sheep, and pig. A minority of domestic ungulate bones were from goat and horse. Where bones bore the distinctive anatomical features of goat they were recorded as such but all other ovicaprid bones were tabulated as sheep, as the overwhelming majority of positive specific identifications were to sheep. The categories of cattle-size ungulate, ie from horse, cattle, or red deer ('c-size'), and sheep-sized ungulate, ie from sheep, goat, or roe deer ('s-size') were kept as broad as possible.

Proportions of species

The overwhelming majority of bones came from food remains and it is therefore only right to discuss first the proportions of the three major food species. Figure 3.3 shows the proportions of cattle, sheep, and pig for groups containing at least 100 identified fragments of the three species.

The overall proportions from pits do not differ much from ditches, but they do not show a rela-

tively higher proportion of cattle bones in ditches than in pits, as is often the case. The 9th- to early 10th-century pits (Phase 10) have an unusually high value for cattle and a low one for sheep, while it is the ditch that has a high proportion of sheep. If the proportions of the three main species are compared with contemporary Saxon Southampton (Bourdillon & Coy 1980, 83), overall, fewer cattle and sheep and rather more pigs were consumed in the western suburb of Winchester. The highest percentage of pig is in the late Saxon pits (Phase 11). In later periods in the western suburb, the percentage of pig is lower overall, but it is high in the Saxo-Norman pit (Phase 13) and the 13th-century ditch at New Road (Phase 15).

Despite the considerable variability revealed between contexts by the taphonomic analyses below, the overall picture of the relative importance of the three common species is of cattle and sheep most numerous for fragments, with pig well-represented and occasionally taking second place after cattle.

Because of their size, cattle would have provided the most meat in all phases. Overall, the second greatest quantity of meat would have been provided by pig. However, in some collections sheep would have taken second place for meat. A comparison of the three species, using the methodology described for Melbourne Street, Southampton (Bourdillon & Coy 1980), would give average meat ratios for the western suburb of: cattle – 77 per cent, sheep – 10 per cent, and pig – 13 per cent.

Parts of the body

The detailed anatomical listings of the main domestic species are shown in Appendix Tables A3.2–3.28. It is clear from these that there are no large specialised

Table 3.5 Percentage and number of head and foot bones, excluding loose teeth, of cattle, sheep, and pig

Phase		Cattle		Sheep		Pig	
		%	n	%	n	%	n
10A		43	(518)	64	(229)	37	(217)
10B		44	(129)	44	(97)	45	(60)
10C		47	(36)	53	(30)	56	(9)
11A		33	(1214)	38	(758)	50	(819)
11B		44	(78)	40	(58)	51	(45)
12A		56	(220)	45	(262)	57	(93)
13A		48	(810)	39	(685)	31	(480)
13B		46	(249)	52	(366)	51	(110)
13C		38	(39)	47	(25)	44	(7)
14A		70	(30)	41	(49)	37	(16)
14B		55	(33)	47	(57)	12	(8)
15A	CT pits	59	(361)	55	(570)	63	(177)
15A	CT well	49	(233)	45	(291)	62	(88)
15A	SXS pits	35	(235)	50	(248)	49	(105)
15B	B2 dem	36	(99)	35	(88)	43	(44)
15C	OA ditch	61	(135)	30	(191)	56	(106)
15C	All ditches	49	(371)	40	(372)	48	(186)

Key to site codes in Table A3.1

deposits in the western suburb during these periods as there were for the Roman contexts where particular anatomical elements of cattle were used for bone-working (Maltby in press). Some localised concentrations are discussed below. Finds of associated bones that would normally articulate – usually ankles, elbows, or feet of the common domesticates – were quite frequent and are detailed in archive.

Table 3.5 gives an overall picture of the distribution of non-meat bones, ie those of the head (skull, upper jaw, and lower jaw but excluding loose teeth) and foot bones (carpals and tarsals, metapodials, and phalanges). Where figures of non-meat bones are higher they suggest the preparation of carcasses or at least the use of whole carcasses rather than sides of meat. What is notable is that so many of the non-meat values are quite low, being well below half the bones found, and that this does not seem to show any change in pattern through time.

There are higher values, suggesting preparation of pig carcasses, in Phase 15, with rather more head fragments in Crowder Terrace pits and rather more foot fragments in Sussex Street pits, but differences are small. Variability in the different deposits does not necessarily demonstrate that there was a change of activities in a period; it may merely mean that the excavations revealed this type of deposit in one period and not in another.

Butchery and carcass utilisation

The method of treating the carcass changed between the late Saxon period and the later Middle Ages. In the late Saxon phases 'paramedian' butchery of the vertebrae was fairly common, but not universal. It often involved butchery with a sharp implement leaving blademarks along one side of the body of the vertebra. An example of a paramedian chop on the axis vertebra of a sheep is shown in Figure 3.4. In most examples, the chops cut through the transverse processes and also often cut slightly into centra. In about one third of the cases recorded there is cutting along the other side of the vertebral column as well, but usually not with such a clean cut. The first paramedian cut may have been to divide the carcass while the second may relate to later, perhaps amateur, butchery. Paramedian butchery can be distinguished by its great accuracy and regularity from other off-centre chops which may have been early attempts at median splitting. The latter attacks the centrum or body of the vertebra itself but fails to go through the central neural canal. Table 3.6 shows the occurrence of median and 'paramedian' butchery (chopping through the transverse process at the side of the vertebra). Where several vertebrae join together and all show splitting this is only counted once. The number of vertebrae of the species in the phase is taken as a baseline. Samples from Phase 15 are

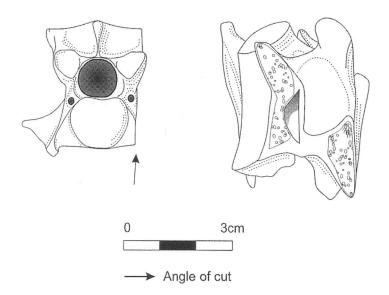

Angle of cut

Figure 3.4 'Paramedian' chop mark on sheep axis from 12th- to 14th-century pit at Crowder Terrace (c.223) (Drawing by P Copeland)

Table 3.6   Paramedian and median axial butchery

Phase	Cattle			Sheep			Pig		
	paramedian	median		paramedian	median		paramedian	median	
	%	%	n	%	%	n	%	%	n
10	20		98			33	8		39
11	17		197	22	2	178	10		155
12	38		26	17	7	40	20		5
13	22	6	162	9	11	118	21	2	87
14	3		7	42		12			
15	1	7	13		9	11		1	9

n = n vertebral fragments; paramedian = chops close to the midline; median = midline chops

Table 3.7   'Blademark' butchery on beef bones

Phase	n	n butchered	n with 'blademarks'	% with 'blademarks'
10A	559	184	29	16
11A	1266	585	193	33
12A	231	99	45	45
13A	858	246	54	22
13B	282	42	11	26

n total identified bones

too small for analysis. In Phase 15 all but one instances of axial butchery were median.

Midline (median) splitting of animal carcasses along the axis of the animal first appears with certainty in the 11th or 12th centuries (Phase 13), although there are some, probably fortuitous, median chops on individual vertebrae before this. This date corresponds with the appearance of the same type of butchery found in medieval Flaxengate, Lincoln (O'Connor 1982,16).

Butchery using a sharp blade was seen from the late Saxon period onward. 'Blademarks' were noted on limb bones as well as vertebrae of the common species. Table 3.7 shows the percentage incidence on cattle bones from the larger collections. Sheep and pigs were sometimes butchered similarly, especially in Phase 11. The blade used appears to have been flexible as the cut surface is not always quite flat, especially when large bones are being cut right through or muscle attachments scooped out. The sharpened metal edge left a characteristic blademark, carrying a record of blade-edge imperfections down the cut surface, as illustrated in Figure 3.5, and in some cases revealing a mark like that of a thin knife blade. The weight behind this butchery, however, carried it through some very

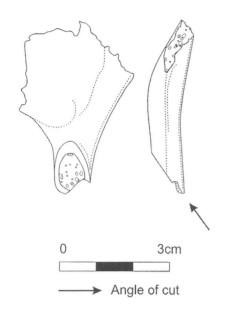

0   3cm

⟶ Angle of cut

Figure 3.5 'Blademark' chopping through sheep or goat ilium from late Saxon Sussex Street (c.1186) (Drawing by P Copeland)

large bones. It is not clear whether the implement was of one type or whether both cleavers and knives were involved.

Similar 'blademark' butchery, often involving scooping out of the muscle attachments from large bones, was noted in Southampton. It is rare in middle Saxon material but more common in late Saxon material from the Six Dials, Downer-Baker, and York Buildings excavations (Bourdillon, pers comm). This butchery is very different from the normal middle Saxon type observed in Hamwic where blademarks were rarely visible (Bourdillon & Coy 1980, 96–7). Instead, the type of butchery found, also observed in Winchester, involved chops right through the main long bones of cattle, especially in the joint areas.

There is a very small amount of sawing. Sometimes it is quite difficult to distinguish this from the blademark butchery because of the parallel lines that the blademark butchery leaves on the cut surface from its blade snags. But blademark butchery often takes a slightly wavy course and the lines run in the direction of the cutting whereas the lines made on the cut surface by a saw are, presumably, at an angle to the direction of the opening cut. When this careful distinction was made, it was clear that saws were mostly in evidence on horn cores and their parent skulls.

Almost all ungulate horn cores showed butchery marks. Some marks could have been made during separation of the skin but sawing through probably indicates removal for exploitation of the horn. Horn cores are discussed further below under species headings.

What were the animals like?

A crucial piece of information that this study has yielded is the difference in gross size of the major

domesticates from period to period. Comparisons can also be made between Winchester and other parts of Wessex. Work at Southampton has shown middle Saxon livestock to have been of a good size whereas in the early post-Saxon periods the size diminished. Cattle then returned to middle Saxon size ranges by the 16th century but sheep did not (Bourdillon 1983).

Selected bone measurements of the main domestic animals are included in the archive and have also been included in the ABMAP computer database of bone measurements *http://ads.ahds.ac.uk/catalogue/specColl/ abmap* (Serjeantson 2005).

Withers heights have been calculated for the main domestic ungulates (Table 3.8). These follow Driesch and Boessneck (1974), using mean values for cattle metapodials, since withers heights calculated for cattle from other long bones need to be interpreted with caution. Height ranges for animals from the western suburb are compared with those from Southampton.

Individual Species

Cattle

Cattle size analysis is complicated by the small samples, sex dimorphism, and other sources of variation in the samples, which are very heterogeneous.

The metacarpus (Fig 3.6) demonstrates this sexual dimorphism. An index of splaying was calculated by dividing the maximum distal breadth, the most distal measurement in this bone, by the breadth at the distal fusion point. This was plotted against a measurement which represented relative size, as the index would be size variable. The separation is very similar in each of the periods plotted, so presumably represents sexual dimorphism. Here it is suggested that the upper cluster probably represents male animals, possibly mostly castrates. In both clusters there is a suspicion of the presence of individuals with more splaying to the right of each distribution.

Comparison between the main periods shows that cattle sizes are remarkably similar. Winchester Saxon cattle bone measurements all came within the Hamwic ranges but averages at Winchester were slightly lower in most cases, often lacking the larger individuals at the top of the Hamwic range. This can be seen in Table 3.8 for the withers heights. Perhaps this compares with the late Saxon start of size diminution noted for medieval Southampton.

Cattle horn core lengths (Table A3.47) in the Saxon deposits ranged from small to medium size using the categories defined by Armitage and Clutton-Brock (1976) for medieval horn cores. There were only two for Phase 13, both short. One from medieval deposits was also in the short category. The more frequent measurements of base dimensions suggest a similar size range in the late Saxon and Saxo-Norman periods. Some horn core shapes were reminiscent of those from middle Saxon Hamwic but others bore similarities to those in the large sample of early medieval cores from Reading Waterfront (Coy 1997).

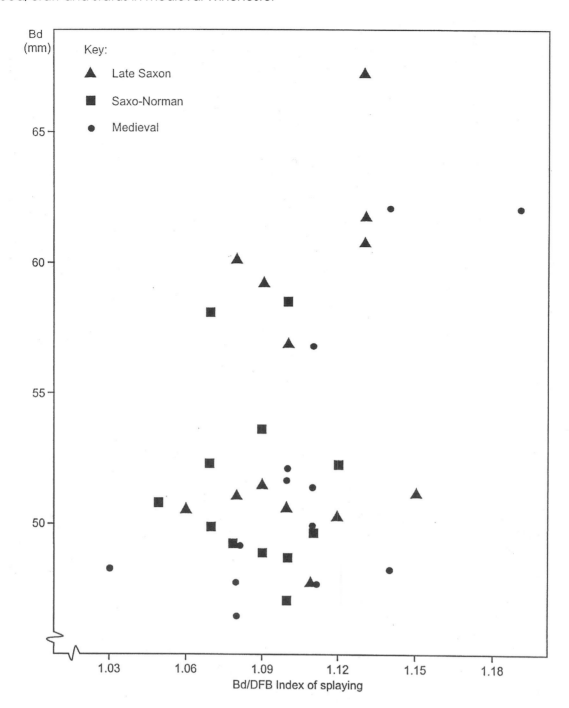

Figure 3.6   Cattle metacarpus: scatter diagram showing distal breadth (Bd) x index of splaying, calculated by dividing the maximum distal breadth by the breadth at the distal fusion point

Age estimates are based on numerical values for tooth eruption and wear, using the method of Grant (1975, 1982). The small sample of jaws from western suburb has been combined as there seemed no noticeable difference in emphasis between phases. Mandibles with ageing data mostly gave values of 41–2 or 44–6, with a few jaws from earlier stages (Fig 3.7). The wear on loose teeth augmented this distribution. This represents animals with quite heavy wear on all the molar teeth. Actual ages can only be guessed at but these animals were at least in their third year and some may have been considerably older. This suggests some concentration on cattle breeding, if not dairying, in the late Saxon and earlier medieval periods in this part of the city.

In order to test this, long bone fusion data was analysed as well as the incidence of porous fragments denoting immaturity and those bones recorded as calf. The evidence is difficult to interpret. There is a high incidence of unfused metapodials and calcanea in Phase 11 pits, bones which fuse nowadays at 2–3 and 3–4 years, respectively. On the other hand two thirds of the (earlier fusing) distal humeri were fused. This suggests there were animals around which would fill in the gaps in the age distribution suggested in Figure 3.7. The anomalies between the dental and fusion

Table 3.8 Withers heights of domestic ungulates (m) compared with Southampton

Species	Phase	Site	n	Range (m)
Cattle	Mid Saxon	Southampton	77	1.02–1.38
	Late Saxon	Southampton	7	1.09–1.22
	Late Saxon	Western suburb	20	1.02–1.22
	Saxo-Norman (FP13)	Western suburb	3	1.06–1.08
	Med	Western suburb	1	1.16
	12–13th C	Southampton	9	0.98–1.19
Sheep	Mid Saxon	Southampton	184	0.50–0.71
	Late Saxon	Western suburb	44	0.49–0.66
	Saxo-Norman	Western suburb	18	0.51–0.61
	Med	Western suburb	17	0.51–0.59
	12–13th C	Southampton	22	0.52–0.59
Pig	Mid Saxon	Southampton	15	0.63–0.78
	Late Saxon	Western suburb	3	0.59–0.71
	Saxo-Norman	Western suburb	4	0.67–0.74
	Med	Western suburb	5	0.64–0.78
?Wild boar	Mid Saxon	Southampton	1	0.83
	Late Saxon	Western suburb	1	0.86

Table 3.9 Epiphyseal fusion of cattle

Phase	distal humerus (1–2y)		distal metacarpus (2–3y)		distal tibia (2–3y)		distal metatarsus (2–3y)		proximal tibia (3–4y)		proximal calcaneum (3–4y)	
	f	nf	f	nf	f	nf	f	nf	f	nf	f	nf
10A	2	4	2	2	4	0	5	5	0	4	1	4
10B			2	1	1	2	0	3			0	3
10C			1	0			1	0			0	1
11A	13	7	11	13	9	6	5	11	1	7	2	14
12A	2	1	2	1	3	2	1	1	1	0	2	1
13A	8	0	13	2	6	2	5	1	3	1	3	1

f fused; nf not fused (approximate modern fusion age is shown)

evidence may be due to differential carcass distribution but the samples involved are very small. In later phases fused bones appear to be more in the majority (Table 3.9).

The frequency of porous bones was no more than 4 per cent, except in a Phase 10 pit containing a partial skeleton of a calf. The consistent but low occurrence of young calf bones, which show no evidence of having been meal remains, supports the picture of cattle breeding, possibly only at a household level comparable with the keeping of a milking cow. The incidence of gross pathology is low and was confined mainly to the foot bones. A few dental anomalies were noted.

Sheep

The vast majority of the ovicaprid bones were from sheep. For the anatomical elements where distinction

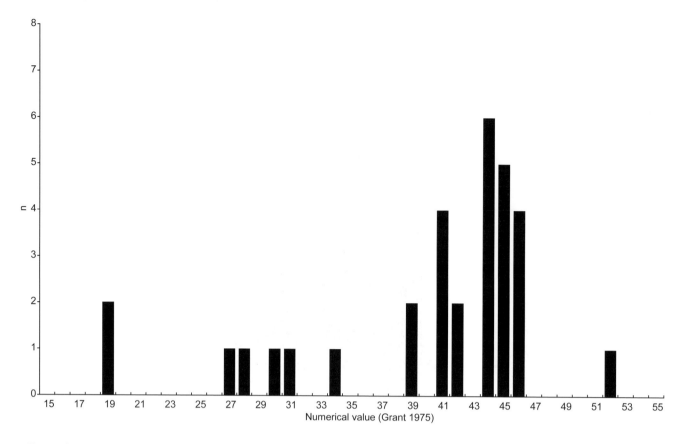

Figure 3.7   Late Saxon – 12th–14th century: dental age stages of cattle (after Grant 1975)

is difficult or impossible, such as mandible and distal tibia, all ovicaprid bones are dealt with together. Where possible though, bones were identified to species (Tables A3.2–3.28), using the anatomical criteria of Boessneck *et al* (1964) and accumulated experience acquired for Wessex at the Faunal Remains Unit.

Sheep bone measurements sit within the Hamwic range in most cases. Figures are given separately for late Saxon, Saxo-Norman and medieval bones. As explained above, a comparison of means is not very useful. Ranges and maxima show some differences between periods. Some of the Saxon bones show a higher maximum and this is sometimes reflected in the other statistics. There is just a suspicion of the post-Saxon size drop that occurred in medieval Southampton. The larger sample from Phase 15 allowed more detailed analysis for distal tibia and trochlea of the distal humerus. In all cases the distributions produced were apparently normal ones with no sign of bimodality: the means for New Road, Crowder Terrace, and Sussex Street were identical.

Horn cores were largely from males. As well as the small quantity which could be measured the many porous and unmeasured cores were also probably mostly from males. A clue to this may be the occasional evidence of hornless sheep. It is likely that at least some females in all periods were hornless. Hornless sheep are certainly present in Phase 15. A number of horn cores showed the characteristic 'thumbprint' marks first mentioned by Hatting

(1975), which was also found at Hamwic. This pathology of sheep horn cores is discussed by Kate Clark in Chapter 6 below.

Tooth wear data for sheep and goats (Fig 3.8) is given in the same format as for cattle using the method of Grant (1975) and includes estimates from jaws where some teeth are missing. The body of the distribution is between numerical values 30 and 42. Data from loose teeth fit this pattern. There are also two small lamb jaws with teeth missing and a jaw of a mature animal with heavier wear on the last two molars than in any of the complete jaws, representing a numerical value of more than 44. According to modern estimates, animals with the lower third molar not yet in wear (ie less than nv30) would be younger than two years although in medieval times the tooth may have taken longer to erupt. This distribution is similar to the much larger middle and late Saxon sample from Portchester Castle, although this had some jaws between nv 26 and 29 (Grant 1976).

In each period there are some distal humeri with unfused distal epiphyses (Table 3.10), confirming the presence of some animals younger than two years. We can as yet only speculate on the real age at death of these animals but it seems that most individuals were at least three years old, some perhaps considerably older. They could represent breeding or milking stock, or animals kept for a number of years for wool. That they also provided mutton is clearly shown by the butchery marks commonly seen on the sheep bones.

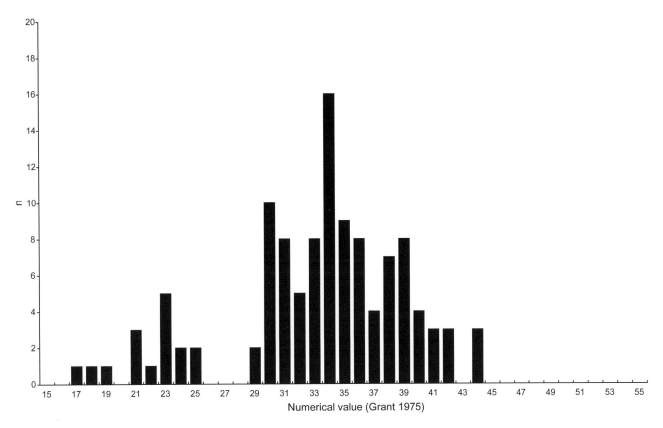

Figure 3.8 Late Saxon – 12th–14th century: dental age stages of sheep and goats (after Grant 1975)

Table 3.10 Epiphyseal fusion data for sheep and goat

Phase	distal humerus (10m)		distal metacarpus (6–12mo)		distal tibia (1–2y)		distal metatarsus (6–12mo)		proximal tibia (3–4y)		proximal calcaneum (3y)	
	f	nf	f	nf	f	nf	f	nf	f	nf	f	nf
10A	6	0	4	2	12	0	1	0	1	0	1	1
10B	2	0	1	1	1	2					2	3
10C	0	1	1	0	1	0						
11A	11	1	14	6	17	6	7	5	1	3	9	4
11B	2	1	3	1	0	2			1	0		
12A	9	0	2	0	10	4	2	2	3	2	1	0
13A	25	2	6	3	23	8	10	5	4	9	4	3
13B	3	0	2	1	6	0	3	1			2	2
13C	2	0			5	0						

f fused; nf not fused (approximate modern fusion age is shown)

There is a consistent background scatter of bones from small lambs in the same way as calf bones occur (these are detailed in archive). This is low throughout the Saxon contexts at up to 3 per cent of bones but is 6–8 per cent in some Crowder Terrace and Sussex Street contexts in Phase 15. Most lamb bones are from partial skeletons in pits but a few appear to have been chewed by people.

Pig

The pig measurements generally fit within the ranges for the much larger collection from Hamwic but lack the upper part of the distribution so means are generally lower.

Two bones may be from wild boar (*Sus scrofa*). In a Saxon period fill of Oram's Arbour enclosure ditch,

Table 3.11 Wear on pig jaws

	M1 not worn	M1 in wear	M2 in wear	M3 coming into wear	M3 full wear	M3 heavy wear
No.	0	16	38	16	6	0
%	0	21	50	21	8	0
nv		9–16	16–25	20–41		

Numerical value (nv) after Grant 1975 is also shown, including estimates

New Road, a lower third molar has a length of 36.1mm. A femur is also of wild boar size and gives a withers height of 0.86m. Immature pig bones large enough to be from wild boar were found in deposits at Sussex Street in all of the main periods. Some hind foot measurements are a little larger for the medieval ranges. This could suggest outbreeding with wild boar but might just be from larger domestic breeding stock. A cranial fragment of pig from Phase 13 demonstrates the shorter face of the domestic pig compared with that of wild boar even at this time. This fits well with the somewhat cramped tooth rows found.

Tooth wear data from the pigs is difficult to interpret or to relate to evidence from loose canine teeth and to fusion data from the bones. There are few complete tooth rows. Jaws from all periods, including estimates, were divided into six groups based on molar wear (Table 3.11). Tooth rows lack the evidence for very young and very old pigs necessary to postulate a breeding economy in the western suburb; rather they represent pigs at a stage of immaturity to provide good meat, with 70 per cent of the jaws from animals less than two years old.

However, there are some remains both from animals of breeding age and of piglets. Older animals are represented by some large male tusks and one or two very fragmentary teeth and jaws in both the late Saxon and Saxo-Norman period. There are some foetal and piglet bones in Phase 11, one bone from a very young pig in Phase 13 and several immature individuals in the Phase 15 pits in Crowder Terrace.

Goat

Bones identifiable to goat are shown with those of the commoner domestic ungulates in Tables A3.2–3.28. Horn cores from both sexes are present in all but Phase 15 and the evidence of cutmarks and working on some cores suggests that horn was used. Goat metapodials turn up in all but Phase 15. In Phase 11, four other postcranial bones were identified and a single humerus in both Phases 13 and 15. A goat metatarsus gives a withers height estimate of 0.65m and other goat measurements compare with the largest sheep.

Horse

Horse bones form less than 2 per cent of domestic ungulate totals throughout, with the only concentration in the demolition layers of the medieval building

714.2 at Sussex Street. Withers height estimates range from 1.25m to 1.43m (or 12 to 14 hands). This is pony size and is comparable with results from other Wessex sites of these periods. Horse bones which were definitely butchered were found in several late Saxon contexts. This was probably for human consumption, as was argued for Saxon Southampton (Bourdillon and Coy 1980).

Other Mammals

Species and anatomy data for the other domestic and larger wild mammals are tabulated for each phase (Tables A3.29–3.46). These include domestic dog and cat as well as the larger wild mammals.

Domestic dog

Only two dogs from the late Saxon period, from Sussex Street, Phase 10, could be measured. Both may be pathological. One was extremely gracile but otherwise compared well with a medium-sized modern dog with a shoulder height of 0.48m. It had suffered a greenstick fracture of the femur but died an adult. The second, also adult, had much shorter, but stouter, very bent limbs. It is not clear whether this was caused by a pathological condition such as rickets or whether such dogs were selectively bred. It would have been about two thirds of the height of the slender dog.

Dog bones from the Saxo-Norman period from Sussex Street (Phase 13) include a rather bent radius from a dog about half a metre at the shoulder, and other bones from two dogs slightly shorter. One has a healed fracture of the tibia and would have been taller if this had not occurred. Two bones are from larger dogs: an ulna and a fragment of mandible, wolf-sized. A skull from of the same date from Sussex Street had a healed facial fracture on the frontal-nasal suture. Such damage is not uncommon in prehistoric and early historic dogs. They were probably struck or kicked by people, perhaps when young and more susceptible to damage.

An interesting collection of dog bones came from the medieval fill of the Oram's Arbour enclosure ditch at New Road. This area was at the back of the King's Mews (Keene 1985). One distal femur was unfused, but otherwise all were mature. The dogs were well built and somewhat uniform in size: it is possible that they were old or sick hounds. The disposal of old hounds in medieval times may have involved death by hanging in a regular place.

Domestic cat

All periods produced skeletons of cats as occasional finds, definitely domestic in the cases where size and cranial evidence was available. There was no evidence of skinning as has been noted elsewhere. Cats became very important for their rat deterrent properties in medieval times, but, although the first rat remains were found in the 13th century, there are occasional finds of cat before that time.

Deer

Remains of red deer (*Cervus elaphus*) and roe deer (*Capreolus capreolus*) were found throughout the late Saxon period in very small quantities, but the former only as antler. In later medieval deposits there are not only a few cranial and foot fragments but also meat-bearing bones of red deer at all three sites and those of roe deer were found at Sussex Street. Fallow deer (*Dama dama*) is presumed to have been introduced after the Norman Conquest and certainly only appears here in the medieval deposits.

Hare

A small number of hare bones were found in late Saxon and medieval contexts. The medieval remains are compatible with brown hare (*Lepus europaeus*), the probable species, based on known chronological and geographical distribution. The only finds in any quantity were in pit F65 in Crowder Terrace. Hare represents high quality food and provides much more meat than a rabbit or fowl.

Other mammals from normal retrieval

There was the pelvis of a badger (*Meles meles*) in Phase 11 and bones of mole (*Talpa europaea*) in Phase 15. Whereas the former could have been meal remains, the bones of the burrowing mole may not necessarily be contemporaneous with the rest of the assemblage.

Birds

Bird bones are shown in Appendix Tables A3.29–3.46. All kinds of poultry, and many species of wild birds were found.

Domestic Fowl

Domestic fowl bones were commonest from pits where bones sometimes represented a partial or nearly whole skeleton. Fowl form the major non-ungulate food species throughout these deposits and would have been very important in the domestic economy.

There were no significant differences in size between bones of the late Saxon and medieval collections. Sizes are close to those from Saxon Southampton but the western suburb material lacks the highest measurements found at Hamwic, which brings down the means. Although there are some quite small fowl, there is also no evidence of the really small bantam cocks found at Hamwic. The Hamwic sample is much larger and that may partly explain its much larger size range.

Adult tarsometatarsi were separated into those with a spur, assumed to be cock birds, those with no spur (assumed to be from hens), and those with a crumbling spur or roughened area in the spur position which may have been castrated birds. Interpretation of spur evidence and caponisation has been the subject of some debate. While Coy (1983) proposed that bones with a rough area in the spur position were from caponised birds, West (1982, 1985) and others have demonstrated that this condition is in fact found in immature male birds. Cockspurs ranged from 6.2mm to 22.2mm in length, measured from the posterior surface.

All femora were checked for the occurrence of medullary bone. A notable find was a partial skeleton from the Saxo-Norman pit F30 at Sussex Street, the limbs of which contained medullary bone (Coy 1983,190). The tarsometatarsus had a small, hard, imperfectly-formed spur. This was presumed to have come from a laying hen and it is possible that this could be an older hen which had developed a spur.

Domestic Goose

Whereas remains of domestic fowl were in all but the very smallest collections, goose bones, although present in each western suburb period, were relatively rare. They were most common in medieval contexts. Sizes correspond with the more common domestic geese from middle Saxon Hamwic. It is presumed that these birds were of similar stock to the domesticated form of the greylag (*Anser anser*), which is found in large numbers from early and middle Saxon settlements in England (Bourdillon & Coy 1980, 117). There are records from the 14th to 15th century of ducks and geese wandering in the streets of Winchester, which they were not supposed to do (Keene 1985, 153).

Ducks

Finds were from all periods. Three categories of duck were recognised (Tables A3.29–3.46). The largest duck bones were either from the wild mallard (*Anas platyrhynchos*) or a domestic form with indistinguishable bones; none showed anatomical distinguishing features which definitely suggested domestication. Rather rarer were bones of smaller species, described in the tables as 'wigeon-sized duck' (*Anas* sp.). These are

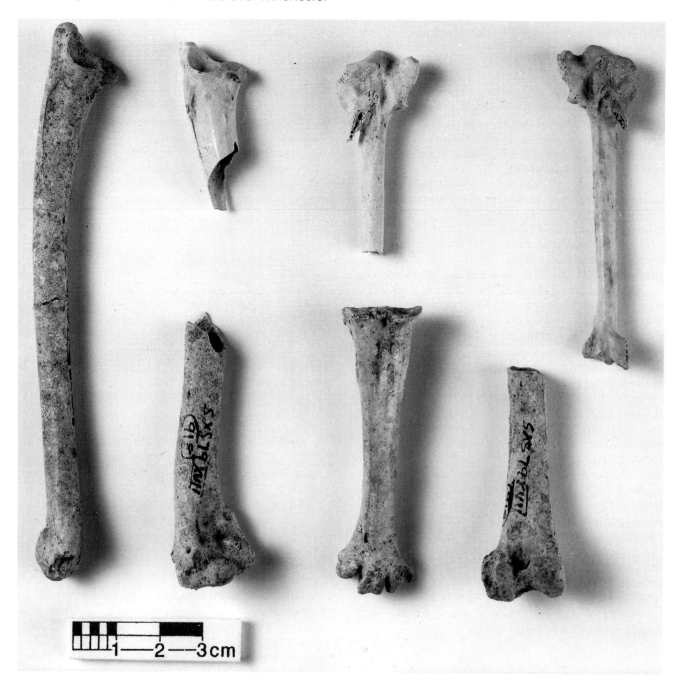

Figure 3.9   Bones of gyrfalcon (Falco rusticolus) from 12th- to 14th-century fill of Oram's Arbour enclosure ditch, New Road, and building 714.2, Sussex Street (Photograph by J Crook)

presumably from a wild duck, but could not be identified to species. A single find from the Saxo-Norman period is of a small duck which was an excellent match for teal (*Anas crecca*).

Waders

Waders were uncommon finds. Woodcock (*Scolopax rusticola*); common snipe (*Gallinago gallinago*); and another wader, probably *Tringa* sp. were found. Woodcock is the only wader which appears in several contexts. There was a single bone of the lapwing (*Vanellus vanellus*).

Game birds

Other wild species were the partridge, probably the grey partridge (*Perdix perdix*); water rail (*Rallus aquaticus*); and wood pigeon (*Columba palumbus*). The smaller pigeon bones included at least one definite identification of a rock or stock dove (*Columba livia/ oenas*). As dovecotes were quite common in Winchester gardens from the later 14th century and may well have been there much earlier (Keene 1985), this is likely to be a domestic or feral rock dove.

A law suit of 1412 which refers to the sale of birds and other food species mentions the sale of 'wood-cocks', doves, geese, partridges, plovers, and 'other birds'

(Derek Keene, pers comm), together with rabbits, capons, chickens, trout, and eels. That all these species could be purchased in Winchester in the 15th century throws new light on such finds from earlier periods. Their presence even in earlier medieval household refuse does not necessarily imply that the household bred, trapped or fished them.

Birds of prey and their quarry

No birds of prey were found in the late Saxon contexts, but three species were recovered from medieval deposits. The buzzard (*Buteo buteo*) and the red kite (*Milvus milvus*) would have been scavengers in the suburbs and probably in the centre of the town itself (Bramwell 1975, 18). In a Sussex Street pit there were several falcon bones (Fig 3.9) These are too large to be from peregrine falcon; they fit the modern size range of gyrfalcon (*Falco rusticolus*), well. The gyrfalcon did not breed in Britain at this time, so this is probably an Icelandic or Scandinavian bird imported for falconry and consequently highly prized. There are further bones of the gyrfalcon in the demolition deposits of the medieval building 714.2 at Sussex Street and one other in Oram's Arbour enclosure ditch (New Road). As is clear from the ulnas (Fig 3.9), the bones are from at least two birds, and may be from more. We know from documentary evidence that in the 14th century a royal falcon keeper was to be found in the Sussex Street area (Keene 1985, 356). The gyrfalcon (see frontispiece) was used to capture large birds, especially mallard, and was considered a hawk of the highest status.

Some bones of other large birds were found, all of which could have been the quarry of birds of prey: grey heron (*Ardea cinerea*) in several contexts; crane (*Grus* sp.), like the gyrfalcon from the Sussex Street building 714.2; and white stork (*Ciconia ciconia*), from an earlier pit. These species have been found on other Wessex sites of the Saxon and medieval period.

Other birds

There were a few fragmentary remains of passerine birds, mostly immature, of which some match immature specimens of house sparrow (*Passer domesticus*), starling (*Sturnus vulgaris*), jackdaw (*Corvus monedula*), blackbird (*Turdus merula*), and crow or rook (*Corvus corone / frugilegus*) in the reference collection of the FRU.

Fish and microfauna

Fish

The fish species with their scientific names are listed in Table 3.12. A summary of the numbers of fish bones recovered from the 1mm sieved samples is given in Table 3.2 and details of the identified species and skeletal elements are in Tables 3.13–3.16. The few fish

Table 3.12 Fish species identified from the western suburb and abbreviations used in Tables 3.13–3.16

ple	Pleurotremata: shark / ray
ray	*Raja clavata*: thornback ray
stu	*Acipenser sturio*: sturgeon
eel	*Anguilla anguilla*: common eel
con	*Conger conger*: conger eel
bre	Sparidae: sea bream
sca	*Trachurus trachurus*: scad or horse mackerel
mac	*Scomber scombrus*: mackerel
gad	Gadidae: cod family
cod	*Gadus morhua*: cod
hak	*Merluccius merluccius*: hake
gar	*Belone belone*: garfish
tur	*Scophthalmus maximus*: turbot
pla	*Pleuronectes platessa*: plaice
flo	*Platichthys flesus*: flounder
p/f	Pleuronectidae: plaice / flounder/ dab
fla	Heterosomata: flatfish
sal	*Salmo* sp.: trout or salmon
her	*Clupea harengus*: herring
b/m	*Dicentrarchus labrax* / Mugilidae: bass / mullet
unf	unknown fish species

bones retrieved from normal trowelling were mainly large conger eel and cod, which, if taken on their own, would have given a highly biased picture of fish consumption. The most useful result of the programme of sampling at Winchester has been the much fuller picture of the exploitation of fish that it has given. The fish bones are generally from pits rather than ditches, even though the latter were also sieved – possibly fish bone did not survive in the ditches where there was a lower density of bone than in the pits. A more detailed discussion of fish recovery bias is given in Coy (1989).

The three main concentrations of fish bone were all from Sussex Street, one came from the earliest group of Saxon pits, another from pits of the Saxo-Norman period, and the third was associated with the medieval buildings 714.1 and 714.2 in Sussex Street. The species and bone numbers shown in Tables 3.12–3.16 may not be a reliable reflection of fish consumption in the western suburb, because not all phases were sieved. Although sieving often leads to recovery of eel and herring bones, the actual number of fish bones retrieved is often fortuitous, depending upon the number and size of the bulk samples processed for each deposit.

Small bones of herring and eel may sometimes be evidence of cesspit material, often appearing crushed after having been subjected to the processes of chewing prior to passage through the alimentary canal (Wheeler & Jones 1989). However many of the herring and eel bones from the western suburb are probably not faecal

Table 3.13   Fish bones from 1mm sieved samples in late Saxon (Phase 10) contexts

	ray	eel	mac	cod	flo	p/f	sal	her	unf	Total
dermal elements	1	–	–	–	–	–	–	–	3	**4**
head bones	–	11	–	–	–	–	–	5	–	**16**
parasphenoid	–	–	–	–	–	–	–	1	–	**1**
premaxillary	–	2	–	–	–	1	–	–	–	**3**
maxillary	–	–	–	–	–	2	–	–	–	**2**
dentary	–	3	–	–	–	–	–	–	–	**3**
articular	–	6	–	–	–	–	–	–	–	**6**
quadrate	–	1	–	–	–	–	–	–	1	**2**
hyomandibular	–	3	–	1	–	–	–	2	–	**6**
preoperculum	–	1	–	–	–	–	–	–	–	**1**
operculum	–	1	–	–	–	–	–	2	–	**3**
branchiostegal	–	–	–	–	–	–	–	–	3	**3**
post temporal	–	–	–	–	–	–	–	2	–	**2**
supracleithrum	–	–	–	–	–	–	–	1	–	**1**
cleithrum	–	19	–	–	–	–	–	–	–	**19**
anal pterygiophore	–	–	–	–	1	–	–	–	–	**1**
thoracic vertebra	–	11	–	–	–	–	–	28	–	**39**
precaudal vertebra	–	291	–	–	1	1	–	395	–	**688**
caudal vertebra	–	636	2	–	–	–	–	378	–	**1016**
vertebra	–	–	–	–	–	–	1	248	71	**320**
ray	–	–	–	–	–	–	–	–	473	**473**
fragment	–	–	–	–	–	1	–	–	904	**905**
Total	**1**	**985**	**2**	**1**	**2**	**5**	**1**	**1062**	**1455**	**3514**

Key to species in Table 3.12

Figure 3.10   Dermal plate of sturgeon (Acipenser sturio) from 12th- to 14th-century building 714.2, Sussex Street (Photograph by J Crook)

in origin as the delicate small bones are perfectly preserved with even their small processes intact.

Species represented include some that could be locally caught, at least at some stage of their life history. Common eel was a frequent find in all periods, and there is a single find of salmon or trout. In the medieval building 714.2 in Sussex Street, Phase 15, there were some dermal bones of sturgeon (Fig 3.10), a highly prized species which now only rarely comes up English rivers.

Otherwise, finds were of marine fish. The incidence of marine fish is greater in the later periods and the finds represent a wide range of families at that time. Remains of the cartilaginous fish are not often preserved, but some ossified vertebral centra of shark or monkfish and the distinctive dermal denticles of the thornback ray were found in several contexts. Some of these elements are from cartilaginous fish which seem to have been of a very large size.

Herring was the most common find in all periods but from Saxo-Norman times there was more variety: cod, hake, garfish, bass, scad or horse mackerel, a species of sea bream, a species of mullet, and mackerel. Hake remains only appear in later medieval deposits (Phase 15). There were occasional flatfish finds throughout; mostly of flounder (which might have come up the

Table 3.14   Fish bones from late Saxon (Phase 11) contexts

	ple	ray	eel	sca	mac	gad	cod	pla	flo	p/f	fla	her	unf	Total
dermal elements	–	2	–	1	–	–	–	–	–	–	–	–	12	**15**
head bones	–	–	–	–	–	–	–	–	–	–	1	3	–	**4**
parasphenoid	–	–	1	–	–	–	–	–	–	–	–	–	–	**1**
premaxillary	–	–	–	–	–	–	1	–	–	–	–	–	–	**1**
dentary	–	–	–	–	–	–	–	–	1	–	–	–	–	**1**
articular	–	–	–	–	–	–	–	–	1	–	–	–	–	**1**
quadrate	–	–	–	1	–	–	–	–	–	–	–	1	–	**2**
hyomandibular	–	–	–	–	–	–	–	–	1	–	–	–	–	**1**
ceratohyale	–	–	–	–	–	–	–	–	–	–	–	1	–	**1**
branchiostegal	–	–	–	–	–	–	–	–	–	–	–	–	8	**8**
pharyngeal	–	–	–	–	–	–	–	–	–	–	1	–	–	**1**
branchial	–	–	–	–	–	–	–	–	–	–	–	–	1	**1**
supracleithrum	–	–	–	–	–	–	–	–	1	–	–	–	–	**1**
cleithrum	–	–	3	–	–	–	–	1	–	–	–	–	–	**4**
anal pterygiophore	–	–	–	–	–	–	–	–	1	–	–	–	–	**1**
thoracic vertebra	–	–	–	–	–	–	–	–	–	–	–	1	–	**1**
precaudal vertebra	–	–	10	–	–	–	–	–	–	–	–	25	–	**35**
caudal vertebra	–	–	24	–	1	–	–	–	15	2	–	71	–	**113**
vertebra	1	–	–	–	–	1	–	–	–	1	–	–	25	**28**
ray	–	–	–	–	–	–	–	–	–	–	–	–	74	**74**
fragment	–	–	–	–	–	–	–	–	–	–	–	–	58	**58**
Total	**1**	**2**	**38**	**2**	**1**	**1**	**1**	**1**	**20**	**3**	**2**	**102**	**178**	**352**

Table 3.15 Fish bones from Saxo-Norman contexts (Phase 13)

	ple	ray	eel	con	bre	mac	gad	cod	pla	p/f	her	b/m	unf	Total
dermal elements	1	–	–	–	–	–	–	–	–	–	–	*(1)	1	2
head bones	–	2	–	–	–	–	–	3	9	–	60	–	3	77
vomer	–	–	1	–	–	–	–	1	–	–	–	–	–	2
maxillary	–	–	–	–	–	–	–	–	1	–	–	–	–	1
dentary	–	–	1	3	–	–	–	–	1	–	2	–	–	7
articular	–	–	–	–	–	1	–	–	1	–	–	–	–	2
hyomandibular	–	–	–	1	–	–	–	–	–	–	–	–	–	1
branchiostegal	–	–	–	–	–	–	–	–	1	–	–	–	–	1
pharyngeal	–	–	–	–	–	–	1	–	–	–	–	–	–	1
supracleithrum	–	–	–	–	–	–	–	1	–	–	–	–	–	1
cleithrum	–	–	–	–	–	–	–	–	–	1	–	–	–	1
anal pterygiophore	–	–	–	–	–	–	–	–	3	1	–	–	–	4
vertebra	1	–	99	1	2	5	1	6	32	3	65	–	83	298
ray	–	–	–	–	–	–	–	–	–	230	–	–	13	243
fragment	–	–	1	–	–	–	–	–	–	–	7	–	122	130
Total	**2**	**2**	**102**	**5**	**2**	**6**	**2**	**11**	**48**	**235**	**134**	**0**	**222**	**771**

*( ) denotes occurrence of scales, not totalled

Table 3.16 Fish bones from medieval contexts (Phase 15)

	ple	ray	stu	eel	con	bre	mac	gad	cod	hak	gar	tur	pla	p/f	fla	her	b/m	unf	Total
dermal elements	–	5	1	–	–	–	–	–	–	–	–	–	–	–	–	–	–	*(2)	6
head bones	–	–	–	–	–	–	–	–	–	–	7	–	–	–	–	–	–	14	21
otoliths	–	–	–	–	–	–	–	–	–	–	–	–	–	–	–	–	–	1	1
vomer	–	–	–	–	1	–	–	–	–	–	–	–	–	–	–	–	–	–	1
premaxillary	–	–	–	–	1	–	–	–	–	–	1	–	–	–	–	–	–	–	2
maxillary	–	–	–	–	–	–	–	–	3	–	–	–	–	–	–	–	–	–	3
dentary	–	–	–	–	3	–	–	–	–	–	3	2	–	–	–	1	–	–	9
articular	–	–	–	–	2	–	–	–	–	–	–	–	–	–	–	–	–	–	2
quadrate	–	–	–	–	1	–	–	–	2	–	–	–	–	–	–	–	–	–	3
hyomandibular	–	–	–	–	–	–	–	–	–	–	–	–	1	–	–	–	–	–	1
preoperculum	–	–	–	–	–	–	–	–	–	–	–	–	–	–	–	1	4	–	5
ceratohyale	–	–	–	–	–	–	–	–	–	–	–	–	–	–	–	–	–	20	20
basihyale	–	–	–	–	1	–	–	–	–	–	–	–	–	–	–	–	–	–	1
branchiostegal	–	–	–	–	1	–	–	–	–	–	–	–	–	–	–	–	–	–	1
supracleithrum	–	–	–	–	2	–	–	–	2	–	–	–	–	–	–	–	–	–	4
cleithrum	–	–	–	–	1	–	–	–	1	–	–	–	1	–	–	–	–	–	3
post cleithrum	–	–	–	–	–	–	–	–	1	–	–	–	–	–	–	–	–	–	1
anal pterygiophore	–	–	–	–	–	–	–	–	–	–	–	–	–	2	–	–	–	–	2
caudal vertebra	–	–	–	–	–	–	–	–	–	–	–	–	–	–	–	–	2	–	2
vertebra	1	1	–	22	8	1	1	6	3	10	–	–	–	7	6	365	2	51	484
fragment	–	–	–	–	–	–	–	–	–	–	–	–	–	–	–	25	–	260	285
Total	**1**	**6**	**1**	**22**	**21**	**1**	**1**	**6**	**12**	**10**	**11**	**2**	**2**	**9**	**6**	**392**	**8**	**346**	**857**

*( ) denotes occurrence of scales, not totalled

river as far as Winchester) and plaice, but there was a single find from a medieval pit at Crowder Terrace of the more luscious turbot.

Small Mammals and Amphibians

The amphibians and small mammals (Table 3.2) tell us little about the surrounding ecosystems as most of the species represented are ubiquitous, even today. The most frequent finds, common frog, common toad and water vole, may be associated with water, the first two breed in water and the last frequently breeds along the banks of the Itchen, although all three species can also be found a long way from water. Other small mammals recovered from the sieved deposits were the common shrew, bank vole, short-tailed vole, house mouse and black rat (scientific names are in the tables).

However, accumulations of small mammal and amphibian bones in certain contexts may indicate a feature left open in antiquity. They may also suggest the time of year. The most spectacular find was a deposit of at least 50 frogs, some very large specimens, in a Late Saxon pit at New Road. Their presence suggests a pit open during the spring and acting as a pitfall trap.

Results by period and site

The account below discusses preservation of the bone and evidence for primary deposition and residuality. Particular points of interest in each context are also described.

Late Saxon – Phase 10

Most of the bones from this phase come from twelve pits in Sussex Street, with smaller samples from two pits (F50 and F51) at New Road (Table 3.1). Smaller assemblages were recovered at Sussex Street from features which possibly comprised the remains of buildings or other structures, from ditches possibly defining property boundaries, and from soil layers which have been interpreted as upcast from the digging of the late Saxon town defences. Some animal bone from Late Saxon fills of F371, the Iron Age Oram's Arbour enclosure ditch (New Road) was also considered here. Detailed results are in Tables A3.2–3.4 and A3.29–3.31.

Sussex Street pits

At a total of 8026 bones, including 3000 of fish, this is the largest collection from the western suburb. Most contexts contained bones of the common domesticates: cattle, sheep, and pig. This assemblage has the highest value for cattle in the western suburb. There were a number of finds of calf, including a part skeleton which had been butchered and later dog gnawed, and other immature cattle.

Horse came from five contexts and one pelvis was butchered. There was a goat axis vertebra in F43. Two dog skeletons were found and an immature cat and a small kitten. All contexts with larger samples contained bones of domestic fowl and goose.

Several associated bones were noted, in addition to the calf skeleton. The largest number were in pit F8, where the articulated foot bones and vertebrae of cattle, two elbow joints of sheep, lumbar vertebrae of pig, and vertebrae, and the partial skeleton of fowl were found.

Wild species (Table A3.29) included red deer antler and roe deer. There was water vole, common shrew, frog (with a deposit of several individuals in F424), toad, and mallard or domestic duck from sieved samples. Fish remains were recovered in most contexts (Table 3.13). This assemblage also constitutes the largest collection of fish bones in the western suburb. Herring vertebrae were by far the commonest element with eel vertebrae in second place.

The chop marks seen included several examples of 'blademark' butchery, discussed above.

New Road pits

This assemblage comprised 1322 bones. The common domestic species were represented throughout. Horse was represented by an incisor from an animal of about ten years and a butchered scapula. There was a goat horn core, which like all the horn cores in this phase, bore traces of sawing or possible blademark butchery at the base. A metapodial was identified as possibly from goat. A medium-sized dog was represented by a metapodial. No fish remains were recorded from these contexts, despite the fact that some were sieved.

The remains of the 50 frogs referred to above were recovered from the pit F50, suggesting, as discussed, that it was open during the summer months.

Sussex Street – various contexts

Only 775 bones were recovered from other features. The species ratios (Table A3.3) showed a higher value for sheep than for the Sussex Street pit deposits of this period, but this may be biased by the small sample. Associations noted were a cattle ankle in F47 and bones of a foetal or newborn pig in F48.

New Road: Oram's Arbour enclosure ditch, F371

These 293 bones show the highest percentage of jaw remains in the western suburb (Table 3.5). The percentage of cattle mandibles is the highest in the late Saxon deposits and the percentage of pig mandibles the highest of all the sites. There was a high percentage of loose teeth, up to 44 per cent for pig, which can be an indication of poor preservation. The percentage of canid gnawing on cattle bones was very high, though gnawing on sheep and pig bones was less common.

Horse bones were found in several contexts, as were cat and fowl bones. As well as disarticulated dog bones, a partial skeleton was found in c.476. Wild species include roe deer and blackbird, and red deer antler. There were no fish bones recovered, although some sieving was carried out.

Late Saxon – Phase 11

Bones were studied from seven pits at Sussex Street, four pits at New Road, and two at Crowder Terrace. Some other features, mostly ditches, at Sussex Street and also Oram's Arbour enclosure ditch at New Road (F371) produced bone which was assigned to this phase (see Table 3.1: detailed results are in Tables A3.5–3.7 and A3.32–3.33). The Sussex Street and New Road pit groups are described below, but it should be noted that the tables combine the figures from all the groups from this phase.

Sussex Street pits

With 6247 bones this is the second of the four large assemblages from the western suburb. The major domestic species were represented and there was much evidence of breeding and of bone associations.

As well as bones with dog gnawing, some on dog bones themselves, many lamb and chicken bones had probably been chewed and sucked by people. One chicken bone from F36 had been chewed by a cat.

There were several lambs and/or kids in pit F36 and also foetal and young piglets. A lateral metapodial from this pit is from a probable bull. The find in F53 of a maxilla of an extremely old pig with teeth worn to the roots may be from an old breeding sow and the same pit contained a collection of sheep or goat jaws of roughly the same age, all with a numerical value of about 34. There was a kitten bone in F500. Domestic fowl was found in most contexts but goose bones were found only in F53.

Wild species included roe deer, domestic duck or mallard, teal, woodcock, and water rail. One pit had several bones of hare, including some from the axial skeleton suggesting the consumption of saddle of hare. Some of the very large unfused pig bones which may have been from wild boar were found in this period. The fish represented are shown in Table 3.14; unlike Phase 10, there were only a few hundred fish bones recovered from sieving.

There were some fine examples of blademark butchery, similar to those seen in assemblage from the Phase 10 pits at Sussex Street. F53 contained a sheep skull carefully cut axially to one side of the midline and also several parts of a butchered cattle skull. In F500 there was a terminal phalanx of cattle apparently cut for removal of the hoof. A horse talus and meta-carpus in F36 both have knife cuts indicating at least skinning. Among the occasional dog bones, one ulna appears to have a knife cut on the medial midshaft, which could conceivably be the result of skinning.

Amphibian bones were found in almost every layer that was sieved.

New Road pits

Only 889 bones were recovered from these pits. The common mammals gave no evidence of local breeding activities although there was a young chicken and some puppy remains. Domestic fowl and some goat remains showed bone associations. There were also associated bones from a cattle elbow and two pig vertebrae. Goat, horse, and kitten were represented. Wild species represented were badger and amphibian (frog or toad), the latter from sieved samples. The Crowder Terrace and New Road pits of this phase produced no fish, although New Road was sampled for sieving.

Late Saxon – Phase 12

The material from this phase dates from the mid-10th to 11th centuries. Most bones are from seven pits at Sussex Street and the later fills of pit F10. They are described below. Further small groups were from a soil layer at Sussex Street and from a property boundary ditch (F74) at Crowder Terrace. The results are shown in Tables A3.8–3.9 and A3.34–3.35.

Sussex Street pits

The assemblage from the pits at Sussex Street comprised 1591 bones. All contexts contained the common ungulates. There is a relatively high value for sheep compared with results from pits in earlier phases (Table A3.8), and a higher value for cattle head and foot bones (Table 3.5), partly because a deposit of horn cores in pit F10 is included. Several contexts contained associated bones from the common ungulates which are detailed in archive.

The cattle horn cores in F10 and some associated sheep and goat horn cores all bore knife cuts at the base and had presumably been exploited for horn. Some horse and dog bones were also recovered from F10.

Wild species were represented by a red deer antler and hare. Domestic duck or mallard bone came from three contexts, and a sternum of a smaller species of duck. Although much sieving was carried out very few fish bones were retrieved. There was a concentration of frog bones in pit F6.

Saxo-Norman – Phase 13

Most of the Saxo-Norman material is from twelve pits at Sussex Street and from the later fills of a ditch (F74) at Crowder Terrace. Small samples also came from other contexts at Sussex Street, six pits and one other feature at New Road, and one layer of fill F371 of the Oram's Arbour enclosure ditch, New Road (see

Table 3.1: detailed results in Tables A3.10–3.12 and A3.36–3.37).

Sussex Street pits

This is the third largest assemblage from the western suburb, having a total of 5015 bones. Specific ratios give the three major species a more even balance than in earlier pit samples (Table A3.10). The proportion of head and foot bones is overall lower than for the Phase 12 pits (Table 3.5), although there is a slightly raised value for cattle mandibles. Whether the lower value for heads and feet indicates the use of prepared carcasses must be balanced against the evidence for young animals. It might even mean that heads and feet were such a delicacy that they went elsewhere. Other indices for taphonomic factors are inconclusive. The fluctuations between phases are difficult to interpret. Fragments were as identifiable to anatomy as for all the major pit deposits in the late Saxon phases (apart from the small ungulates in Phase 10) although more fragments were identifiable to species than in earlier phases. This might indicate differences either in depositional processes or in taphonomic history. Two bones had obviously been around on the surface; they were similar to bones found in a stony area of Stoner Motors excavations, Southampton, where the bones were distinctively marked from having rubbed against gravel and large stones (J Bourdillon, pers comm).

Bone associations, including epiphysis and shaft found together, may suggest some input of fairly fresh material.

There were a number of part skeletons of pigs in pit F30 with unfused bones. The high number of bones with associated epiphyses contributes to the unusual proportions of the main species in the pit: 18 per cent cattle, 15 per cent sheep or goat, and 67 per cent pig. There is a high proportion of pelvis fragments and plenty of evidence of butchery, including a pelvis with evenly spaced knife marks suggesting that a number of evenly thick slices of pork or bacon had been cut from it.

Horse is represented in small numbers but consistently. There was a butchered humerus in F30 but otherwise cuts are confined to a calcaneum in F82, a metapodial in F436, and a splint bone in F506, all of which may be associated with skinning. Several of the other bones are dog gnawed. The bones are similar in size and shape to those of a large strong pony. Goat horn cores came from several contexts.

There were a few cat and dog bones, including several cat bones from F436, which may be from the same animal. The dogs have been discussed above. These pits, especially F30, had a high proportion of domestic fowl bones, many of which were recovered from bulk sieving. The fowls include the possible hen with spurs, which has been discussed above, and at least eight further birds, several of them laying hens and at least one immature. Some of the fowl bones showed butchery marks. The phenomenon of a high proportion of laying fowl in what may have been food

deposits has been noted elsewhere in Wessex (Coy 1983).

Goose bones were in five contexts, and there were bones of domestic duck or mallard in F506. Wild species were represented in F30 by common snipe, grey heron, and wood pigeon. A fragment or red deer antler was recorded in F506, woodcock in F54, and stork in F80. The pits produced 755 fish bones, with a wide range of species represented. There was a deposit of flatfish bones – plaice or flounder – in F30, but overall the commonest finds from sieving were common eel and herring (Table 3.15).

The sieved samples commonly produced frog, toad, and small rodent bones, including some definite identifications of house mouse, bank vole, and shrew.

Crowder Terrace

In the assemblage of over 2000 fragments from the upper layers of ditch F74 there was no particular evidence of the bone associations usually found in pits. These deposits contained fewer ungulate bones at least half complete than did other assemblages and also a high proportion of bones unidentifiable except as large or small ungulate (Table 3.4). This, and the lack of associated bones, suggests that material was possibly transported from elsewhere. The finds have been tabulated separately as 'other layers' (Tables A3.11 and A3.37). There are a few bones with abrasion marks similar to those from the Sussex Street discussed above.

The common ungulates were represented, with a bias towards sheep. Lambs and a fragment of calf skull were found. There were some goat bones, and a few of horse of about fourteen hands, the size of a large pony but of rather delicate build. Other horse bones were also found, none butchered. There was a small amount of domestic dog, cat, fowl, and goose bone. Wild species were teal, another duck species, woodcock and pigeon, which match domestic pigeon or rock dove. There are no sieved samples but fish bones were recovered from normal excavation.

Medieval (12th–14th century) – Phase 15

A small group of material from pits or other features from Sussex Street was originally treated as a separate phase (14), but is now regarded as part of Phase 15. The mammal and bird bones are shown separately in Tables A3.13–3.15 and A3.38 and fish bones in Table 3.16.

In studying the medieval bones, the aim was to answer questions about the relationship between different areas of the western suburb and the function of the different features. The Tables A3.16–3.28 and A3.39–3.46 show more finds divided into more context groups than in earlier periods and the account of the material is more detailed.

Most of the medieval assemblage is from pits and a well at Crowder Terrace, from pits at Sussex Street, and from two buildings (714.1 and 714.2) on tenement 714 at Sussex Street (shown in 15B in the tables). Assemblages from property boundary ditches at Sussex Street and Crowder Terrace, from the recut Oram's Arbour enclosure ditch (New Road), F391, and from the boundary ditch of the medieval cemetery at Crowder Terrace were also studied. Material from the remains of buildings and other structures at New Road and Crowder Terrace and from soil layers and a few other contexts were recorded, but have not been described in detail here.

Crowder Terrace pits and well

At 6768 bones, this is the fourth large sample from the western suburb. Bones are from three pits: F60 (Tables A3.16, A3.39); F65 (Tables A3.17, A3.40); and F71 (Tables A3.18, A3.41); and a well, F70 (Tables A3.19, A3.42). The assemblage from the well differed from that from the pits in some respects, so has been considered separately.

The taphonomic results are quite different from those obtained from the Sussex Street pits discussed above. For both pits and well, 64 per cent of the ungulate bones were unidentifiable to species (Table 3.3). This contrasts with 45 per cent for the 'earlier' pits at Sussex Street and is the highest result for the western suburb. It is only matched by Oram's Arbour enclosure ditch, New Road, discussed below. Bones that are even more fragmented are often even unidentifiable to anatomical element. In the Sussex Street pits discussed below, 39 per cent of large ungulate fragments and 26 per cent of small ungulate fragments were unidentifiable to anatomical element, but in the pits at Crowder Terrace these values were even higher – 55 per cent and 44 per cent respectively and were also higher for the well. Such a high percentage of unidentified fragments is only otherwise found in ditches, including the Crowder Terrace ditch material discussed below. Confirming the atypical deposit there is a raised value (20 per cent) for all ungulate loose teeth compared with the Sussex Street pits (7 per cent). These results do compare though with the 19 per cent overall result for Phase 15 ditches. The percentage of dog gnawing is high, but it is high over most of the western suburb and this sample does not seem to be particularly extreme here (Fig 3.2).

There are at least two possible reasons for the severe fragmentation of these bones. The bones may have become fragmented because the deposits were not associated with domestic activity but were associated with the industrial work being carried out in the western suburb at the time, in particular non-ferrous metal working. Some of the pit fills may have been broken up on the surface before inclusion. Another possibility is that the pits were excavated with extraordinary care and that more small and featureless pieces of bone were retrieved than would normally be the case. Two contexts in particular, 188 in F70 and 225 in F71, were very carefully retrieved, with many sheep incisors and other bones recovered that are sometimes missed in normal excavation. The fragmentary bones

are mostly splinters. These two layers may have largely contributed to the high values for unidentified fragments in the two features involved. Confirmation of good retrieval in these features is the find of two herring bones from normal retrieval in F65. The western suburb material was, however, very well retrieved overall, so the most likely conclusion is that the formation processes of these fills were not the same as those associated with the other pits studied.

As explained above, the pits especially show a preponderance of sheep bones, with cattle the next most frequent find and pig in relatively low numbers. There are quite high values for head and foot fragments; for pig this is due to some concentration of head fragments (Table 3.5). This could contribute slightly to the loose teeth figures already mentioned, although every effort was taken to ensure that loose teeth had not come from jaws with modern breaks.

Crowder Terrace pit, F60

Preservation of bone varied in the pit, with c.23 containing very well-preserved material, including some with an ivory like texture, whilst c.216 contained some highly eroded bones, suggesting different origins. Of the approximately 900 bones found, a high proportion was unidentifiable, as discussed.

There was a notable concentration of bones of the head and neck of the main domestic species. Among the bones of the three main domestic animals, there were sixteen of lamb, one of calf, and three of piglet. In additions remains of horses (of nine years and eleven to twelve years), cat, fowl, goose, hare, mole, and woodcock were recorded. Fish from normal retrieval were conger, cod, and turbot and sieving added plaice to the list of fish remains found.

Butchery was noted on a sheep skull, a cattle neck and some sheep vertebrae which were cut axially, but not very efficiently, midline. There was occasional blademark butchery and a lot of chop marks carried out at right angles to the axis of the body on both sheep and cattle bones, showing that carcasses were cut into relatively small pieces.

Crowder Terrace pit, F65

There were approximately 1600 fragments from pit F65, of which a high proportion again was unidentifiable. The remains of two articulated pigs' feet and three feet of a roe deer probably entered the pit in a relatively fresh state.

Sheep were in the majority, and pig remains relatively few. Other species included one metacarpus from a possible goat and an incisor from a horse of at least twelve years. There were no calf remains but 27 lamb bones and seven piglet bones. Dog, cat, fowl, goose, fallow deer, brown hare, and starling were recorded. Despite an apparent lack of sieving, conger, herring, cod, bass, plaice or flounder and the first hake remains were recorded.

Ungulates, even lamb, were extensively butchered with axial splitting, not very uniformly carried out. There was also a lot of evidence of blademarks on both cattle and sheep bones. The high frequency of the use of this technique, which was otherwise characteristic of the late period at Saxon Sussex Street, suggests the possible idiosyncratic nature of localised food preparation.

Crowder Terrace pit, F71

Sheep bones are again in the majority, but there is definite evidence also for goat from two horn cores and an immature metapodial. There are a dozen bones of horse and dog, and cat (including a kitten). Fowl (including two young birds) and goose were also recorded. For the first time in the western suburb there is bone as well as antler of red deer and evidence for fallow deer. Hare was also present. Shark, conger eel, and hake came from normal retrieval as well as herring from the only sieved context.

Butchery showed the same off-centre axial splitting seen in the other pits, on cattle skull and thoracic vertebrae, and sheep vertebrae; no blademark butchery was noted, and one cattle humerus showed an atypical medio-lateral clean chop. A cattle toe had skinning marks.

The upper and lower layers probably represent different stages of deposition in the pit. Most of the animal bone is from the upper layer of fill (c.225). It included a typical collection of highly fragmented, chalky, butchered bone, very eroded and with more dog-gnawing than for the two other pits. The gnawing may be linked to the eroded nature of the bones.

The lower layers included the partial skeleton of a chicken, and also about seven frogs and six toads (some very large) suggesting the pit was open at some stage. It also contained as well some bones of a horse, from an animal of large pony size but fairly gracile. The lowest layer contained skull and mandible fragments of red deer. These larger bones may have dropped down from later deposition. Herring vertebrae were recovered on sieving. These were mineralised, so possibly from a cesspit, although they are not damaged in a fashion suggesting they have been through the gut

Crowder Terrace well, F70

The largest sample from Crowder Terrace, is from the well, with over 2000 bones. Sheep and cattle were more evenly balanced in this collection than in the pits (Table A3.19) with less stress on head bones, at least for cattle and sheep (Table 3.5). There were 28 lamb fragments but no calf or piglet. Horse was represented, mostly by loose teeth, and a metatarsus similar in dimensions to that from a New Forest pony of about fourteen hands.

Dog, cat, fowl, goose, all three species of deer, hare, partridge, and a medium-sized duck were recorded. Fish represented were thornback ray, cod, hake,

garfish, and a large turbot, probably in excess of seven pounds. Sieving also produced black rat, small rodent, frog, and toad (Table 3.2).

Much of the bone came from the top fill (188) which was similar in many criteria to pit F71. However, percentages of the main species were not significantly different from the percentage for the feature as a whole. There were some fragments of unusually large cattle rib that could be later contamination. Quite accurate axial splitting of pig and sheep atlas and axis bones was noted, sheep ribs were cut and some sheep mandibles were cut through in a decisive manner, cutting off the coronoid process. Cattle bones were cut in a variety of ways but there were no blademarks. This evidence suggests that the deposit is more like the upper layer (c.225) in pit F71 than the two other pits.

Sussex Street pits

Altogether, a total of 1367 bones was recovered. A small quantity of material from F389 is shown separately (Table A3.21) but is similar to the remainder so the pits are discussed together below. The bones were on the whole well-preserved and a high proportion was measurable. Associated bones found were part of a cattle forelimb and an ankle.

The percentage of cattle bones was smaller than in the Sussex Street pits of earlier periods. The ratio of cattle to the smaller species tends to be higher in large features at all periods, not least because of the need for large spaces into which to throw the bigger bones, but this does not appear to be the main factor at work here. The overall results from the Sussex Street pits do seem to confirm a genuine drop in the importance of cattle in the diet from late Saxon to medieval times. The ratio of the main species was similar to that in the Crowder Terrace well, though sheep were fewer than in the Crowder Terrace pits.

Horse, domestic cat, fowl, goose, domestic duck or mallard, a medium-sized wild duck, and red deer (antler) were represented. Four of the gyrfalcon bones referred to above came from F405. All the fish remains came from normal excavation. There was no herring or eel and this could be because of the few sieved samples. The 'later' pits contained two species not found in the earlier ones – a tibia fragment from fallow deer with blademark butchery and herring remains from sieving.

Sussex Street medieval buildings, 714.1 and 714.2

There were a few bones from the occupation layers of building 714.1, including cattle, sheep, hare, goose, and a bone of oystercatcher; also herring, hake and flatfish from sieved samples. The hearth within the medieval building 714.2 produced only a small unidentified fish fragment and a few unidentifiable mammalian bone crumbs from sieving, all calcined. Three other contexts produced eroded mammalian fragments probably from dog droppings; frog bones; and ray, herring, common eel and flatfish bones from sieving. Some of the fish remains might be associated with human faeces as they included some very tiny bones. A fourth context produced sheep, pig, fowl, and the sturgeon scute referred to earlier from normal retrieval, and an abundance of herring and some mackerel bones from sieving. The general lack of bones from the floor layers is not surprising as these areas would tend to be kept fairly clear whilst in use.

The majority of the bone, about 600 fragments, was from demolition levels on building 714.2 (Tables A3.23 and A3.44). There was a relatively higher percentage of identifiable bones and apparently less residual material than in the medieval pits at Crowder Terrace described above, or ditches described below. Some were clean, white, and well-preserved; others were stained, and about half the mammal bone had the ivory like texture also seen in material from the Crowder Terrace pits.

The largest group of associated horse bones from the western suburb was recovered from c.973, and other horse bones were spread through the layers. The bones which could be measured compared well with bones from a pony of fourteen hands. No butchery was noted on these.

Of the three common ungulates, cattle was slightly in the majority, with a bias towards meat-bearing fragments like vertebrae and ribs, reminiscent of the Phase 11 pits. Dog, a partial skeleton of a cat, fowl, goose, red deer (antler and immature femur), roe deer (associated ulna and radius), and hare were recorded. Three pig bones, two of which were immature, were large enough to be from wild boar.

The percentage of bird bones was higher than usual. The wild birds included heron, crane, buzzard, two further fragments of gyrfalcon, and pigeon. The heron and crane bones were from the wing, with a heron ulna which was butchered distally. The wings could have provided feathers for arrows and the birds were both likely quarry of birds of prey. The finds complement the remains of falcons and documentary evidence that falcons were kept nearby. Fish included common eel from normal retrieval and eel and herring from sieving. Frog bones were also retrieved from sieving.

Some examples of butchery were distinctive and of a kind not seen before on the sites. They show determined and heavy chopping through of articular ends, for instance a cattle astragalus and proximal femur of sheep. A single instance of paramedian butchery in sheep, of the type seen in late Saxon deposits, may suggest contamination with earlier material or an individual butchery method, perhaps home-based.

The wide variety of species and the unusual butchery make the assemblage from these houses a distinctive one.

Sussex Street ditches, F126 and F401

The bones from the two ditches excavated in Sussex Street show a variety of preservation, suggesting a mixed origin.

The larger collection is from ditch F126, a recut of a Saxo-Norman ditch, with over 800 fragments (Tables A3.25 and A3.45) and the smaller from F401 with just over 100 fragments. Unlike the results for pits of this phase, cattle were slightly better represented than sheep, and pig frequency low. Horse was quite common, as were dog, cat, fowl, and goose. Goat, red deer, roe deer, brown hare, heron, and red kite were also present. Remains have some affinities with those from the medieval building 714.2 – in the species range, identifiability, varied preservation, and some very determined butchery with a sharp chopper.

F401 (Table A3.26) produced just over 100 more fragments which were more gnawed by canids and more eroded than those from ditch F126. A higher percentage was unidentifiable (Table 3.4). The species present, as well as the common domesticates, were dog, cat, fowl, goose, and red deer. Sieving produced no fish.

New Road: property boundary ditch, F391

Virtually all medieval bones from New Road came from ditches or gullies, about half (over 1700 bones) from a property boundary ditch (F391) cut into, and on nearly the same alignment as the Oram's Arbour enclosure (Tables A3.27, A3.46). This is comparable with collections from earlier phases of ditch fill. Preservation was often excellent with a high proportion of measurable bones. Bone colour varied and may indicate different origins. But there was also a high proportion of bones unidentifiable to anatomical element, as in the Crowder Terrace pits described earlier.

Like the earlier New Road ditch deposits, there was a high value for sheep fragments but here pig remains were also better represented than elsewhere at this time. Head and foot fragments were high for cattle and pig, as in the earlier fills of the ditch, but not for sheep (Table 3.5), suggesting that sheep heads and feet went elsewhere. The only fish came from unsieved contexts.

Four similarly butchered sheep axis vertebrae cut just to one side of the midline suggest some standardisation of sheep butchery. An unexpected feature of this material was the high frequency of blademark butchery – unusual for this period. There are examples on cattle bones throughout the deposit, and on one pig pelvis.

The partial skeletons of dogs may have been those of old hounds, as discussed earlier. Horse remains were mostly distal limb bones and again represented animals around fourteen hands. Cat, fowl, and goose are also represented. The wild species included red deer (antler), fallow deer, hare, wood pigeon, buzzard, gyrfalcon, wader, and a few remains of passerines (Table A3.46). Despite some sieving, the only fish bones came from normal retrieval. Conger, mullet, sea bream, and plaice or flounder were identified.

Discussion

This material is important in the overall picture which is emerging for Winchester. Finds from the pits seem to represent the most down to earth picture of urban domestic life and suggest the much more direct involvement of people with their animals than is found today. Frequent evidence that cats gnawed on chicken bones and dogs on dog bones and that late Saxon horses were eaten and dogs skinned adds up to a complex picture of life in the backyards of the western suburb for a period before documentary evidence is available. The written records for later medieval times (Keene 1985, 153) confirms the proximity of the domestic species to human habitation.

In the late Saxon period the animal bones, especially the major deposits in the Sussex Street pits, are important assemblages for giving a picture of life in early Winchester. They show evidence of the local breeding of some species in the large number of very young animals that were found. The presence of calf bones, especially, is quite unlike what is found in middle Saxon Hamwic. Some cattle breeding seems to have taken place even if only to supply the occasional lactating cow for household milk. However, the lower emphasis on cattle overall and greater emphasis on pig,

except in the Sussex Street Phase 10 pits, is a noticeable difference from Hamwic, as is the smaller size for many of the bone measurements. Some inhabitants of the western suburb possibly had access during the late Saxon and medieval periods to meat of the wild boar or to hybrid stock.

In post-Saxon times there is evidence here for an increase in the breadth of wild species exploited and for fallow deer, probably a post-Norman introduction. Interestingly there were no signs of rabbit, another Norman introduction, although the native hare was exploited throughout. At all periods the role of wild species in the diet is difficult to quantify. There is no doubt that a wide variety of species supplemented the normal domestic ungulate meat and the dietary consequences of this should not be underestimated (Coy 1982).

Some deposits of the 12th–14th centuries show links with hunting and falconry, from the presence of possible hounds, falcons, and their quarry. It seems some of the inhabitants of the western suburb may have had a role in these activities. It is unlikely too that large numbers of dogs would have been allowed to ordinary inhabitants of New Road at this time and for this reason those found in New Road ditch may well have been hounds.

4 Late Saxon animal bone from the northern and eastern suburbs and the city defences *by J Bourdillon*

Introduction

No one needs animal bones to know that late Saxon Winchester was of the highest status both in Wessex and in the wider country. Its bones are those from a known special place and they may be taken as such in discussion. Even special places, though, have their less special areas, and what is not known in advance is how each present assemblage of bone waste relates to waste from the place as a whole. Here, however, it should be remembered from the outset that the material is from the periphery of the city, rather than its central area.

The late Saxon bones from the northern and eastern suburbs are discussed here. This period has also been covered in the report on the western suburb sites (Chapter 3). Furthermore, comparisons are possible with significant middle and late Saxon deposits from Southampton, from which a large corpus of animal bone has been published (Bourdillon 1980b, 1985, 1988; Bourdillon & Coy 1980). These deposits displayed some interesting points of difference during the transition from the middle to the late Saxon periods: for example, smaller sizes for the main domestic mammals; and a wider range of species; and styles of butchery that were neat and more precise. To assess how far the material from Southampton reflected the pattern of a wider region was one of the objectives of the present study.

This chapter is intended both as a full description of the animal bones of the late Saxon period from the present Winchester sites, and as a tool to help in the assessment of site and assemblage formation and the interpretation of features. After a short survey of the overall results and their likely reliability, the assemblages are described by site and phase. There is then the main analysis, by species, with a broader discussion at the end. The main supporting quantification is given in Tables 4.1–4.26 and Figures 4.1–4.3 and 4.6; the tables show number of identified fragments. Graphic representation of measurement is shown in Figures 4.4 and 4.5, and statistics are located in the Appendix (Tables A4.1–A4.7). Recording followed the methods codified by Jones *et al* (1981).

The system of phasing used in Winchester has already been briefly explained (Chapter 1). Individual bone assemblages have often been referred to by their site code and phase only and the explanation of these references is given below. Reference to individual contexts has only been made where this might possibly have some significance within a phase or feature, but a full list of the contexts studied is available in the archive. References to property boundaries are after Keene (1985). Most of the bones were recovered by hand in the trench, but the bone

fragments from 28 soil samples have also been considered.

The Sites

Ten assemblages from contexts of late Saxon date were selected for study. These comprised one assemblage each from 27 Jewry Street (27JS) and Henly's Garage (HG) on the city defences, two assemblages from Chester Road (CHR) in the eastern suburb, and six assemblages from Victoria Road (VR) in the northern suburb. The selection from Victoria Road included material that had been deposited in a ditch and in clay silt layers, but the other assemblages were from pits.

For the most part, the late Saxon occupation of the sites under discussion is characterised by large cut features (mostly pits, with some ditches). Evidence for the structures and properties to which these features belong tends to be somewhat ephemeral and difficult to interpret, not only, very often, due to truncation in later times, but also, sometimes, because of the small size of the trenches available for investigation. It is worth noting at the outset that investigation of the animal bone assemblages has allowed a fuller interpretation of the activities carried out on these sites, in the absence of better stratigraphic evidence. Conversely, the stratigraphic evidence has dictated the relatively small size of the sample.

City defences

At 27 Jewry Street, within the northern arm of the city defences, deposits of likely late Saxon date were few in number. The remains of a probably late Saxon street were recovered in one part of the site, whilst in another, levelling during the late medieval period had truncated earlier occupation allowing the survival of negative features (pits and a well) only. The animal bone assemblage from one of these, a rectangular feature, probably a cesspit (F54) (Phase 11), is discussed here.

At the Henly's Garage site on the southern city defences, a good animal bone assemblage was recovered from F121 (Phase 18B), one of a group of cesspits respecting the street pattern, which is believed to be of late Saxon origin.

Eastern suburb

The site at Chester Road produced two of the assemblages discussed here. Two pits of Phase 45 (F21 and F28) produced the stratigraphically earlier of the

55

assemblages from Chester Road. These were associated with a possible structural feature which could not be interpreted easily.

The other assemblage was from a pit of Phase 47 (F24), cut through a soil accumulation (probably the result of erosion of the hill slopes above the site) which had sealed the pits of Phase 45.

Northern suburb

Like other sites that produced animal bones discussed in this chapter, most of the late Saxon deposits and features at Victoria Road were badly damaged by later activity leaving minimal stratigraphic remains. Two assemblages were from F588, one of three ditches demarcating property boundaries or functioning as drains at late Saxon Victoria Road. The ditch seems to have been largely silted up by the end of the late Saxon period (Phase 493), but the uppermost fills (Phase 494) produced later pottery. The two phases of infilling have been treated separately here. A further assemblage was from clay silt deposits post-dating the cutting of the ditch (Phase 503). Three assemblages were from pits. Pit F569 (Phase 507) was possibly associated with the remains of a timber building (on tenement 935) of late Saxon date. The remaining two assemblages were both from pits – F976 (Phase 508) and F762 (Phase 636), which could not be associated easily with contemporary structures, as the remains of the latter were so badly truncated and difficult to interpret.

The range and state of the material

Table 4.1 lists the species identified from trench recovery. Cattle fragments were dominant, but sheep/goat were represented too. The abundance of pig varied greatly by site and by context; that of horse was high for its time. The tally for dog was inflated by a group of puppy bones from the eastern suburb; but even if these are discounted as coming from a likely single skeleton there would still be a heavy bias of dog bones against those of cat.

For a known rich settlement, there was little deer. Domestic fowl was well represented, but goose was rare. Other bird bones were mainly of duck, either mallard or domestic: most were found from the eastern suburb, in pits F21 and F28 (Phase 45) at Chester Road. Fish bones were incidental from the trench.

When the results from the soil samples were taken in comparison (Table 4.2) amphibians, absent from trench recovery, were represented in three occurrences. The remains of bird were still quite low against the mammal fragments as a whole – there were passerine fragments from sieving, but the fragments listed as of 'other bird' could perhaps have come from domestic fowl. Goose was not found from the samples – and it must be said that the low rate from normal recovery is likely to be a valid comparison with those for the fragments from domestic fowl. Fish fragments were more numerous and well outnumbered those of bird. The samples gave no horse, dog, cat, goat, or deer.

Apart from the sieved results, there are clues from the condition of the trench material as to its reliability – for though likely residual assemblages were omitted, there is still the chance of taphonomic bias. The rate of identification is fair (Table 4.1). The general rate of erosion was found to be moderate (Table 4.3), and that of heavy erosion may be seen as very low; the incidence of burning was minimal. Such points are encouraging. Chewing, though, was more common, and with quite a high rate of heavy chewing it may be that other bones (most likely the smaller ones) had been chewed completely and removed from the record altogether.

One check on recovery is to look for the presence not just of the smaller species but of the smaller bones of somewhat larger species, and Maltby's (1985, 38) index of sheep/goat phalanges is useful here. A disparity between the rates for first, second, and third phalanges must show a loss at some point in the taphonomic process: when the larger phalanges are the best recovered, it may be that the smaller ones were overlooked in the trench. No sheep/goat phalanges were found from the soil samples and it was not possible to use the sieving as a check, but the recovery from the trench overall was 17:4:2 for first, second, and third phalanges (Table 4.3). This is a great loss of the smaller ones – and at some point since death a loss even for the first ones, since each individual sheep or goat has eight and a great many sheep and goat were represented in the study as a whole. Incisors of sheep/goat, too, are easy to miss. None was found from the samples (out of 21 sheep/goat fragments, seven of which were from teeth), and only two incisors were found from 1148 fragments of sheep/goat from the trench (a total which included 117 loose teeth). Arguments from absence of smaller material must therefore be treated with some caution.

The assemblages by site and context

City defences

27, Jewry Street, Phase 11 (pit F54)

Animal bones were found in a total of eleven contexts of pit F54, of which c.580 gave by far the most.

Many bones had been chewed, some lightly, some more heavily but they were hard and well preserved, with a high rate of identifiable material and a low rate of erosion and loose teeth. The pit group contained some whole and near-whole vertebrae of cattle, mainly from the neck and from at least two individuals.

As well as the main food mammals there were four fragments of dog, including bones of small individuals (or of the same small individual). The five bones of horse came from three contexts, and included a whole fused radius of a small pony. There were also two fragments of roe deer – an adult mandible and distal tibia. With only four roe deer fragments from the whole study, these two finds are notable. The twenty bones

**Table 4.1 Late Saxon northern and eastern suburbs and city defences:
summary of animal bones by site and phase: hand recovery**

	27JS 11	HG 18B	CHR 45	CHR 47	VR 493	VR 494	VR 503	VR 507	VR 508	VR 636	Total
horse	5	–	24	6	7	3	5	15	13	10	**88**
cattle	141	36	333	136	129	67	111	158	163	137	**1411**
c-size rib frgts	35	9	60	116	25	23	29	42	30	63	**432**
sheep	25	20	36	15	14	13	54	34	19	12	**242**
sheep/goat	90	25	150	145	46	36	160	104	90	60	**906**
s-size rib frgts	58	8	54	120	13	14	45	52	52	45	**461**
goat	–	–	11	2	–	2	–	1	–	12	**28**
pig	58	8	146	144	42	9	49	65	67	82	**670**
dog	4	–	26	1	3	12	–	5	1	5	**57**
cat	–	2	–	–	1	–	–	2	–	2	**7**
red deer	–	–	–	1	1	1	1	–	–	1	**5**
roe deer	2	–	–	1	–	–	1	–	–	–	**4**
hare	–	–	5	–	–	2	–	–	–	–	**7**
domestic fowl	20	3	33	34	2	2	1	11	31	24	**161**
goose	–	–	–	2	–	–	–	–	3	1	**6**
duck	1	–	12	–	–	–	–	–	–	1	**14**
other bird	–	–	–	–	–	–	1	–	–	1	**2**
fish	–	–	–	4	–	–	1	–	–	1	**6**
Total identified	439	111	890	727	283	184	458	489	469	457	4507
% identified	79	85	55	58	66	63	51	56	64	64	60
unidentified fragments											
cattle-size	41	7	223	90	131	54	144	271	74	95	**1130**
sheep-size	76	13	497	433	16	52	294	112	187	159	**1839**
Total	**556**	**131**	**1610**	**1250**	**430**	**290**	**896**	**872**	**730**	**711**	**7476**

Key: 27 JS 27 Jewry Street; HG Henly's Garage; CHR Chester Road; VR Victoria Road

of domestic fowl were spread over several contexts. A radius shaft fragment of bird was not diagnostic, but could well have been from duck: it was too long for fowl and too small for goose.

The relative representation of the main domestic mammals was near par for the study as a whole. Cattle long bones were well represented, but there was a shortage of their head fragments. Indeed, this was the only assemblage in which there were no ageable mandibles. Pig long bones were also well represented, but there were only two pig foot bones. Sheep/goat

gave many ribs. There were also several bones of young animals, which were spread over the species and throughout the pit. There were calf bones, two very young mandibles from sheep/goat, a young pig mandible, and small porous bones of domestic fowl.

Henly's Garage, Phase 18B (pit F121)

This material came from five contexts in pit F121, the infilling of which is dated to the late Saxon period.

Table 4.2   Summary of animal bones by site and phase: sieved recovery

	CHR 47	VR 493	VR 494	VR 503	VR 507	VR 508	VR 636	Total
cattle	–	1	1	3	2	1	2	**10**
sheep/goat	2	6	4	4	3	–	2	**21**
pig	–	2	1	1	1	1	–	**6**
larger mammal	–	1	5	3	11	–	1	**21**
mammal	9	24	11	32	54	73	18	**221**
smaller mammal	1	3	3	7	3	2	4	**23**
domestic fowl	1	–	–	–	1	3	–	**5**
bird	–	–	1	–	1	–	1	**3**
passerine sp.	2	–	–	–	–	1	–	**3**
amphibian	2	–	1	–	–	8	–	**11**
herring	3	–	–	1	3	1	1	**9**
mackerel	–	–	–	–	–	1	–	**1**
flatfish	–	–	–	–	–	–	1	**1**
gadoid spp.	–	–	–	–	–	–	1	**1**
fish	5	–	–	1	1	–	2	**9**
Total	25	37	27	52	80	91	33	**345**
samples, n	1	5	3	6	7	2	4	**28**

Note: 'bird' and 'fish' comprise fragments not further identified and contexts lacking sieved material have been omitted

Table 4.3   Condition of the identified material (n and %)
and the number of phalanges of sheep/goat, an index of retrieval

	27JS 11	HG 18B	CHR 45	CHR 47	VR 493	VR 494	VR 503	VR 507	VR 508	VR 636	Total
% identified	79	85	55	58	66	63	51	56	64	64	**60**
n fragments											
all eroded	11	5	22	25	30	8	77	56	9	12	**255**
very eroded	1	1	5	3	6	2	11	16	2	3	**50**
all chewed	64	12	151	44	31	17	36	45	57	41	**498**
very chewed	36	2	69	15	12	7	17	19	33	17	**327**
burnt	3	1	3	1	1	3	2	1	1	2	**18**
loose teeth	7	2	67	35	33	11	59	57	24	25	**320**
by percentage											
all eroded	3	5	2	3	11	4	17	11	1	3	**5**
very eroded	0	1	<1	<1	2	1	2	3	<1	<1	**1**
all chewed	15	11	17	6	11	9	8	9	9	9	**11**
very chewed	8	2	8	2	4	4	4	4	5	4	**7**
burnt	<1	1	<1	0	<1	2	<1	0	0	<1	**<1**
loose teeth	2	1	8	5	12	6	13	12	5	5	**7**
phalanges of sheep/goat											
phalanx 1	2	–	5	1	–	–	3	4	2	–	**17**
phalanx 2	–	–	2	–	–	–	1	–	1	–	**4**
phalanx 3	–	–	–	–	1	–	1	–	–	–	**2**

These bones form the smallest of the present assemblages, and only c.1203 gave a good sample of material. The range of species was limited. There were three bones of domestic fowl and a skull and femur of cat. All other fragments were from the main domestic food mammals. The pit group gave two near-whole neck vertebrae of cattle (one of a calf, the other adult) and a near-whole thoracic vertebra of a juvenile. It also gave a near-whole adult mandible of cattle. Sheep/goat remains include mainly long bones and bones from the head, and there were only eight fragments of pig.

Eastern suburb

Chester Road, Phase 45 (pits F21 and F28)

A total of nine contexts in two pits, F21 and F28, produced this sample of animal bone. The largest assemblage was from c.133 (F28), and there were good assemblages also from contexts 103, 106 (F21), 136, and 137 (F28). Other contexts gave minimal bone.

There was a high rate of unidentifiable material, and a high rate of chewing (with the most heavily chewed material in F28). Erosion, however, was limited.

There were 26 fragments of dog from F28; these were all of neonatal puppy and may have come from a single individual. The 24 fragments of horse were mostly loose teeth and bones of the leg, and they came from at least three individuals. There were bones of the lower right front leg of smallish adult from F28 and from the same feature came the whole fused tibia of a much larger individual. Two deciduous premolars, upper and lower, both in light wear and two unworn lower teeth, an incisor and a canine, were also from F28. The horse bones from F28 included a clear case of pathology with first and second phalanges fused rigidly together.

Goat was quite well represented with seven horn cores and (more rarely in archaeological material) with four post-cranial fragments. These were found in both F21 and F28. There were also five fragments of hare, mostly lumbar vertebrae, again from both features.

The 33 fragments of domestic fowl were found mainly from F28, and there were twelve fragments of duck (either mallard or domestic) from the same contexts. There was no goose.

For the main domestic food mammals, head fragments were well represented. There were horn cores from five contexts, including worked material from both pits. There were many ageable mandibles of cattle and pig in F28, and others of pig in both features. There were many large fragments of cattle from the two pits: whole or near-whole bones included a radius and femur, metapodials, and also neck, thoracic, and lumbar vertebrae. Large fragments from cattle, and a bias to head waste, are not usually expected from pits.

Though there was puppy and youngish horse, there was no very young material from pig. Nor was there much calf. There were however some larger but still quite porous bones of sheep/goat – six from F28.

Chester Road, Phase 47 (pit F24)

This was the largest assemblage of animal bones and it came from a single pit at Chester Road, F24. Of the eight contexts, the best assemblages came from contexts 127, 115, and 118. Like CHR Phase 45 (F21 and F28), the pit gave the contrast of much unidentifiable material but few eroded bones; unlike those features, its rate of chewing was low. One soil sample (c.127) was taken from this feature.

Though there was a fair range of species, the fragment count from the various minor species was low for an assemblage of this size. There were six fragments of horse, two fragments of goat (a skull fragment and a horn core) the maxilla of a smallish dog, an antler fragment, most likely of red deer, and a tibia of roe deer. There were 34 fragments of domestic fowl and two of goose. By normal trench recovery, no fragments were found from other birds, but the single soil sample gave three bird fragments – a sesamoid probably from domestic fowl, and a distal ulna and foot phalanx of a passerine, chaffinch-size. The sample also gave two amphibian bones (a vertebra and a long bone fragment).

For the main domestic mammals there was much pig, with a bias to fragments from the head. Cattle was poorly represented, with few head or vertebra fragments – and without the whole or near-whole cattle bones that had been notable from CHR Phase 45 (F21 and F28).

There was much young material from the main food mammals, with three fragments each of neonatal sheep/goat and pig, in addition to five sheep/goat mandibles where the deciduous fourth premolar was barely in wear. Porous bones of somewhat larger lambs and young pigs were found in several contexts, as were bones of calf.

Northern suburb

Victoria Road, Phases 493 and 494 (ditch F588)

Phase 493 at Victoria Road refers to the lower fills of a ditch, F588, of late Saxon date, and Phase 494, the upper, and discernibly later fills. Of the seven contexts in Phase 493 yielding animal bones, contexts 2358, 2360, and 2364 were most productive. Four soil samples (contexts 2348, 2360, 2363, and 2365) were taken from this phase.

There were more loose teeth and more eroded bones than for the study as a whole (12 per cent against a mean of 7 per cent, and 11 per cent against 5 per cent): erosion was highest for the cattle fragments. Some of the bones in these two contexts were also stained. The rate of chewing was standard for the study as a whole.

As often in ditch contexts, this assemblage showed some bias towards larger species (see Maltby 1981, 166). Of the main food mammals cattle was the best represented, and there were several whole or near-whole cattle neck vertebrae and metapodials. There were seven fragments of horse from four contexts, including a pelvis fragment and two loose incisors and a distal metatarsus with small sharp cut marks but this is quite a normal incidence for this study.

Both dog and cat, which are common species from ditches, were present: from dog there were two loose upper premolars and a small fragment of skull with strong sagittal crest; from cat there was one very large distal femur. There was also a fragment of red deer antler. Bird bones are often less common in ditch deposition. Here there were only two bones, both of domestic fowl. Both were radii but they were not a pair.

For distribution over the body of the main domestic mammals, material from the head was well represented – though for cattle there was some bias to long bone fragments as well. Sheep/goat gave many head bones and also foot bones, with some shortage of long bones and ribs. There were many pig long bones, but bones of the feet were scarce. There was no evidence of young individuals of any species.

The five sieved samples gave only mammal fragments and most of these (28 out of 35) were too small to be identified. All three contexts (2299, 2343, and 2344) of the later phase (494) of ditch F588 were quite productive. Soil samples were also taken from all three.

The preservation was better and the rate of loose teeth was lower than in Phase 493, though there were some burnt bones. Apart from one whole metacarpal from a small individual – almost certainly a cow – all the cattle bones were much fragmented.

Horse fragments were scarce for a ditch; there were only three. There was, however, evidence of three or probably four dogs: the twelve fragments included a scapula, a tibia, a neck vertebra, and a maxilla, which were very small indeed, together with some bones which were small but not tiny, and which were most likely from a different dog, and also, two left pelves of dogs of medium-size. There were also two goat horn cores. Again bones of bird were scarce: only two, both of domestic fowl were present. There were also two fragments of hare.

For the main domestic ratio, cattle were well represented, but the ratio of cattle to sheep/goat was normal; what was strange about this phase of the ditch was the marked shortage of pig. Cattle gave few vertebrae, but otherwise a fair distribution over the body. Sheep/goat were poor on head bones, and quite rich on long bones. There were no young individuals at all.

The three sieved samples gave mainly mammal bones. Context 2299 also gave a tibia of frog, and a long bone fragment of bird which could not be further identified.

Victoria Road, clay silt deposits (Phase 503)

This phase consisted of ten contexts. Of these, contexts 2213, 2211, and 2214 were the most productive of bone, and contexts 2212, 2217, and 2218 were the least. Six soil samples were taken from this group of contexts (2209, 2211, 2213, 2216, and 2218).

Of the various groups in this study, these deposits gave the highest proportion both of unidentified and of eroded bones (especially from c.2211, where some highly eroded bones were also stained). The rate of chewing, however, was quite low. Many contexts gave a high rate of loose teeth both of cattle and of sheep/goat, and apart from one near-whole radius in c.2214 the cattle bones were generally much fragmented.

Site layers seem often to contain quite casual deposition, with general bone rubbish added to the usual food waste. Here, however, there were no bones of dog or cat. The five bones from horse, including three heads of horse ribs, was standard for the study; all the larger mammal rib fragments were examined carefully for further fragments of horse, but all were good for cattle, both on texture and on shape. A distal humerus of horse had been heavily cut.

Two deer bones seem a sign of rich diet for such contexts as these – there was a chewed proximal humerus of red deer and a mandible of a sub-adult roe deer. The group also contained one of the securely identified bones of wild bird from the whole study – a humerus which was an excellent match for that of brent goose (*Branta bernicla*) in the reference collection housed at the Faunal Remains Unit. There was no domestic goose and no duck. A further humerus was the only fowl bone from this group of contexts, with no bird at all from the samples.

For the main domestic mammals, bones of sheep/goat were abundant, with many skull fragments and some horn cores. Cattle and pig, though both were quite poorly represented, had a fair distribution over the body.

The five soil samples gave a total of 52 fragments, but these included many small unidentified fragments.

Victoria Road, Phase 507 (pit F569)

This pit produced animal bone from eight contexts, mainly from contexts 2068, 2109, and 2118. Seven soil samples were taken from the pit (contexts 2066, 2068, 2070, 2118, 2146, and 2147).

There were many unidentified fragments and a high rate both of eroded bones and of loose teeth. This is uncommon from pit material, but on the evidence of the pottery, residuality is largely discounted. The bones were likely contemporary but in a poor state at burial.

There were five fragments of dog – a small pelvis, a larger one, loose teeth, and a neck vertebra. There were also two loose teeth of cat. From goat, there were no horn cores but there was a distal humerus and although it was a small fragment the identification seems secure. There were fifteen fragments of horse. Most were from the back leg, but there were also a humerus of a small individual, a cut radius, and loose teeth. There were eleven bones of domestic fowl; this is a higher rate than in the ditch (VR, F588, Phases 493 and 494) or the clay silt deposits (Phase 503), but not high for pits in general. There were no other bird fragments from the trench, though there was one unidentified long bone fragment and a radius of domestic fowl from the soil samples.

The relative representation of the main domestic mammals was standard for the study, with some shortage of head fragments for sheep/goat and for pig.

Context 2070 gave the youngest pig mandible from the study the fourth deciduous premolar was barely in wear and the first molar was only just visible in the gum. There was no other very young material by normal recovery, but one of the samples gave a small fragment of neonatal ilium, which was either from lamb or from dog.

Victoria Road, Phase 508 (pit F976)

Both contexts from this pit (contexts 3817 and 3832) gave large assemblages of bone with excellent preservation: only one of the bones showed signs of erosion. Both contexts also contained many of the larger fragments from cattle. Two soil samples were taken from c.3832.

The group contained the left mandible of an old dog, where the third and fourth premolars had both been lost antemortem. There was also part of the right back leg of a large horse, with a whole tibia, a matching fibula, and calcaneum and astragalus; a rib head and a left patella could have been from the same individual. The seven horse fragments included a mandible fragment with small sharp cuts, and the neck vertebra of a large individual.

There were 31 fragments of domestic fowl – for their relative representation, this was the best assemblage in the study. There were also three fragments of goose, but there were no other bird species from the trench.

The relative representation of the main domestic mammals was standard for the study, with normal distribution over the body for cattle and sheep/goat. For pig, there was a strong bias to bones of the feet. Both contexts gave some very small and very porous bones of cattle and of sheep/goat, and rather larger but still porous bones of these species and also of pig.

The two sieved samples were gave three bird ribs which could have been from fowl, and a mandible of a small passerine which matches sparrow. Both also gave amphibian fragments, with a femur and humerus of a small frog and a pelvis, urostyle and other fragments from a somewhat larger individual. There was a preoperculum of herring and a caudal vertebra of mackerel.

Victoria Road, Phase 636 (pit F762)

This pit contained ten contexts with bone, of which four were very productive – in order of abundance, contexts 3217, 3222, 3216, and 3103. Preservation was good, with a low rate of erosion and few loose teeth. There were several large fragments from cattle, especially neck vertebrae in c.3222. Four soil samples were taken (contexts 3018, 3036, 3100, and 3102).

There was a good range of species. Two bones of cat (a pelvis and a loose tooth) and a much-sawn fragment of red deer antler were included. Ten horse

fragments, were all from the head. Bird was quite well represented; 24 fragments of domestic fowl were present, along with a coracoid of goose, a humerus of woodcock, and a carpometacarpus of a mallard or domestic duck.

Of the main food mammals, pig was very well represented, though with no evidence of young material. By contrast, there were two bones of neonatal calf, and two from neonatal sheep/goat. In addition, there was a mandible of a young sheep/goat with the first molar not yet in wear. This assemblage was the richest for horn cores, with twelve from goat, many of them sawn or cut near the base. There were also three horn cores of cattle and two from sheep.

There were some bones of fish from normal trench recovery and there were several fish species from the soil samples. Context 3100 had produced no bones at all from the trench, but its sample gave a caudal vertebra of herring, a supracleithrum from a flatfish (cf plaice about 35cm in greatest length), and also two fin rays. A caudal vertebra from the gadoid family (probably cod) came from a sample. A small fragment of bird could not be further identified.

Contextuality

Before taking the material as a whole and drawing from it on the basis of topic, it is useful to look for any points of comparison between the assemblages. In particular, were there changes that could have related to context type?

The two phases of the VR ditch F588 have some factors in common, factors which are often seen as linked with ditches: there was very little bird, for instance, and no bones of young animals; and in the ratio of the main food mammals, cattle fragments were notably common, with some bias to fragments from the head. There were a fair number of dog bones, and a certain amount of horse. In all these ways the present ditch material was like that from the early ditch on the Six Dials sites at Hamwic (Bourdillon 1984).

At Winchester, though, the ditch/pit distinction may not be so simple. The high ratio of cattle in the later ditch phase seems not to have been intrinsic but to have stemmed directly from the dearth of pig; and the cattle head fragments, though quite abundant, make a poor showing beside the pit assemblages of Phase 45 from Chester Road.

Horse may be common in ditches, but from the present study it seems to have been common in pits as well. Isolated horse teeth were found in most context types, and articulated limbs were present in pits. There was a contrast in preservation between the two phases of ditch, with far more erosion in the lower fills of VR F588 (Phase 493). There were more large fragments there as well. It may be that by the time of the upper filling of the ditch, the pattern of deposition had changed. It may be, too, that in late Saxon Winchester the pits themselves were dumping grounds for casual bone waste and that distinctions from ditch contexts were less marked.

Table 4.4 Anatomical distribution in horse

	27JS 11	CHR 45	CHR 47	VR 493	VR 494	VR 503	VR 507	VR 508	VR 636	Total
skull fragment	–	–	–	–	–	–	1	1	6	8
mandible	–	–	1	–	–	–	–	–	1	2
loose teeth	–	4	1	2	1	1	4	–	3	16
cervical vertebrae 3-7	–	–	–	1	–	–	–	1	–	2
thoracic vertebrae	–	–	–	–	–	–	–	1	–	1
rib head	–	–	–	–	–	3	–	2	–	5
scapula	1	–	–	–	–	–	1	–	–	2
os coxae	–	–	1	1	–	–	–	1	–	3
humerus	–	1	–	1	–	1	1	–	–	4
radius	1	1	–	–	1	–	1	–	–	4
ulna	1	–	–	–	–	–	–	–	–	1
femur	–	1	–	–	–	–	1	1	–	3
tibia	–	–	–	–	–	–	–	1	–	1
fibula	–	–	–	–	–	–	–	1	–	1
carpal	–	5	–	–	–	–	–	–	–	5
astragalus	1	–	1	–	–	–	1	1	–	4
calcaneum	1	–	–	–	–	–	1	1	–	3
other tarsal	–	–	–	–	–	–	1	–	–	1
metacarpal	–	3	–	1	–	–	–	–	–	4
metatarsal	–	2	–	1	–	–	1	–	–	4
phalanx 1	–	2	1	–	–	–	1	–	–	4
phalanx 2	–	1	1	–	–	–	–	1	–	3
phalanx 3	–	1	–	–	1	–	1	–	–	3
sesamoid	–	3	–	–	–	–	–	–	–	3
patella	–	–	–	–	–	–	1	–	–	1
Total	**5**	**24**	**6**	**7**	**3**	**5**	**15**	**13**	**10**	**88**

Note: contexts containing no horse have been omitted

The material from the clay silt deposits (VR Phase 503) was notably eroded; the rate of identification was low and there were many loose teeth. There may have been real site and taphonomic differences in the formation of these contexts.

There were differences too between the three main areas the northern suburb, the eastern, and the city defences. Eroded bones are less common from the eastern suburb and from the defences.

The material by species

Horse

For the period, there was a fair amount of horse (Table 4.1): the 88 bones in a total of 4507 identified fragments compare well with 49 in 49,000 fragments from the Melbourne Street excavations in middle Saxon Hamwic. The main groups were in the pits of Phase 45 at CHR (F21 and F28), where there was a minimum number of three or four individuals, in VR Phase 507 (F569) and in VR Phase 508 (F976). HG Phase 18B (F121) was the only assemblage with no horse, and the total sample here was small.

For distribution over the body (Table 4.4), loose teeth were quite common; otherwise there was not much material from the head (save for the fragments in VR Phase 636, F762, which have been seen as from a single skull). As often found for horse, there were many bones of feet and ankles. There were also several of the main limb bones, two of which were from articulated legs. There were only three vertebrae, two cervical and one thoracic, though it should be remembered that the five rib heads would have articulated with the spine in the thoracic area.

Size

Six withers heights (Table A4.1) could be estimated by the factors of Kiesewalter (Driesch & Boessneck,

Table 4.5 Butchery cuts in horse

	27JS 11	CHR 45	CHR 47	VR 493	VR 503	VR 507	VR 508	Total
skull	–	–	–	–	–	1	1	2
cervical vertebrae	–	–	–	1	–	–	–	1
humerus	–	–	–	–	1	–	–	1
radius	1	1	–	–	–	1	–	3
ulna	1	–	–	–	–	–	–	1
femur	–	–	–	–	–	1	–	1
astragalus	–	–	1	–	–	–	–	1
metatarsus	–	1	–	1	–	1	–	3
phalanx 1	–	1	1	–	–	–	–	2
Total	2	3	2	2	1	4	1	15

Note: contexts with no horse have been omitted

1974). These heights confirm the impression given by handling the whole collection: that many bones were close in size to those of a modern New Forest mare in the reference collection, which was the common size from Hamwic; that there was also some very small material; and that at least one more substantial individual was represented (by a metatarsus in one of the CHR pits of Phase 45, F28) (Table A4.2). The two small radii come from ponies of smaller stock than any seen so far in the material from middle Saxon Hamwic, though they were no smaller than was common in the New Forest in the eighteenth century (Tubbs 1986, 116). The tibia is from a horse at the upper end of the Hamwic range – though it must be said that by Witt's scale based on material from continental Europe (Driesch & Boessneck 1974, 331) it would be taken as of only medium size. The other two individuals gave heights which would have fitted easily into middle Saxon Southampton, or would fit the New Forest today. All would have made good riding ponies or pack animals.

Age

All horse epiphyses were fused, but in CHR F28 (Phase 45) there were some loose teeth from younger individuals – deciduous upper premolars in light wear, and an unworn incisor and canine (both lower teeth, and both permanent). Such evidence of young horses is quite rare. Horse bones found from towns are almost always old enough to have been fully trained.

Pathology

Several of the horse bones gave signs of pathology, and all serious problems were from the ankles and feet. The gravest case was from CHR F28 (Phase 45), where first and second phalanges were fused rigid with a great deal of surrounding exostosis. The same pit also gave a whole left metatarsus which showed some exostosis on the front of the shaft towards the proximal end, but which had no pathological signs on the distal shaft nor at either articulation. Other troubles of the feet came from VR Phase 507 (F569), where a right third tarsal was fused to the central, and from VR Phase 508 (F976), where a left second phalanx showed bad exostosis on the shaft.

A near-whole right scapula of horse from 27JS Phase 11 (pit F54) had a much extended outgrowth on the glenoid knob and from CHR Phase 47 (F24) a right mandibular fragment showed lesion or distortion on the hinge.

No fewer than fifteen of these horse bones had been cut, many of them repeatedly, and Table 4.5 shows that such cutting was both widespread over the body and widespread over the site. Ten of these bones had surface cuts only, often very small; and sharp ones (for example, on the condyles in one of the fragments of skull from VR Phase 508, F976, and repeatedly on the distal joint surface of a third metatarsal in one of the lower fills, Phase 493, of ditch F588 at VR). By contrast, the humerus from the clay silt deposits at VR (Phase 503) had been cut through several times on the lateral side of the distal end, apparently with strong smooth movements and a large heavy blade.

Cattle

The three-way reckoning by fragment count of cattle, sheep/goat, and pig is a useful indicator of changing abundance (Fig 4.1). For the purist, secure identifications only would be counted, which includes the heads of ribs but not their ventral fragments. To count all rib fragments and assign them to species gives a result which is based on some assumptions and no doubt on some mistakes, but which even so may be a fairer reflection of relative representation in the past. Both sets of figures are given, and the reader may make the choice. It has been seen that the relative representation

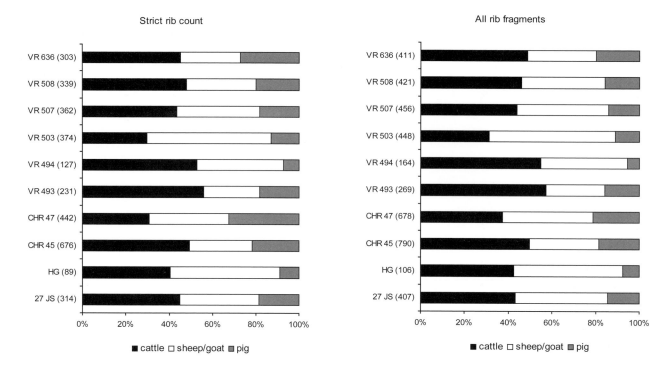

Figure 4.1   Late Saxon northern and eastern suburbs and city defences: representation (%) of the main food mammals by strict rib count (left) by all rib fragments (right) (sample size in brackets; key to site codes in Table 4.1)

of cattle was at its highest in the ditch F588, Phases 493 and 494, at VR (56 per cent and 53 per cent if one takes rib heads only, or 57 per cent and 55 per cent more generously), but that in the upper ditch (Phase 494) this stemmed from a major dearth of pig, and that the lowest was in the clay silt deposits at the same site, VR Phase 503 (31 per cent or 30 per cent). The figures for assemblages that were wholly or very largely of pit material space out quite evenly between the two extremes (from 49 per cent or 50 per cent in the pits of Phase 45, F21 and F28, at CHR down to 31 per cent or 37 per cent in CHR Phase 47, F24).

To some extent these differences in relative abundance fit with different distributions over the body (Table 4.6; Fig 4.2, *see* colour section): head fragments of cattle were high in both ditch phases (493 and 494) at VR (F588) and also in CHR Phase 45, and in the VR layers they were low (though there were many loose teeth in the layers, so that heads plus teeth added up to much the same). It is to be noted that cattle head fragments and loose teeth were very low in the two pit assemblages recovered from the city defences (27JS Phase 11, F54; and HG Phase 18B, F121). Another marked change was the rise in ribs in CHR Phase 47 (F24), and also in VR Phase 636 (F762) even though rib heads as such were low there.

Butchery

Of the main cattle bones, most had been extensively chopped and those few which were whole or near-whole were conspicuous: data for these are given in Table 4.7. The percentage of the bone fragment present was coded following Jones *et al* (1981, 76). Of the 90 fragments of scapula, for example, only one (in one of the pits of Phase 45 at CHR) reached the size-range from half to three-quarters. For long bones ten out of 314 fragments were of more than three-quarters of a bone, and fifteen were just below this size; the bias was to CHR Phase 45. For vertebrae there were 40 and 25 respectively with the same degree of preservation out of 226 total fragments, with CHR Phase 45 again the most abundant, but with 27JS Phase 11 (F54) and VR Phase 508 (F976) quite productive as well. These assemblages were all from pits. There were proportionally more of the larger fragments of metapodials (which is fair enough for bones that are somewhat smaller and less rich in marrow, and are also disposed of more easily); these were more evenly spread throughout the sample.

A total of nine whole or near-whole cattle mandibles seems high, but this was not a concentration, for the material came from several features and contexts. The two near-whole mandibles from VR Phase 507 (F569) were a pair; both were pathological and they are described below. Those from CHR F28 (Phase 45) were both from the same context (133), but they came from two individuals.

For the style of butchery on the cattle bones there are three main points of interest (Table 4.8). First, a fair number of the long bones had been split vertically in the anterioposterior direction, and this suggests more careful cutting than the rough chopping of the long bones for marrow which was common in the middle Saxon period. Such splitting of the cattle bones was a noted form of Roman butchery (Maltby 1989; in press), but in the present material the split bones were

Table 4.6 Anatomical distribution in cattle

	27JS 11	HG 18B	CHR 45	CHR 47	VR 493	VR 494	VR 503	VR 507	VR 508	VR 636	Total
horn core	1	–	16	4	3	3	2	1	1	3	**34**
skull fragment	3	–	52	1	10	1	1	12	13	6	**99**
maxilla	–	1	1	1	2	2	1	2	1	4	**15**
mandible	4	1	19	8	8	7	10	12	8	3	**80**
hyoid	–	–	–	4	–	1	–	1	–	–	**6**
loose teeth	2	1	22	7	13	4	14	13	10	8	**94**
atlas/axis	6	–	15	1	4	–	2	1	5	1	**35**
cervical vertebrae 3-7	7	2	8	6	2	1	6	7	9	8	**56**
thoracic vertebrae	10	2	15	7	11	2	6	8	8	9	**78**
lumbar vertebrae	6	3	7	8	3	1	3	8	8	10	**57**
sacral vertebrae	4	1	2	1	2	–	1	–	1	–	**12**
caudal vertebrae	–	–	–	–	–	–	–	2	–	–	**2**
vertebra fragment	–	–	14	–	–	–	–	–	–	–	**14**
rib (head)	9	–	10	11	–	2	8	5	13	3	**61**
scapula	10	5	15	15	3	5	4	11	15	7	**90**
os coxae	10	5	14	8	9	4	6	7	8	7	**78**
humerus	7	–	24	7	9	4	3	7	11	12	**84**
radius	7	1	18	2	13	2	9	8	7	12	**79**
ulna	4	–	6	4	4	3	5	5	2	6	**39**
femur	12	4	11	13	8	4	3	3	11	6	**75**
tibia	12	3	16	11	5	6	6	6	6	5	**76**
patella	1	–	2	–	–	–	–	–	1	1	**5**
carpal	–	–	5	2	–	–	4	3	3	1	**18**
astragalus	2	–	5	1	2	1	2	1	–	2	**16**
calcaneum	3	1	4	–	5	4	3	6	3	6	**35**
centroquartal	1	–	1	–	–	1	–	–	–	1	**4**
other tarsal	–	–	–	–	–	–	–	1	–	–	**1**
metacarpal	4	–	12	2	4	2	4	6	2	4	**40**
metatarsal	7	3	6	5	5	3	5	4	4	3	**45**
metapodial fragment	1	–	–	–	–	–	–	–	–	–	**1**
phalanx 1	5	3	4	3	3	2	3	6	5	4	**38**
phalanx 2	–	–	4	3	–	2	–	5	2	–	**16**
phalanx 3	3	–	5	1	1	–	–	5	6	4	**25**
Sub-total	141	36	333	136	129	67	111	158	163	137	**1411**
rib fragments, cattle-size	35	9	60	116	25	23	29	42	30	63	**432**
Total (including all rib)	176	45	393	252	154	90	140	200	193	200	**1843**

Table 4.7   Fragmentation in selected cattle bones

	27JS 11	HG 18B	CHR 45	CHR 47	VR 493	VR 494	VR 503	VR 507	VR 508	VR 636	Total
mandibles											
less than 1/2 present	4	–	17	7	8	6	9	10	7	2	**70**
1/2-3/4 present	–	–	–	–	–	–	–	–	1	–	**1**
more than 3/4 present	–	1	2	1	–	1	1	2	–	1	**9**
Total	**4**	**1**	**19**	**8**	**8**	**7**	**10**	**12**	**8**	**3**	**80**
vertebrae											
less than 1/2 present	18	3	27	18	14	3	15	21	20	22	**161**
1/2-3/4 present	4	1	8	3	1	–	2	2	2	2	**25**
more than 3/4 present	7	3	10	1	5	1	–	1	8	4	**40**
Total	**29**	**7**	**45**	**22**	**20**	**4**	**17**	**24**	**30**	**28**	**226**
scapula											
less than 1/2 present	10	5	14	15	3	5	4	11	15	7	**89**
1/2-3/4 present	–	–	1	–	–	–	–	–	–	–	**1**
more than 3/4 present	–	–	–	–	–	–	–	–	–	–	**–**
Total	**10**	**5**	**15**	**15**	**3**	**5**	**4**	**11**	**15**	**7**	**90**
long bones											
less than 1/2 present	37	8	60	32	33	15	20	22	29	33	**289**
1/2-3/4 present	1	–	3	–	2	1	–	1	5	2	**15**
more than 3/4 present	–	–	6	1	–	–	1	1	1	–	**10**
Total	38	8	69	33	35	16	21	24	35	35	**314**
metapodia											
less than 1/2 present	9	1	14	4	4	4	8	12	5	7	**68**
1/2-3/4 present	1	1	3	2	3	–	1	–	1	–	**12**
more than 3/4 present	2	1	1	1	2	1	–	–	–	1	**9**
Total	**12**	**3**	**18**	**7**	**9**	**5**	**9**	**12**	**6**	**8**	**89**

no more eroded than the others; they are not taken as residual from Roman times, but simply as a sign of quite careful butchery in the late Saxon period. The style was most common in the bones from CHR Phase 45 and (pro rata) in VR Phase 636 (F762), and there were five examples from the early phase (494) of the ditch F588 at Victoria Road. It was rare from both of the city defences sites.

Splitting was most likely carried out with a chopper. Other long bones (or even other areas of the same split long bone) gave signs of very smooth cutting, most likely with localised pressure and with a large heavy blade. This style may also represent a measure of extra care. Again the long bones affected were most frequent from CHR Phase 45 and VR Phase 636 (F762). The city defences sites showed four examples; there was none from the early phase (493) of the ditch F588 at VR.

There was also sagittal cutting on the cattle vertebrae. When this is clean and central (or very nearly so) it indicates a lengthwise division of the carcass, and this was discussed by O' Connor (1982, 16) in connection with the Flaxengate site at Lincoln. He found widespread evidence for the practice from the later medieval

period, but there were some hints of its introduction perhaps from the 11th century, a time when building styles were changing to give structures strong enough to support the suspended carcass and withstand the force of the necessary blows. No central sagittal cutting was seen in the present material – and indeed it was not found from the western suburb of Winchester until the later medieval period. There, sagittal cutting which was found on the cattle vertebrae from the late Saxon period was notably off-centre (termed 'paramedian' in Chapter 3). It was sufficiently common to be seen on 20 per cent of the material (n=98), and such cutting has been interpreted as a sign of growing professionalism in the butchery. This cutting in the sagittal plane was seen also from the present sites, though on only 4 per cent of the bones (1 out of 226 of the cattle vertebrae). Save for a single fragment of a lumbar vertebra, only the thoracics had been so cut.

There was a total of 34 fragments of cattle horn core; no polled material was seen. Nine of the fragments had been cut or worked, and these were spread through the assemblages. All of the assemblages except the small one from HG Phase 18B (F121) contained the occa-

Table 4.8 Butchery cuts in selected cattle bones

	27JS 11	HG 18B	CHR 45	CHR 47	VR 493	VR 494	VR 503	VR 507	VR 508	VR 636	Total
fragments split											
humerus split	–	–	8	1	1	1	–	1	–	4	**16**
humerus n	7	–	24	7	9	4	3	7	11	12	**84**
radius split	–	–	5	–	3	1	2	1	1	2	**15**
radius n	7	1	18	2	13	2	9	8	7	12	**79**
femur split	1	1	1	2	–	1	–	–	1	1	**8**
femur n	12	4	11	13	8	4	3	3	11	6	**75**
tibia split	–	–	3	1	1	–	–	1	1	1	**8**
tibia n	12	3	16	11	5	6	6	6	6	5	**76**
long bones split	1	1	17	4	5	3	2	3	3	8	**47**
long bones n	38	8	69	33	35	16	21	24	35	35	**314**
long bones with smooth cuts											
humerus smooth	1	–	3	2	–	–	–	–	–	4	**10**
humerus n	7	–	24	7	9	4	3	7	11	12	**84**
radius smooth	1	–	4	–	–	–	–	–	–	1	**6**
radius n	7	1	18	2	13	2	9	8	7	12	**79**
femur smooth	1	1	–	–	–	1	–	–	–	1	**4**
femur n	12	4	11	13	8	4	3	3	11	6	**75**
tibia smooth	–	–	2	1	–	–	–	–	–	–	**3**
tibia n	12	3	16	11	5	6	6	6	6	5	**76**
long bones smooth	3	1	9	3	–	1	–	–	–	6	**23**
long bones n	38	8	69	33	35	16	21	24	35	35	**314**
vertebrae with sagittal and paramedian sagittal cuts											
cervical sagittal	2	2	2	–	–	–	1	2	3	2	**14**
cervical paramedian	–	–	–	–	–	–	–	–	–	–	**–**
cervical n	13	2	23	7	6	1	8	8	14	9	**91**
thoracic sagittal	3	1	6	–	2	–	2	2	4	4	**24**
thoracic paramedian	1	1	1	–	2	–	–	1	3	–	**9**
thoracic n	10	2	15	7	11	2	6	8	8	9	**78**
lumbar sagittal	2	2	4	5	–	–	1	2	3	1	**20**
lumbar paramedian	–	–	–	–	–	–	–	1	–	–	**1**
lumbar n	6	3	7	8	3	1	3	8	8	10	**57**

sional core fragment but only CHR Phase 45 contained them in any concentration. Mostly the material was found in quite small fragments, but there was one near-whole core from one of the lower fills (Phase 493) of VR F588: this was medium in length, oval in cross-section, and curved, and it was most likely from a female. There was the rounded tip of an oval, curving core in VR Phase 508 (F976); and a fragment in

Table 4.9 Stages of tooth eruption and wear in the mandibles of cattle

Stage	1: M1 unworn	2: M1 in wear	3: M2 in wear	4: M3 in wear	5: M3 in full wear	Total	plus loose LM3 stage 5	Total
HG 18B	–	–	–	–	1	1	–	1
CHR 45	–	–	1	1	3	5	2	7
CHR 47	–	–	1	–	–	1	–	1
VR 493	–	–	–	–	1	1	–	1
VR 494	–	–	–	–	1	1	–	1
VR 503	–	–	–	1	1	2	–	2
VR 507	–	–	–	1	2	3	1	4
VR 508	–	–	1	–	–	1	–	1
VR 636	–	–	1	–	–	1	–	1
Total	–	–	**4**	**3**	**9**	**16**	**3**	**19**

Note: contexts with no data have been omitted

CHR Phase 47 (F24) was also gently curving. An oval fragment from one of the later fills of ditch F588 at VR (Phase 494) was deeply grooved and very heavy. Most distinctive was a fragment from VR Phase 507 (F569): this was large, heavy and rounded, and though there was neither base nor tip, the lines suggest that the full core may have been quite long.

There were few signs that the cores had been worked. From the sixteen fragments in CHR Phase 45, two cores had been chopped obliquely from the skull and another showed many oblique surface cuts though it had not been removed. A distal fragment from 27JS Phase 11 (F54) had been neatly cut round the circumference just above the base. In VR Phase 636 (F762), on the other hand, though there were several worked horn cores of goat (below), the three fragments from cattle were all small and showed no cuts.

Size

Five withers heights could be calculated from whole fused bones of cattle (Table A4.1). For the fragmented bones, a summary of measurements where the sample size is greatest is given in Table A4.3.

The five withers heights range from 1.07m to 1.25m. The figure from the whole radius is notably high, for in this period the measurements from the long bones often convert into lower withers heights than do those from the metapodials: this may be from changed conformation in the stock, from having to use the factors of Matolsci, or even from butchery bias, but the point should be made that the radius from one of the pits of Phase 45 at CHR gives a size considerably larger than expected. The minimal total of five calculated withers heights gives a mean of 1.16m, very close indeed to that from the far larger sample from the Melbourne Street excavations in middle Saxon Hamwic (1.154m, n=77). The Hamwic cattle sizes have been claimed as good and generous for their period (Bourdillon & Coy 1980, 106) and it is

clear that the cattle in Southampton declined in size thereafter (Bourdillon 1980, 185).

For measurements of breadth the present figures may also be compared with those from Hamwic Melbourne Street. From measurements of fused articulations only, with the data compared with the respective Hamwic means and with the results then percentaged, the measured bones from the Winchester cattle come out with an overall breadth of 98.6 per cent of their middle Saxon equivalents from Hamwic (Table A4.7). This is closer than the figure which was calculated for the new town of late Saxon Southampton (96 per cent – Bourdillon 1988, 186). A fall-off in size from the middle Saxon period to the first post-Conquest centuries seems to have been established over central southern England, and perhaps more widely, in that no data have been found to challenge the pattern from Southampton. One would expect the cattle of late Saxon Winchester to show some decline, and they do so minimally on the present measurements. One may see them perhaps as animals that were selected for their size.

Age

Only sixteen mandibles of cattle had the main cheek teeth in place and could therefore be aged (Table 4.9). None was younger than stage 3, when the second molar is in wear but not yet the third. Animals from stage 3 and from stage 4 (when the third molar comes into wear), offer good and tender eating, and these two stages account for seven mandibles out of the total of sixteen. For the other nine mandibles and for the three loose third molars, all molar cusps were fully in wear – the culmination of a long process of maturation. The only concentration of mandibles came with the five from CHR F28 (Phase 45), and one of the loose third molars. For ages these gave a fair cross-section of the study as a whole.

Although the mandibles included no young individuals, there was some evidence of calves from other

Table 4.10 Evidence of very young material in cattle

| | By porous fragments | | | By epiphyseal fusion | | | |
	neonatal	older calf	all fragments	scapula unfused	scapula fused	Hdl/Rpx unfused	Hdl/Rpx fused
27JS 11	–	3	141	–	2	–	5
HG 18B	–	1	36	–	–	–	–
CHR 45	–	2	333	–	4	–	22
CHR 47	–	2	136	–	–	–	6
VR 493	–	1	129	–	–	–	10
VR 494	–	–	67	–	2	–	1
VR 503	–	2	111	–	1	–	4
VR 507	–	1	158	–	1	1	6
VR 508	2	4	163	–	4	–	8
VR 636	2	–	137	–	1	–	9
Total	4	15	1411	–	15	1	71

Note: Hdl/Rpx: distal humerus and/or proximal radius epiphysis

bones of the body (Table 4.10). From the epiphyses, one bone from the early-fusing group was not yet fused – a distal humerus from VR Phase 507 (F569). Porous material, however, is perhaps the best indicator of youth, since it is an indicator to which all bones of the body may contribute. There were four calf bones which were very porous and so small that they are likely to have come from neonatal individuals – two bones from VR Phase 508 (F976), a humerus shaft and a thoracic vertebra which, small as it was, had been butchered; and two from VR Phase 636 (F762), a shaft of radius, and a horn core. These therefore establish the presence of some breeding animals near the site. In addition there were fifteen bones which were quite porous but not so small; these are likely to have come from individuals of several weeks or perhaps a few months old. Of this group, four bones were from VR Phase 508 (F976). Another (a much-chewed metacarpal shaft) came from the early phase (493) of the ditch F588 at VR.

Pathology

In the pair of cattle mandibles from VR Phase 507 (F569), both the permanent fourth premolars were twisted at right angles to the main tooth row. The right had *ante-mortem* loss of all three molars. In the left the fourth premolar had an extra fork to the root and there was an extra hole in the gum behind the third premolar: abnormal stresses had produced a strange pattern of molar tooth wear, but this could be roughly translated into Grant's (1975) stages k, j, and g. The individual was certainly fully mature. One loose lower third molar out of the twelve recovered lacked its final cusp.

From the post-cranial skeleton there was a case of serious damage from VR F588 (Phase 494), where a fused right distal tibia had set so awkwardly after a

fracture that it was hard to see how the animal could have continued to place any weight on that leg.

There were only two cases of exostosis on the cattle foot bones, and neither was grave. A right distal metatarsal from 27JS Phase 11 (F54) showed light exostosis round the joint, and also some splaying, and from CHR F28 (Phase 45) a whole fused first phalanx had exostosis on both its medial and its lateral shafts, but not on either joint. There were also two ribs that showed damage: on one from VR F588 (Phase 493) there was major exostosis, perhaps following an infection, and on one from VR Phase 636 (F762) there were signs that a fracture had not fully healed. From their broad thin cross-section these two ribs probably came from cattle.

Two distal humeri showed a lateral protuberance above the trochlea – one was from a large, well-marked, and probably quite old individual from CHR F28, Phase 45 (Bd 92.3, BT 75.7mm) and the other from CHR Phase 47 (F24) and was from a sightly smaller individual (Bd 81.0, BT 68.8mm). The lumps on two bones were so strange but so similar (and quite unlike the exostosis commonly seen at the elbow in sheep, as discussed in Chapter 6) that one might hazard a guess that the condition was genetic rather than pathological.

There were other minor anomalies. From HG Phase 18B (F121) came the ventral fragment of a very lopsided lumbar vertebra; the bone was fused, but only caudally. Three first phalanges showed small lesions on their joint surfaces – proximally in CHR Phase 47 (F24) and distally in 27JS Phase 11 (F54) and CHR Phase 47 (F24).

The upper ditch fills of F588 at VR (Phase 494) gave three acetabula that were misshapen either at laterally or medially – a left one, and two right ones – and a left acetabulum from Phase 503 (one of the clay silt deposits from the same site) showed a slit near the lateral edge.

Table 4.11 Anatomical distribution in goat

	Horn core	Skull	Humerus	Radius	Os coxae	Total
CHR 45	7	–	2	1	1	**11**
CHR 47	1	1	–	–	–	**2**
VR 494	2	–	–	–	–	**2**
VR 507	–	–	1	–	–	**1**
VR 636	12	–	–	–	–	**12**
Total	**22**	**1**	**3**	**1**	**1**	**28**

Note: contexts in which securely identified goat was absent have been omitted

On a left ulna from VR Phase 636 (F762) the articular surface curved back over the upper shaft.

Sheep and Goat

In addition to 22 horn cores, and one fragment of skull from CHR Phase 47 (F24), only five post-cranial fragments of goat were identified (Table 4.11). Apart from a right distal humerus in VR Phase 507 (F569), all were from the pits of Phase 45 at CHR. In F21 there was a large and very straight humerus shaft which was certainly from goat, and a pelvis with morphology which exactly matched that of a male goat in the reference collection. The similar texture of these two bones stood out within the assemblage. A right distal humerus and a right proximal radius were recovered from F28; both were cut obliquely and could have been from the same individual.

For sheep, all horn cores are distinguished to species in the archive, along with several skull fragments, the distal scapulae, most of the long bone material except for the tibiae, and nearly all the metapodials. The identification of one conspicuous os coxae also seemed secure for goat (Table 4.11). The rest of the ovicaprid bones appear in the archive as 'sheep/goat'. For ease of data handling this included all the mandibles, though it should be noted that all the deciduous fourth premolars were of sheep. It has to be accepted that some bones of goat may have been missed, especially those from young individuals, but it is likely to be more realistic to take the undifferentiated sheep/goat bones as having come very largely from sheep and to treat them as such in the discussion.

It was suggested above that many of the smaller sheep/goat bones (those of the foot and ankle, and loose incisors) had most likely been lost in trench recovery; even so, sheep/goat were a good second to cattle by fragment count overall, although they were more abundant, both in the clay silt deposits at VR (Phase 503) and in the small assemblage of pit-material from HG Phase 18B (F121). They were at their lowest in the early phase of the ditch at VR (F588, Phase 493) and in the large assemblage from the two pits of Phase 45 at CHR (F21 and F28), and also in VR Phase 636 (F762) where pig was notably high.

For distribution over the body in Table 4.12, the head fragments of rib have been recorded separately from their body fragments. On size and shape, however, it is very likely that most of these sheep-size rib fragments came from sheep/goat rather than from pig, and they have been shown by percentage accordingly in Figure 4.1. For Table 4.12 there is also the caution that if some numbers of small bones have been lost, as seemed likely from the discussion above, the overall groups in Table 4.14 would need some correction in interpretation; yet one may take it that any loss would be constant over the sites, and they provide a useful template against which the overall distributions may be set.

Head fragments were notably abundant in the clay silt deposits at VR (Phase 503); they were low in the later phase of the ditch F588 (Phase 494) and in the pit assemblage from VR Phase 507 (F569). It should be remembered that the figures for ribs may include a few ventral rib fragments from pig; but sheep/goat ribs were notably well represented in VR Phase 636 (F762), and in CHR Phase 47, F24 (where bones of the feet were very low indeed). By contrast ribs were low in CHR Phase 45, and long bones were plentiful there in all the main contexts (Fig. 4.3, *see* colour section).

Hornless sheep have been found among the material from Roman Winchester (Maltby in press) and a close watch was kept for hornless skulls in the present assemblage. Both male and female sheep seemed generally to be horned. Two fragments, however, may show the results of possible polling: one from the ditch F588 at VR (Phase 494) had no horn core but was very rough in that area, and from HG Phase 18B (F121) there was an apparently adult fragment with a small strange bud for a core.

Size

The measurements of sheep (Table A4.1) on which the withers heights are based (Fig 4.4) are all from bones of the body where the identification is secure; and even of the measurements of breadth (Table A4.4), it is only the tibiae (Fig 4.5) which have to be classed as from sheep/goat.

On Teichert's withers height factors for prehistoric and protohistoric sheep (Teichert 1975), the upper end of the Hamwic range is missing from the late Saxon Winchester material: the mean height was 0.55m, with a range from 0.51m to 0.62m, compared with the

Table 4.12 Anatomical distribution in sheep and sheep/goat

	JS 11	HG 18B	CHR 45	CHR 47	VR 493	VR 494	VR 503	VR 507	VR 508	VR 636	Total
horn core	2	2	2	2	1	1	3	5	–	2	**20**
skull fragment	5	5	23	10	1	2	48	5	10	6	**115**
maxilla	1	–	5	7	3	1	9	–	3	1	**30**
mandible	8	4	15	15	8	1	10	5	8	9	**83**
hyoid	–	–	–	–	–	–	–	–	–	1	**1**
loose teeth	–	1	20	12	8	5	39	21	9	2	**117**
atlas/axis	4	2	6	1	2	1	2	2	5	2	**27**
cervical vertebra 3-7	12	–	2	9	1	4	5	5	1	1	**40**
thoracic vertebra	4	–	7	8	3	1	13	4	6	3	**49**
lumbar vertebra	4	–	7	11	–	1	4	6	2	4	**39**
sacral vertebra	–	–	–	1	–	–	1	–	1	–	**3**
caudal vertetbra	–	–	–	–	–	–	–	–	1	–	**1**
rib head	28	8	8	23	2	5	12	14	17	8	**125**
sternum	–	–	–	–	1	1	–	–	–	1	**3**
scapula	5	2	6	12	2	3	5	9	7	3	**54**
os coxae	7	2	8	4	8	3	3	3	4	2	**44**
humerus	5	1	7	6	1	1	5	5	5	2	**38**
radius	7	4	12	8	1	4	8	9	6	6	**65**
ulna	4	–	9	4	–	–	–	–	2	3	**22**
femur	1	1	4	4	–	1	3	6	–	–	**20**
tibia	6	5	19	14	6	6	11	13	7	3	**90**
fibula	–	–	–	–	–	–	–	–	1	–	**1**
carpal	–	–	–	1	–	–	1	–	–	–	**2**
astragalus	1	–	–	–	1	–	4	–	1	2	**9**
calcaneum	–	–	4	–	–	–	2	–	1	–	**7**
centroquartal	–	–	–	–	–	–	1	–	–	–	**1**
metacarpal	3	3	5	4	5	2	7	15	3	2	**49**
metatarsal	6	5	10	3	5	6	13	7	6	9	**70**
phalanx 1	2	–	5	1	–	–	3	4	2	–	**17**
phalanx 2	–	–	2	–	–	–	1	–	1	–	**4**
phalanx 3	–	–	–	–	1	–	1	–	–	–	**2**
Total	**115**	**45**	**186**	**160**	**60**	**49**	**214**	**138**	**109**	**72**	**1148**
rib fragments, sheep-size	58	8	54	120	13	14	45	52	52	45	**461**

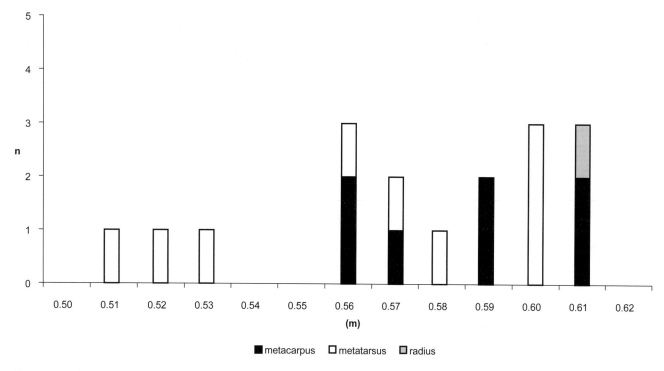

Figure 4.4   Sheep: distribution of withers height (calculated from Teichert 1975)

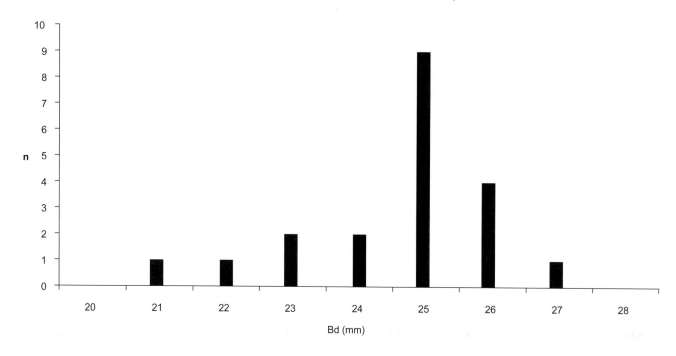

Figure 4.5   Sheep and goat tibia: distal breadth (measurement after Driesch 1976)

figures from Hamwic Melbourne Street of 0.62m with a range of 0.50m to 0.71m (n=223). The overall figure for bone articular breadths, calculated as described above for cattle, is 96.4 per cent of the respective means from middle Saxon Hamwic (Table A4.7). This seems to mark a real falling off in sizes at Winchester, and indeed some of the material from the western suburb was even smaller, down to 0.49m (Chapter 3). It is an interesting contrast that a sample of thirteen sheep heights from late Saxon Southampton showed less of decline (to 0.59m, with a range of 0.54m to 0.65m),

and that the articular breadths there were very close indeed to those from Hamwic (99.4 per cent). There seem to be several points of difference in the late Saxon flocks of sheep as represented in Winchester and in Southampton.

Age

Table 4.13 shows a high rate of very young sheep mandibles (on the evidence of the deciduous fourth

Table 4.13 Stages of tooth eruption and wear in the mandibles of sheep and sheep/goat

	27JS 11	HG 18B	CHR 45	CHR 47	VR 493	VR 494	VR 503	VR 507	VR 508	VR 636	Total
Stage											
1	2	–	1	5	–	–	–	–	–	1	9
2	–	–	1	–	–	–	–	–	–	–	1
3	1	1	1	–	–	–	1	–	–	–	4
3 or 4	–	1	–	–	–	–	–	–	–	–	1
4	2	1	2	2	1	–	3	–	2	1	14
4 or 5	–	–	–	1	–	–	1	–	–	–	2
5	1	1	2	3	2	–	2	1	3	2	17
Total mandibles	**6**	**4**	**7**	**11**	**3**	**–**	**7**	**1**	**5**	**4**	**48**
plus loose DPM4 and LM3											
Stage											
3	–	–	–	–	–	1	–	–	–	–	1
4	–	–	–	–	1	1	1	1	1	–	5
5	–	–	–	–	–	–	–	1	1	–	2
Total	**6**	**4**	**7**	**11**	**4**	**2**	**8**	**3**	**7**	**4**	**56**

Note: all fourth deciduous premolars were from sheep

Table 4.14 Evidence of very young material in sheep and sheep/goat

	By porous fragments			By epiphyseal fusion			
	neonatal	young lamb	all fragments	scapula unfused	scapula fused	Hdl/Rpx unfused	Hdl/Rpx fused
27JS 11	1	–	115	–	–	–	7
HG 18B	–	1	45	–	–	–	7
CHR 45	–	6	186	–	3	–	12
CHR 47	3	9	160	–	1	1	3
VR 493	–	–	60	–	1	–	1
VR 494	–	2	49	–	–	1	2
VR 503	–	4	214	–	1	–	2
VR 507	–	8	138	–	1	–	6
VR 508	2	4	109	1	2	2	5
VR 636	2	3	72	1	–	1	2
Total	**8**	**37**	**1148**	**2**	**9**	**5**	**41**

Note: Hdl/ Rpx: distal humerus and / or proximal radius epiphysis

premolars, none of them was from goat). This contrasts with the absence of very young mandibles from cattle. There was a concentration in CHR Phase 47 (F24); others were found from 27JS Phase 11 (F54); from CHR F28, Phase 45 (the pit which gave the only mandible from the second stage, with the first molar recently in wear); and from VR Phase 636 (F762). There were four mandibles from stage 3, with the second molar in recent wear, and a good number from stage 4, with the third molar coming into wear but with the last cusp still unworn (fourteen, plus five loose teeth). These two groups form the prime eating ages. There were also many older adults (seventeen mandibles, plus two loose teeth).

The evidence from other bones of the body supports that from the mandibles (Table 4.14): there is more young material than from cattle. There are several unfused epiphyses from the early-fusing group, and the incidence of porous bones was higher – both for likely neonatal material (six out of 148 fragments, against four out of 1411), and for the porous but rather larger bones (sheep: 37 out of 1148; cattle: 5 out of 1411).

Table 4.15 Distribution of horn core fragments

	Cattle	Sheep	Goat	Total
27JS 11	1	2	–	**3**
HG 18B	–	2	–	**2**
CHR 45	16	2	7	**25**
CHR 47	4	2	1	**7**
VR 493	3	1	–	**4**
VR 494	3	1	2	**6**
VR 503	2	3	–	**5**
VR 507	1	5	–	**6**
VR 508	1	–	–	**1**
VR 636	3	2	12	**17**
Total	**34**	**20**	**22**	**76**

It would seem that the flocks of sheep/goat represented here were culled to provide for tender eating as well as run to provide for wool; and from the general rate of young material it seems that there was breeding nearby.

Horn cores

The fragment count for horn cores was given separately by species in the tables (Tables 4.11 and 4.12) that show distribution over the body, but they are collected in Table 4.15; cattle horn core fragments are included for comparison. Though even on the strictest reckoning the post-cranial bones of sheep far outnumbered those of goat, goat gave more fragments of horn core. By site and context there was a clear concentration of these in VR Phase 636 (F762) and CHR Phase 45, with twelve in VR Phase 636 and seven in CHR Phase 45. One goat core from VR Phase 636 was eroded and stained, but otherwise all were hard and in good condition.

Of these 22 goat cores, eleven had been cut or sawn or both. Five from VR Phase 636 (F762) showed saw-marks, and some of these had also been cut. From CHR Phase 45 only one was sawn, but five had been cut. Where such marks of working were seen, the core had been cut obliquely at the base; none had been removed by cutting straight across the forehead, a cut which had been standard practice at middle Saxon Hamwic.

The goat horn cores were all alike in that they were hard, straight and slightly oval in cross-section, similar in shape to the male goat horn cores from Hamwic (Bourdillon & Coy 1980), and although smaller than these, they appear to be from mature animals. Because of the way they had been cut it was hard to take any measurements, but an estimate of 210mm for the greatest length is likely to be fair for the core which was the most complete and which otherwise seemed to be quite typical (CHR F21). The male goat cores from Hamwic were over 300mm in greatest length, with about 200mm for the much slighter female cores.

For Winchester it may be said that a selection of solely female cores would be very unlikely for horn working, and one must assume that the material came from males; but it was not from the same stock of goats that was found from middle Saxon Hamwic (and indeed which seems to have continued there through medieval times).

The horn core fragments from sheep were spread quite evenly over the sample, VR Phase 508 (F976) yielding none at all. With five sheep cores, VR Phase 507 (F569) was the richest: by contrast this pit gave only one core from cow and none from goat. Two of its sheep core fragments were from rams, but none showed cut marks. The next richest group was also from VR, in the clay silt deposits of Phase 503, with a male core, and one porous and one adult core fragment. Again there were no cut marks.

There were few cores of sheep from the two assemblages where goat horn working showed some concentration, and these cores, though few, had been worked. The two from CHR F28 (Phase 45), one of them male, had both been cut obliquely from the head, and the two from VR Phase 636 (F762) had also been cut, sagitally at the base for a heavy male core, and obliquely from a probable female core. The only other core of note came from HG Phase 18B (F121); this was still quite young, but seemed more curved than usual.

Pathology

There were several cases of impaction on the sheep/goat mandibles. In three cases this impaction occurred between the fourth premolar and the first molar (27JS Phase 11 (F54); CHR Phase 47 (F24); and CHR Phase 45 (F28), where the tooth row had worn very unevenly; and in two it was in the molar row itself (CHR Phase 45, F28; and VR Phase 636, F762). A further mandible from CHR F28 (Phase 45) had likely periodontal disease and loose back molars, and a left maxilla from CHR F21 was puffy as from an infection, with the molars showing caries.

From the body, several bones showed troubles at the elbow, as is often seen on archaeological material from sheep (Baker & Brothwell 1980, 127) – see also Chapter 6. A humerus and radius from VR (a clay silt deposit of Phase 503), both with distal exostosis, articulated well, and from VR Phase 508 (F976) three fragments with exostosis (humerus, radius, and ulna) formed a single elbow joint. There was also some mild lateral exostosis on a distal humerus from 27JS Phase 11 (F54), and three radii from VR Phase 507 (F569) showed lipping at the joint. All these bones were certainly from sheep.

Sheep exostosis at the elbow was reported from Hamwic Melbourne Street where it was seen as a probable indication of considerable age as well as a sign that one part of the body had been subjected to serious strain (Bourdillon & Coy 1980, 92).

One serious case of sheep pathology was a whole right-fused metatarsus from HG Phase 18B (F121) where the front shaft was badly swollen as if from an

Table 4.16   Anatomical distribution in pig

	27JS 11	HG 18B	CHR 45	CHR 47	VR 493	VR 494	VR 503	VR 507	VR 508	VR 636	Total
skull fragment	7	–	9	25	3	–	8	7	7	8	**74**
maxilla	1	–	15	8	1	1	1	3	3	2	**35**
mandible	5	2	22	28	5	1	3	4	1	5	**76**
loose teeth	5	–	21	15	8	–	5	15	5	12	**86**
atlas/ axis	1	–	–	2	–	–	3	–	1	3	**10**
cervical vertebra 3-7	1	–	–	–	2	1	–	1	2	–	**7**
thoracic vertebra	1	–	3	5	3	–	2	2	–	4	**20**
lumbar vertebra	4	–	1	3	–	–	1	2	1	1	**13**
sacral vertebra	–	–	1	–	–	–	–	–	–	–	**1**
rib head	3	–	2	9	3	–	3	3	3	3	**28**
sternum	–	–	–	–	–	–	–	–	–	2	**2**
scapula	6	1	12	10	1	2	2	2	5	2	**45**
os coxae	1	–	3	3	–	1	2	7	1	6	**24**
humerus	3	1	9	4	3	–	3	1	3	4	**31**
radius	4	–	5	3	3	–	5	3	1	–	**24**
ulna	3	–	7	4	2	2	1	1	2	3	**25**
femur	2	–	9	4	1	–	1	3	1	2	**23**
tibia	9	–	10	1	2	1	1	2	3	3	**32**
fibula	–	1	–	6	1	–	2	–	2	1	**13**
astragalus	1	–	1	–	–	–	1	1	2	–	**6**
calcaneum	–	–	2	–	–	–	–	–	3	1	**6**
other tarsal	–	–	–	–	–	–	–	–	1	1	**2**
metacarpal	–	1	3	4	1	–	1	2	4	6	**22**
metatarsal	–	2	3	2	1	–	2	2	5	2	**19**
metapodial fragment	–	–	4	6	–	–	1	–	6	7	**24**
phalanx 1	1	–	2	–	1	–	1	1	5	3	**14**
phalanx 2	–	–	–	2	1	–	–	–	1	1	**5**
phalanx 3	–	–	2	–	–	–	–	–	1	–	**3**
Total	**58**	**8**	**146**	**144**	**42**	**9**	**49**	**65**	**67**	**82**	**670**

infection; and there were rough lumps near the cranial end of a right sheep/goat pelvis from CHR F28 (Phase 45), as from an unusual join (or rubbing) with the sacrum.

Pig

Overall, pig accounted for 21 per cent of total representation of cattle, sheep/goat, and pig – but group by group there were great variations in its abundance (Table 4.1). The high rate of pig from CHR Phase 47 (F24) may be linked with the low rate of cattle there; in VR Phase 636 (F762) the abundance may have stemmed partly from a marked concentration in in a single context (3217). The variation does not seem to be linked with context-type: there were minimal pig fragments from later phase of the VR ditch F588 (Phase 494) and from the small assemblage of pit material from HG Phase 18B (F121), and it was also low in the VR clay silt deposits (Phase 503). Only six fragments of pig were identified from

Table 4.17   Stages of tooth eruption and wear in the mandibles of pig

stage	1	2	3	3 or 4	4	5	Total
27JS 11	1	–	1	–	–	1	**3**
CHR 45	–	3	5	1	3	3	**15**
CHR 47	–	1	5	–	4	2	**12**
VR 493	–	–	–	–	1	–	**1**
VR 503	–	1	2	–	–	–	**3**
VR 507	1	–	–	–	–	–	**1**
VR 508	–	1	–	–	–	–	**1**
VR 636	–	–	2	1	–	–	**3**
Total	2	6	15	2	8	6	**39**

Note: contexts with no data have been omitted

Table 4.18   Evidence of very young material in pig

	By porous fragments			By epiphyseal fusion			
	neonatal	young pig	all fragments	scapula unfused	scapula fused	Hdl/Rpx unfused	Hdl/Rpx fused
27JS 11	–	1	58	–	2	–	4
HG 18B	–	1	8	1	–	–	1
CHR 45	–	–	146	2	5	1	6
CHR 47	2	6	144	3	3	1	3
VR 493	–	–	42	–	–	2	1
VR 494	–	–	9	–	1	–	–
VR 503	–	1	49	–	–	1	3
VR 507	–	5	65	–	–	1	1
VR 508	1	2	67	–	–	–	1
VR 636	–	1	82	–	–	–	1
Total	3	17	670	6	11	6	21

Note: Hdl/Rpx : distal humerus and / or proximal radius epiphysis

the sieved samples. Three of these were from ditch contexts (including the later Phase 494 of VR ditch F588), two were from pits and one was from the clay silt deposits (VR Phase 503).

By distribution over the body (Table 4.16 and Fig 4.6, *see* colour section) there were contrasts with cattle and with sheep/goat. Head fragments were much more abundant (especially in the two assemblages from the eastern suburb – from CHR Phase 47 (F24) and from CHR Phase 45, (F28). Loose teeth were common in the early phase of the ditch at VR (F588, Phase 493), but also in the pit material from VR Phase 507 (F569). Vertebrae were lacking. Ribs, too, were lacking – and the heads of ribs are fully distinctive to species, even if other pig rib fragments may be missed. Foot bones were scarce save in the marked concentration from VR Phase 636 (F762). Long bones were relatively common in pit F54 (Phase 11) at 27JS (where bones of the feet were very scarce), and also in the early phase (493) of the ditch F588 at VR.

Age

Ageing as assessed from mandibles is usefully complemented by evidence from other bones (Tables 4.17 and 4.18). The pigs represented in this study were certainly much younger than the cattle and there is nothing surprising in that. However, only on fusion of the earliest-fusing bones may they be taken as younger than sheep/goat. Neonatal pig bones were found in CHR Phase 47 (F24) and in VR Phase 508 (F976); and there were two very young mandibles with the first molar not yet in wear, one each from 27JS Phase 11 (F54) and from VR Phase 507 (F569). However, there was an even higher proportion of mandibles of young animals among the sheep/goat.

For those individuals that were young but not neonatal, pig was better represented in VR Phase 494. There were seventeen porous bones of this size, several in CHR Phase 47; and five from VR Phase 507 (F569). By fusion evidence from the first-fusing group

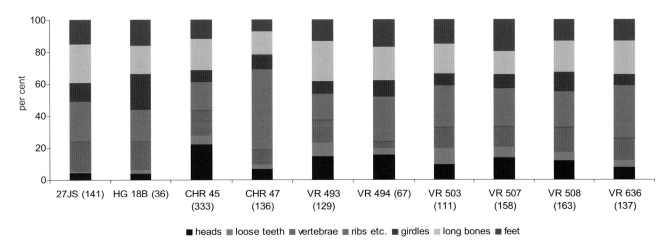

Figure 4.2 Distribution by main body groups in cattle (%) (sample size in brackets; key to site codes in Table 4.1)

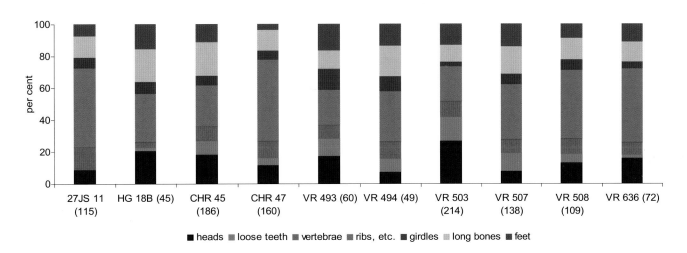

Figure 4.3 Distribution by main body groups in sheep and sheep / goat (%) (sample size in brackets; key to site codes in Table 4.1)

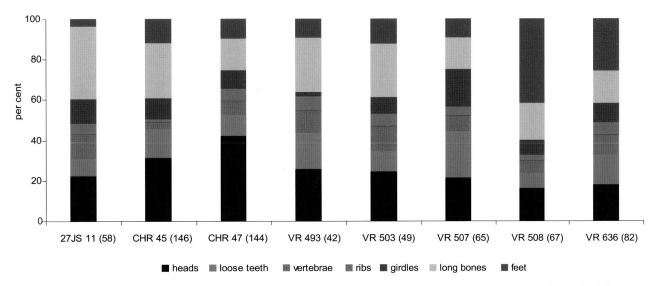

Figure 4.6 Distribution by main body group in pig (%) (sample size in brackets; key to site codes in Table 4.1)

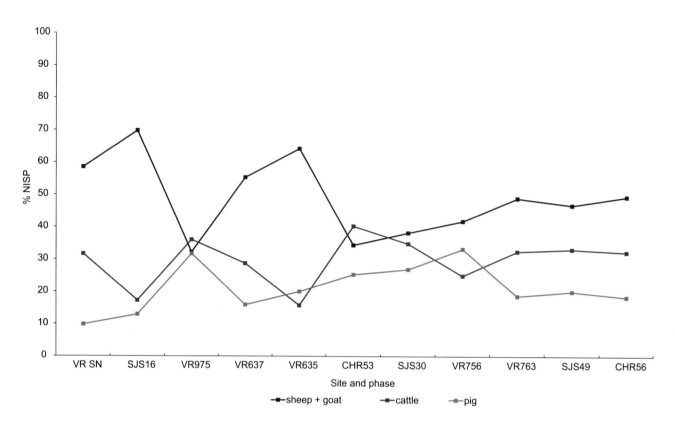

Figure 5.1   Medieval northern and eastern suburbs: relative proportions of cattle, sheep, and pig in the largest groups studied: % NISP (key to site codes in Table 5.1) SN Saxo-Norman. Sites arranged in date order

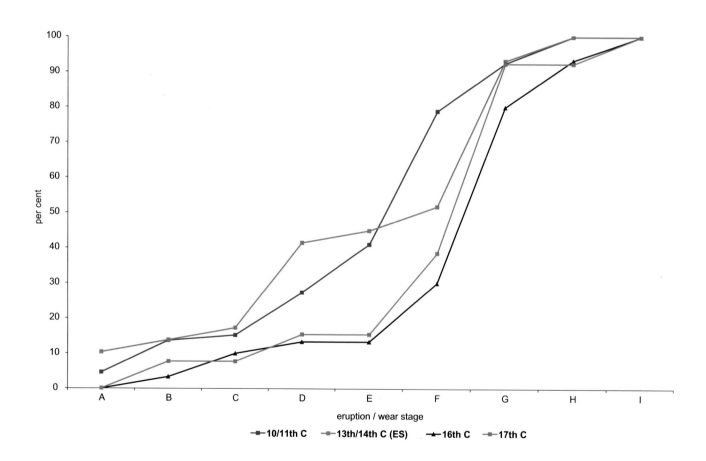

Figure 5.36   Sheep and goat: age at death from dental eruption and wear: cumulative percentages (age stages after Payne 1973) ES Eastern suburb

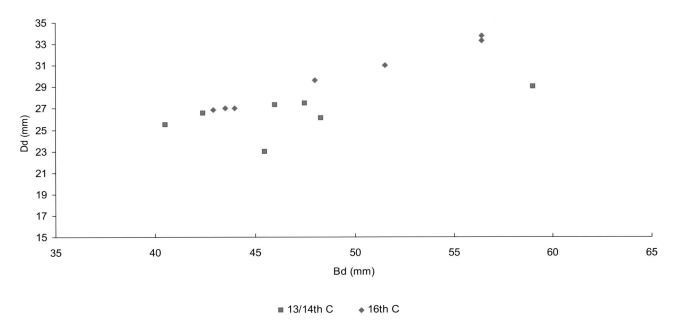

Figure 5.37   Cattle: size of proximal metacarpals (Bp x Dp) (after Driesch 1976)

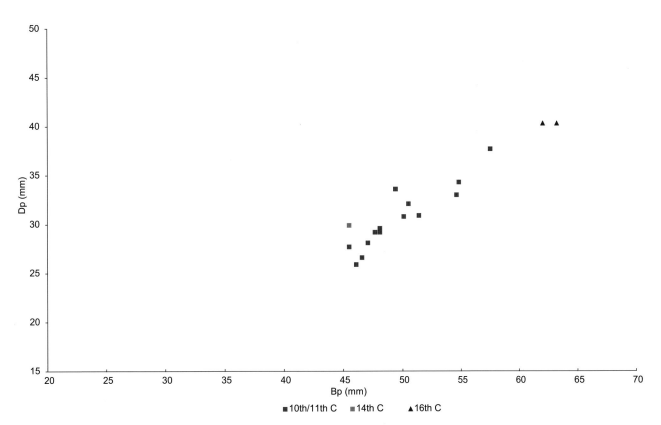

Figure 5.38   Cattle: size of distal metacarpals (Bd x Dd) (after Driesch 1976)

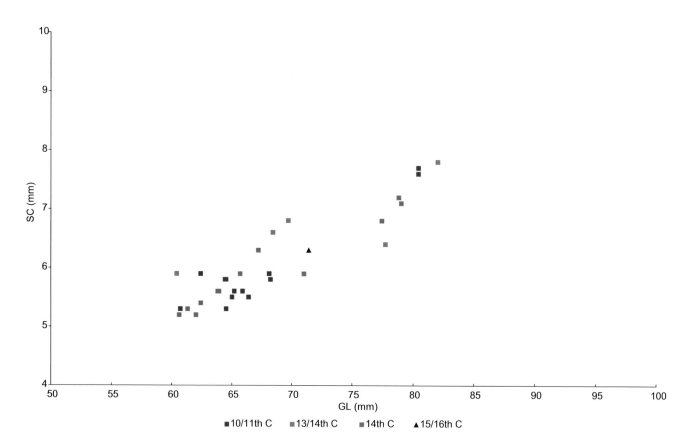

Figure 5.41   Domestic fowl: tarsometatarsus size (GL x SC) (after Driesch 1976)

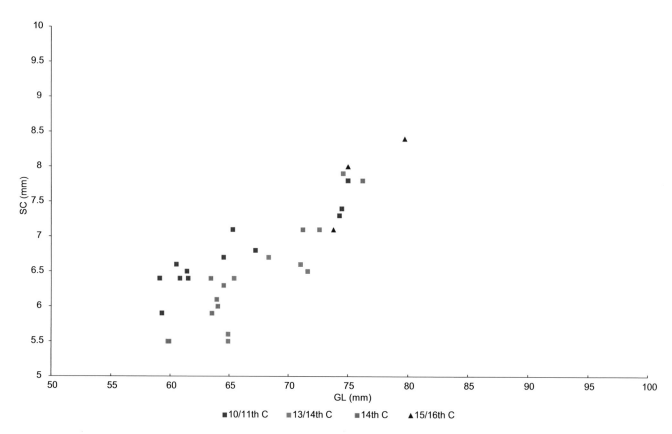

Figure 5.42   Domestic fowl: humerus size (GL x SC) (after Driesch 1976)

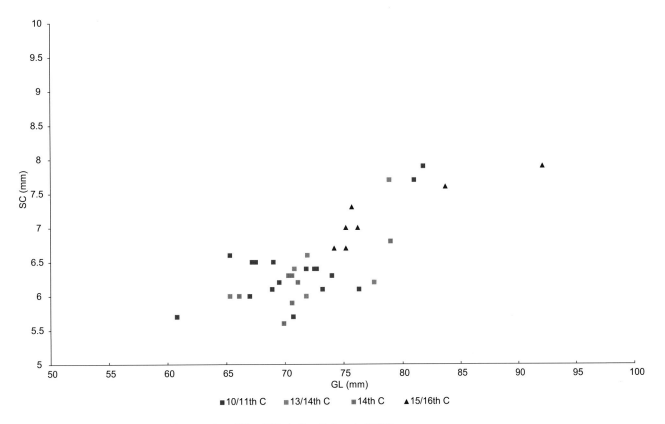

Figure 5.43   Domestic fowl: femur size (GL x SC) (after Driesch 1976)

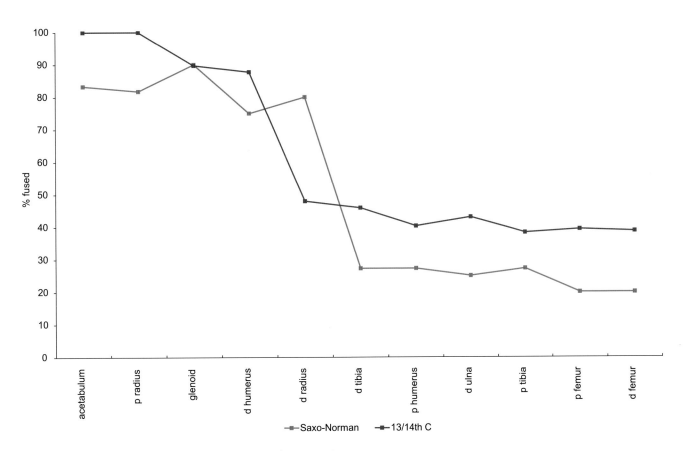

Figure 5.51   Saxo-Norman and 13th–14th century: age at death of cats: from bone fusion

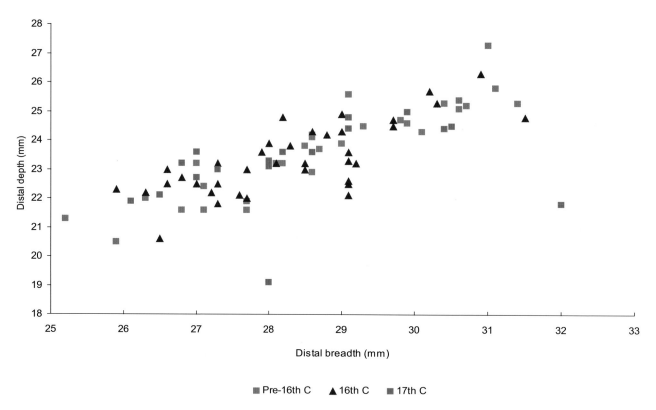

Figure 6.2   *Sheep humerus: bivariate of plot of distal breadth (Bd) x distal depth (mm) (after Driesch 1976)*

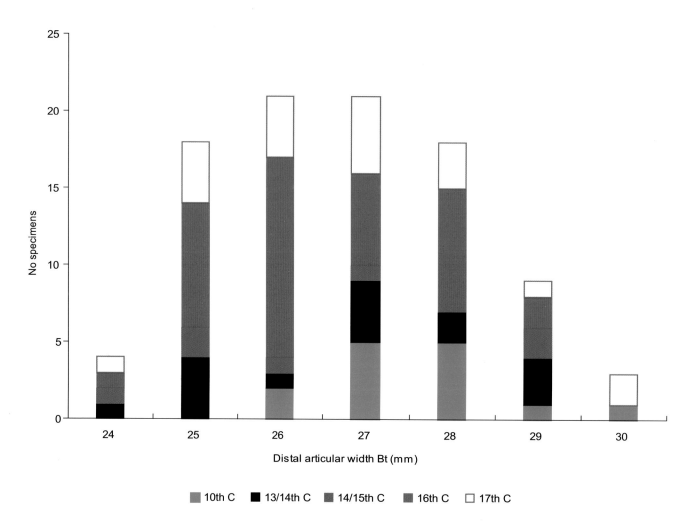

Figure 6.3   *Sheep humerus: distal articular breadth (Bt) (after Driesch 1976)*

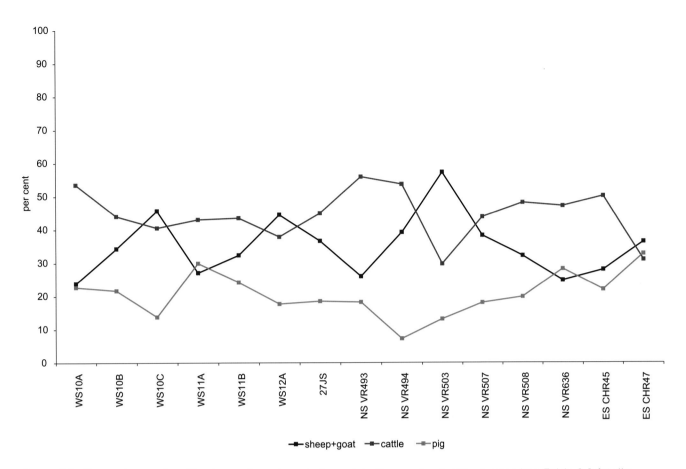

Figure 7.2   Percentage of cattle, sheep / goat, and pig on late Saxon sites in Winchester (see Table 1.1 for site codes)

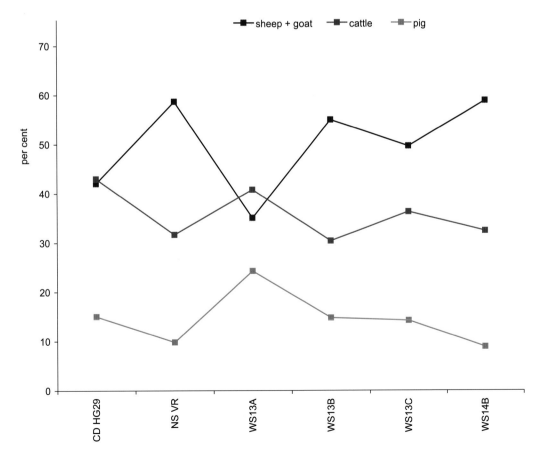

Figure 7.3   Percentage of cattle, sheep / goat and pig on Saxo-Norman sites in Winchester (arranged as Fig 7.2)

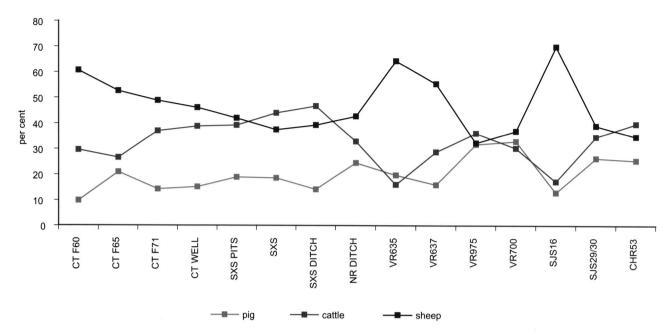

Figure 7.5   Percentage of cattle, sheep / goat, and pig on 13th- to 14th-century sites in Winchester (arranged as Fig 7.2)

Table 4.19 Anatomical distribution in dog

	27JS 11	CHR 45	CHR 47	VR 493	VR 494	VR 507	VR 508	VR 636	Total
skull fragment	–	–	–	1	1	–	–	–	2
maxilla	–	–	1	–	3	–	–	–	4
mandible	–	1	–	–	–	–	1	–	2
loose teeth	–	–	–	2	1	2	–	–	5
atlas/ axis	–	–	–	–	1	1	–	–	2
thoracic vertebra	–	–	–	–	1	–	–	–	1
rib	1	14	–	–	1	–	–	–	16
scapula	1	1	–	–	1	–	–	–	3
os coxae	–	–	–	–	2	2	–	1	5
humerus	–	3	–	–	–	–	–	1	4
radius	1	3	–	–	–	–	–	1	5
ulna	–	3	–	–	–	–	–	–	3
tibia	1	1	–	–	1	–	–	1	4
phalanx 1	–	–	–	–	–	–	–	1	1
Total	**4**	**26**	**1**	**3**	**12**	**5**	**1**	**5**	**57**

Note: contexts from which no dog was recovered have been omitted

of epiphyses, there is more young material from pig; and there were six mandibles in stage 2, with the first molar in wear but not the second.

Of the remaining pig mandibles, many were from stages 3 and 4, so were from tender and prime eating animals. The rest, with the third molar in wear, including the third cusp, were from fully mature animals.

Pathology

A right fragment of pig mandible from 27JS Phase 11 (F54) had lost all its main cheek teeth *ante-mortem* and there was a very large lateral swelling by the alveolus of the fourth premolar. This was a large and very heavy specimen, and although it was toothless it seemed fair to class the mandible as fully adult and to include it in Table 4.17.

A right fused distal tibia from CHR F28 (Phase 45) showed strong roughness as from rubbing or irritation. Lateral damage at this height on the tibia has been found on pigs from time to time and has been taken to suggest contraction from tethering, first by Boessneck *et al* (1971, 78) for several examples from Manching; and by Bourdillon & Coy (1980, 96) for some from middle Saxon Hamwic. It seems not impossible that the present case could have been caused by the irritation of tethering, even though the damage showed on the medial side.

A whole fused fourth metacarpal from VR Phase 636 (F762) had several tiny holes on the proximal joint and at the proximal end of the front shaft. It may be that these had been produced by some form of parasite.

There was exostosis on two third metatarsals – mildly

on the proximal articulation of a bone that was distally unfused (VR F588 Phase 493), and seriously over the whole joint surface of a left proximal fragment also from VR (a clay silt deposit of Phase 503).

With so much quite young material, the sample of measurable bones and teeth was generally small (Table A4.5). Four lower third molars were in sufficient wear to be measured, and their greatest lengths ranged from 26mm to 30mm. These figures are low. When set against the measurements of bone articular breadths from Hamwic Melbourne Street, the data for pig bones gave a comparison of 97.7 per cent, which is very close to the figure from late Saxon Southampton (98.0 per cent).

Dog

Dog was widely represented (Table 4.19), though 26 of the total 57 bones were from a single puppy skeleton (CHR Phase 45, F28). There were no fragments of dog in the clay silt deposits at VR, nor in the small assemblage of pit material from HG Phase 18B (F121). No other dog bones were unfused.

Size

There were bones from individuals of several sizes, often in a single group. From 27JS Phase 11 (F54) there was a small radius shaft, a small and rather bowed fragment of distal tibia (Bd 17.3mm, shaft breadth SC 9.3mm), a scapula, and rib of medium size. CHR Phase 47 (F24) gave the front of a right maxilla of a smallish dog, with the adult third premolar in wear. The early

Table 4.20 Anatomical distribution in cat

| | HG | VR | VR | VR | Total |
	18B	493	507	636	
skull	1	–	–	–	1
loose teeth	–	–	2	–	2
os coxae	–	–	–	1	1
femur	1	1	–	–	2
metapodial	–	–	–	1	1
Total	**2**	**1**	**2**	**2**	**7**

Note: contexts with no cat have been omitted

phase of the ditch F588 at VR (Phase 493) contained a skull fragment with a strong sagittal crest; this came from a dog of medium size. Also in this phase of the ditch were two loose left upper premolars, either or both of which could have come from this same individual.

The upper phase of the ditch F588 at VR (Phase 494) yielded bones of at least three individuals. There was a back dorsal fragment of a small skull, and a pair of small maxillae, both with the fourth premolar and first molar in wear. There was also a distal scapula fragment of a tiny individual: the length across the glenoid (LG) was only 18.3mm, the size of a fox, but the bone was of dog and not fox on morphology. There was also a tiny fused proximal tibia, with a breadth (Bp) of 23.1mm; this had tiny cuts on the lateral surface of the joint. These bones may have come from two individuals or perhaps just from one – it is not impossible for a dog which has a tiny body to have a small but not diminutive head. The group also produced two fragments of pelvis, both left and both from the cranial end, from two further individuals, both of medium size.

There was contrast again in VR Phase 507 (F569). The group gave a small left pelvis with an acetabular length (LA) of 16.0mm; a left pelvis, but this one was medium-to-large (LA 27.9mm); a medium-sized atlas; and also two fragments of loose teeth.

VR Phase 636 (F762) produced quite a small humerus, too badly chewed to give a measurement of greatest length but with a distal breadth (Bd) of 24.3mm and a minimum shaft (SC) of only 8.0mm, and a small and rather bowed radius shaft and a whole fused tibia. The tibia had a greater proximal breadth than that in the upper ditch (Bp 27.3mm compared with 23.0mm), but at 105.2mm its length was short in proportion, and would convert by the factors of Koudelka to a withers height of only 0.31m. The bone, however, was strangely curved and the animal could not have carried itself normally. This group also gave the fragment of very small pelvis.

Excavations from middle Saxon Hamwic have so far given dogs only of medium size, and the small individuals in the assemblage from late Saxon Winchester are therefore notable. It seems clear that dogs were quite common there and that many but not all of them were small ones, and it seems likely that abnormal bowing of some of the bones was linked to their very small size.

Cat

There were far fewer bones of cat than of dog (Table 4.20). From HG Phase 18B (F121) there was a fragment from the back of a skull and a whole left femur, fully fused but so chewed at the distal end that measurements could not be taken. One of the earlier fills of the ditch F588 at VR (Phase 493) gave a large right distal femur (Bd 24.2mm). There were two loose canine teeth from VR Phase 507 (F569): an upper and a lower.

VR Phase 636 (F762) gave two fragments from two individuals. There was a right ilium with so clean a break obliquely across the acetabulum that it had probably been cut, though in spite of a close examination no cut marks could be seen. The bones were in good condition and seemed to be from a mature individual. There was also a metapodial fragment which was porous, eroded, and stained.

Deer

The few fragments of deer were scattered over several assemblages though there was none from the largest, the pits (F21 and F28) of Phase 45 at CHR (Table 4.21).

From red deer there were three small fragments of antler. One had been sawn in several planes (VR Phase 636, F762); those from CHR Phase 47 (F24) and VR Phase 636 (F762) may also have been worked but gave no signs of it. There were also two post-cranial fragments, both from good-sized red deer. A left proximal humerus from VR (Phase 503 clay silt deposits) was too badly chewed to be measured, but it handled as much larger than the humerus in the modern comparative collection of the Faunal Remains Unit. A whole left fused metatarsal from the later phase (494) of the VR ditch F588 had a greatest length of 270.0mm; this bone showed several surface cuts at the proximal end, both on the medial shaft and on the surface of the joint.

Two mandibles of roe deer were recovered. A left one from 27JS, Phase 11 (F54), had a tooth row in quite heavy wear; this had a small surface cut on the lateral surface near the back. The other, also left, was from VR (a clay silt deposit of Phase 503) and was from a younger individual, with the permanent fourth premolar visible just as a lingual slit below the deciduous tooth. There were also two tibiae of roe deer,

Table 4.21 Anatomical distribution in deer

	Red deer				Roe deer			Total
	antler	humerus	metatarsal	all	mandible	tibia	all	
27JS 11	–	–	–	–	1	1	2	**2**
CHR 47	1	–	–	1	–	1	1	**2**
VR 493	1	–	–	1	–	–	–	**1**
VR 494	–	–	1	1	–	–	–	**1**
VR 503	–	1	–	1	1	–	1	**2**
VR 636	1	–	–	1	–	–	–	**1**
Total	**3**	**1**	**1**	**5**	**2**	**2**	**4**	**9**

Note: contexts with no deer have been omitted

a fused left distal fragment in 27JS Phase 11, F54 (Bd 24.1mm), and a small butchered fragment of proximal shaft in CHR Phase 47 (F24). There were no other deer bones.

Hare

Fragments of hare were found in three groups (Table 4.22). A fused third metacarpal from CHR F28 (Phase 45) was a little large for the brown hare (*Lepus europaeus*) in the reference collection, but the proximal articulation was an exact match and this identification seems likely. The same group gave an unfused lumbar vertebra and three further lumbar vertebrae; all of these latter had the cranial epiphysis fused and caudal epiphysis not fused.

The other two bones of hare were both from the upper fill of the VR ditch F588 (Phase 494). There was a fused right proximal tibia (Bp 20.2mm) and a fused lateral metapodial, perhaps from the same individual.

Domestic fowl

There was a fair amount of domestic fowl, though there was a dearth in both phases (493 and 494) of the ditch F588 at VR and also in the site layers of Phase 503 (Table 4.23). Best representation came in the assemblages from the eastern suburb, and in the pit group from VR Phase 507 (F569). Five bones of probable domestic fowl were also found in the soil samples.

Table 4.22 Anatomical distribution in hare

	CHR	VR	Total
	45	494	
lumbar vertebra	4	–	**4**
tibia	–	1	**1**
metacarpal	1	–	**1**
metapodial	–	1	**1**
Total	**5**	**2**	**7**

Note: contexts with no hare have been omitted

Mostly this material was of good food bones. There was a small amount of waste – three fragments from the head (two of skull, and a mandible) from CHR Phase 45 and a foot phalanx of good size for fowl from VR Phase 507 (F569). Butchery cuts were seen on 24 of the 161 bones; these cut bones were from various parts of the body and were found in most assemblages.

Several fragments were porous (Table 4.24). These were not the very large and rather shapeless bones which are quite often found on medieval sites and which could perhaps be signs of castration. The present porous material was smaller and neater and is likely to have come from young individuals.

There were few bones at all from large individuals, and some bones were very short indeed (Table A4.6). Two very short bones, both from CHR F28 (Phase 45), may have been from a single deformed individual. One of these was a left ulna, a slightly bowed specimen with a greatest length of 47.0mm and a shaft breadth of 3.7mm; this bone was slightly bowed. The other was a left tibiotarsus (greatest length of 69.5mm and a shaft breadth of 5.5mm) with the fibula fused to it at its distal end. There was a further tibiotarsus (again a left one and this time just a fragment), which also had the fibula fused to it just above the distal joint. From VR Phase 636 (F762), a right distal tibiotarsus showed minor exostosis on the shaft. More common as fowl pathology was a healed fracture on a right ulna from CHR F28 (Phase 45).

Domestic goose

There was surprisingly little evidence of domestic goose (Table 4.25), for this is a species which in the Saxon period often rivalled fowl, by weight if not by fragment count, and its large bones are not likely to have been overlooked.

Birds of Wild and Possibly Wild Species

Bones of birds from species other than fowl and goose are listed in Table 4.26. The VR clay silt deposits (Phase 503) gave a humerus of Brent goose (*Branta*

Table 4.23   Anatomical distribution in domestic fowl

	27JS 11	HG 18B	CHR 45	CHR 47	VR 493	VR 494	VR 503	VR 507	VR 508	VR 636	Total
skull fragment	–	–	2	–	–	–	–	–	–	–	**2**
mandible	–	–	1	–	–	–	–	–	–	–	**1**
vertebra	–	–	–	–	–	–	–	1	2	–	**3**
rib	–	–	1	–	–	–	–	–	1	–	**2**
furcula	–	–	–	–	–	–	–	–	1	–	**1**
scapula	3	–	2	3	–	–	–	–	2	1	**11**
coracoid	–	–	4	4	–	–	–	1	–	4	**13**
sternum	1	–	1	2	–	–	–	1	1	1	**7**
os coxae	6	–	1	4	–	–	–	–	3	1	**15**
humerus	–	–	4	4	–	1	1	2	–	4	**16**
radius	1	1	–	–	2	–	–	–	4	3	**11**
ulna	–	–	2	5	–	–	–	–	2	1	**10**
carpometacarpus	–	–	–	1	–	–	–	–	2	–	**3**
femur	3	1	4	2	–	1	–	3	6	3	**23**
tibiotarsus	5	1	5	7	–	–	–	2	4	4	**28**
tarsometatarsus	1	–	6	1	–	–	–	1	2	2	**13**
foot phalanx	–	–	–	–	–	–	–	–	1	–	**1**
long bone fragment	–	–	–	1	–	–	–	–	–	–	**1**
Total	**20**	**3**	**33**	**34**	**2**	**2**	**1**	**11**	**31**	**24**	**161**

Table 4.24   Incidence of porous bones in domestic fowl

	Very porous	Porous	All fowl bones
27JS 11	–	3	20
HG 18B	–	–	3
CHR 45	–	3	33
CHR 47	1	2	34
VR 493	–	–	2
VR 494	–	–	2
VR 503	–	–	1
VR 507	–	–	11
VR 508	–	6	31
VR 636	–	–	24
Total	**1**	**14**	**161**

Table 4.25   Anatomical distribution in goose

	CHR 47	VR 508	VR 636	Total
rib	–	1	–	1
sternum	–	1	–	1
coracoid	–	–	1	1
humerus	1	1	–	2
tibiotarsus	1	–	–	1
Total	**2**	**3**	**1**	**6**

Note: contexts with no goose have been omitted

bernicla) and there was a tarsometatarsus of woodcock (*Scolopax rusticola*) from VR Phase 636 (F762). These are not exotic species: woodcock has been reported regularly from Saxon and medieval sites, and large flocks of Brent geese may be seen in the Solent today. From normal trench recovery these were the only species of bird that were certainly wild, though there were passerine bones from the soil samples – an ulna and foot phalanx that were the size of chaffinch (cf *Fringilla coelebs*) from CHR Phase 47 (F24), and a

mandible like that of sparrow (cf *Passer domesticus*) from VR Phase 508 (F976). No butchery cuts were seen on these bones.

The bones of other birds from trench recovery were likely all to have been from duck, and were either of mallard (*Anas platyrhynchos*) or were from domestic stock. Nearly all were from CHR F28 (Phase 45). Seven of these were ribs and as such cannot be securely identified even to family group, but they were too large for the small bones of domestic fowl that were present in the same group, and both on relative size and on staining they matched the accompanying fragments of duck. Of the other duck bones, two were a good match for those of a male mallard in the reference collection – a scapula with greatest length of 72.0mm, and a carpometacarpus with one of 58.5mm. Two

Table 4.26 Anatomical distribution in duck and other birds

	27JS 11	CHR 45	VR 503	VR 636	Total
rib	–	7	–	–	7
sternum	–	1	–	–	1
scapula	–	1	–	–	1
coracoid	–	2	–	–	2
humerus	–	–	1	1	2
radius	1	–	–	–	1
tibiotarsus	–	1	–	–	1
tarsometatarsus	–	–	–	1	1
Total	**1**	**12**	**1**	**2**	**16**

Note:
VR 503: one bone of brent goose *Branta bernicla*
VR 636: one bone of woodcock *Scolopax rusticola*
Other material from domestic duck or mallard *Anas platyrhynchos*

coracoids were quite large – a left with greatest length of 58.0mm, a right with one of 58.2mm. One suspects that these may represent domestic material, but with so small a sample it is safer to leave the options open for the moment.

Discussion

The bones tell much about the animals. The cattle which were brought in to late Saxon Winchester seem to have been of a good size for the period (though a larger sample of measurements would be useful). The sheep, on the other hand, were small and slender. In this they were like the sheep of the early post-Conquest centuries (who carried the wealth of the country on their small backs and are not to be despised), but their age groups spanned more than just a wool-flock, and some of them were so young that they must have been bred nearby. By the size of their horn cores, the goats could be seen to come of different stock from those of Saxon or medieval Southampton – and indeed from those common on archaeological sites of the period in the south. The pigs were just small pigs.

If one takes these bones as indicators of the diet of late Saxon Winchester, the picture is sound but not rich. There were signs of prime meat groups of cattle and sheep, with variable quantities of pig (which were also from these prime groups, but this is standard in archaeological material). Goose was inexplicably rare, but there was a fair amount of domestic fowl,

and even if these fowls were small, some of them at least were young and tender. There were ducks, and some of them perhaps were from domestic stock. All these things suggest a sound and well-organised food supply. Yet signs of a more distinctive diet were rare: these sites gave no equivalent style in food to the Winchester style of art, in its heyday at this time. Dishes special to the menu may be listed in a sentence: three occurrences of hare; only two bird bones, other than duck, that were certainly from the wild (and from common wild species at that); and a few post-cranial fragments of deer. When set against the venison from the late Saxon enclosures at Trowbridge (Bourdillon, 1989) or the wild birds found by Eastham (1977) from the thegn's house at late Saxon Portchester, the delicacies from the present sites make a very meagre list.

The assemblages, however, were made up of more than simply food waste, and other aspects of an urban way of life may be inferred from the remains. There was careful butchery on many of the cattle long bones, and some of their vertebrae showed sagittal paramedian cuts which most likely foreshadowed a growing professional style. The high rate of horse bones (nearly all of them from ponies) gave signs of much activity in the transport of people or of goods. There were horn cores from cattle, goats and sheep, and those from goat had been selected by sex and brought to the town to be worked. Lastly, there were dogs of several sizes: some were very small lapdogs which were surely kept as pets, the signs of style and surplus in an urban way of life.

5 Medieval and post-medieval animal bone from the northern and eastern suburbs and the city defences
by D Serjeantson and P Smith

Introduction

In this chapter, *c* 22,000 bones from 23 different groups or phases are discussed (Table 5.1). Most are from the Victoria Road excavations in the northern suburb. Other major groups are from the eastern suburb, and one is from the Henly's Garage site in the area of the southern city defences. These date from every period from Saxo-Norman to 17th century, with the possible exception of the 12th century, from which time no single group was identified as large and intact enough for inclusion. The largest number of groups studied are from the medieval period (13th to 14th centuries), but there are also substantial early medieval (Saxo-Norman, including the

10th and 11th and possibly but not certainly the 12th century) groups and bones from the later medieval and post-medieval period (Table 5.2).

The first part of this chapter contains a discussion of the bones by period and phase, which concentrates on the origin of the deposits and the light the groups can shed on the occupation or use of the area excavated. In the second part, the individual species are discussed. The balance between the discussion of context and of species is weighted more heavily towards the former than is usual in animal bone reports. The first part, by emphasising that the collection is from restricted areas of the town with very disparate deposits, demonstrates that the usual assumption, implicit in most

Table 5.1 Medieval northern and eastern suburbs and city defences: summary of animal bones by phase: number of identified bones: NISP

Date	Phase	Mammals + birds		Fish		Total
		Hand	Sieve	Hand	Sieve	
10th–11th	VR529	708	7		35	750
10th–11th	VR530	1390	986	11	46	2433
10th–11th	VR532	1387	31	24	170	1612
10th–11th	HG29	988	35	20	49	1092
13th	SJS13	212		3		215
13th	SJS16	433		4		437
13th–14th	SJS29	119				119
13th–14th	CHR53	2489	9	14		2512
13th–14th	VR616	125	11	1	3	140
13th–14th	VR635	869	10	20	112	1011
13th–14th	VR637	519	21	2	125	667
13th–14th	VR743	273		28		301
13th–14th	VR783	284		3		287
13th–14th	VR975	1276	9	20		1305
14th	SJS30	1074	6	(35)		1080
late 14th	VR700	842	46	9	44	941
14th–15th	VR685	183				183
15th–16th	VR792	855	273	6	12	1146
15th–16th	VR756	795	9	22		826
16th	VR763	1472	1	15	16	1504
16th	SJS49	2046		23		2069
17th	CHR56	1427		7		1434
Total		**19766**	**1454**	**232**	**612**	**22064**

Key: VR Victoria Road; HG Henly's Garage; SJS St John's Street; CHR Chester Road
Note: numbers in brackets ( ) are preliminary count, no detailed record

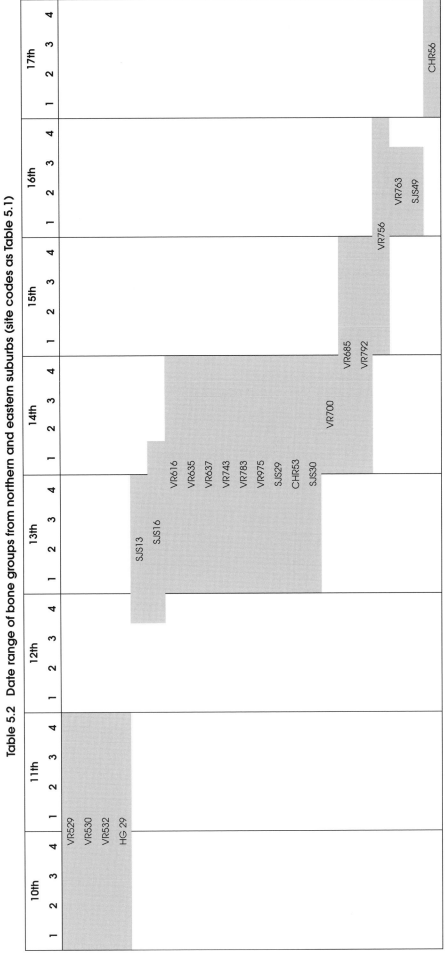

Table 5.2 Date range of bone groups from northern and eastern suburbs (site codes as Table 5.1)

1, 2, 3, 4 = 1st, 2nd, 3rd, 4th quarter

reports, that the bones are a representative sample from which to infer diet or animal husbandry of the period, cannot be made without qualification.

Classification of species

In the second part of this chapter, the role of the various species present is discussed. They have been grouped for this purpose according to how they were perceived (as far as we can tell) – and exploited – by the human population. This classification has been explored further (Serjeantson 2000).

The domestic animals that were routinely eaten, having been raised and kept at least partly for meat, are discussed first. These are sheep, cattle, pigs, goat, and domestic fowl. Records such as urban market regulations and cellarers' accounts show that they were offered for sale and bought for consumption, either as complete carcasses or as joints. The archaeological evidence confirming that these were food comprises finds of bones that are disarticulated and have evidence for dismemberment of the carcass and other butchery. The main mammal limb bones have normally been chopped for marrow extraction. This is more common with cattle than with sheep and pigs. More paradoxical evidence for human consumption is the presence of chewing or gnawing by dogs of the disarticulated bones, discussed below. It is common on food remains, whereas it is rare or absent on the groups of industrial material.

The second group is those animals which were eaten, but whose domestic status is uncertain. These are geese, ducks, and pigeons. Domestication or close control of all three is attested in the Middle Ages, but bones may not be morphologically distinct from the wild counterparts. From the evidence of documentation and treatment of the carcass, geese here have been interpreted as mainly domestic, even where they cannot be distinguished by size and shape from wild geese. Records and depictions refer to domestic ducks but the status of the mallards from which bones were identified is uncertain. Few bones of pigeon have been recovered from the deposits studied, and all match the rock or stock dove (*Columba livia / oenas*). None is from the woodpigeon (*Columba palumbus*), which is distinctly larger. The domestic pigeon or dove is the domestic form of the rock dove, and it is likely that all are domestic birds.

The three species of deer (red, roe, and fallow), the hare, and the rabbit are discussed together in the section on wild mammals, despite the fact that the status of the fallow deer and the rabbit was not fully wild. The fallow deer from the time of its introduction, though regarded as a hunted animal, was kept in parks. The rabbits, at first kept in warrens, had similar status, though 'hunting' was carried out with ferrets and nets. Later, these were more fully domesticated. There is ample evidence from the butchery that the bones found were from food animals.

Fish are discussed after the other food species. All, with the possible exception of a single bone of stickle-back recovered from a well or pit, were brought to the city as food.

The domestic animals not usually eaten are discussed separately from the food animals. For each the question is considered of whether they were in fact sometimes eaten. Of these, the horse and dog were considered animals of higher status, and closer to the human condition, than the food animals (Thomas 1983). This did not inhibit use of the skins, though it was at least part of the inhibition on human consumption of the flesh. An ordinance of 1558 stipulates that by that period 'no dead horses, dogs or carrion of any kind' were to be thrown in the road (Victoria County History 1912, V, 31). From this is it clear that once dead these were regarded as carrion, but there is nevertheless some archaeological evidence that horses were occasionally eaten. Horses and dogs were often found as skeletons or part skeletons; some carcasses were buried with care, and others clearly disposed of with less care. The cats were of lesser status and were undoubtedly then, as today, less closely controlled, but were exploited for their fur, as discussed below. There is no evidence here that these were eaten.

Finally, there are the wild animals and commensals which became incorporated in the deposits by accident. These are discussed with the phase group in which they were found. Most numerous are the frogs and toads, mostly found in the bottom of wells and pits which had held water, but commensals such as the black rat and house mouse were also found. The status of the small number of wild birds found is uncertain. There are a few that might not have been indigenous in or around the town, but, as discussed in Chapter 3, wild fowl were offered for sale in Winchester at least in the later Middle Ages. The bones which were found gave few clues as to whether they were food species or accidentals.

Method of analysis

A summary table for each phase shows the number of identified bones (NISP), with the bones from the sieved samples shown separately from those collected by hand. The tables include the percentage of identified bones, fragments assigned to size class, and the unidentified fraction. The percentages of sheep, cattle, and pigs shown relate exclusively to the proportions of these three main food species. Fish are listed separately, with scientific names, in the tables. Sheep and goats are amalgamated as 'sheep+goat', and goat bones when found are listed separately in brackets. The total number of amphibians and rodents is shown, and presence of an identified species is indicated in the tables. The bones recorded as 'bird NFI' (not further identified) include vertebrae and ribs, as well as wing and limb bone splinters that could not be identified. Many – in some cases most – of these will be from domestic fowl and goose. The cat / rabbit size fragments may include some of hares and small dogs.

Of the main domestic mammals, only the axis and atlas vertebrae were identified to species systemati-

Table 5.3 Percentage of gnawed bones, calculated on the limb bones (LBs) only

Date	Phase	LBs	Gnawed	Gnawed
		n	n	%
10th–11th	VR529	113	42	37.2
10th–11th	VR530	250	93	37.2
10th–11th	VR532	185	52	28.1
10th–11th	HG29	291	71	24.4
13th	SJS13	40	5	12.5
13th	SJS16	60	16	26.7
13th–14th	CHR53	331	97	29.3
13th–14th	SJS29	13	5	38.5
13th–14th	VR616	78	25	32.1
13th–14th	VR635	97	18	18.6
13th–14th	VR637	103	28	27.2
13th–14th	VR975	118	20	16.9
14th	SJS30	149	22	14.8
late 14th	VR700	150	34	22.7
14th–15th	VR685	34	8	23.5
14th–15th	VR792	265	6	2.3
15th–16th	VR756	80	18	22.5
16th	VR763	312	79	25.3
16th	SJS49	309	39	12.6
17th	CHR56	326	136	41.7
Total		**3304**	**814**	**24.6**

cally. Other vertebrae and ribs were identified as either sheep-size, which includes pig and other middle-size mammals; or cattle-size, which in a few contexts will include horse, and possibly fragments of fallow deer.

Tables showing the anatomical distribution of the main species in each assemblage or group are also given in the appendix. Where more than 100 bones were identified, both NISP and minimum number of elements (MNE) are given. MNE has been calculated for the left- and right-hand side from the most frequent part of the bone present. The parts of the bone present were recorded using the eight 'zones' defined for each bone (Serjeantson 1996). The zones defined are described and illustrated in the archive. The presence of zones 1–8 respectively is summed for each element and each side. Comparison between NISP and MNE for any element will give an approximate guide to the degree of fragmentation of the bone. The fourth field in the tables giving anatomical distribution shows the number of bones as a percentage of the maximum which would have been expected if the whole animal was present (Brain 1976). The figure used as 100 per cent is the notional minimum number of individuals derived from the most frequent element, and multiplied by two. The tables, and the figures on which they are based, therefore show which elements are most numerous.

It has been pointed out that calculation of the minimum number of individuals is inappropriate for groups of bones from towns where it is not likely that the origin of the deposit was whole animals. Here, the use of MNE and MNI is a device which allows relative percentages of parts of the skeleton to be shown, and is not intended to reflect the notion that whole skeletons were present.

Destruction by dogs

In all deposits with food remains, a high proportion of the bones have been chewed or gnawed. There are several animals which could have done this. First, and certainly the most common cause of the gnawing, was the domestic dog; most gnawed bones have the scoring round the damaged end and punctures of the type made by dogs or foxes, and of these two the dog is much the most likely. Some of the bird bones have tiny punctures characteristic of the tooth marks of a smaller mammal, most likely the cat, but possibly the ferret. Pigs also chewed bones, producing a pattern of destruction similar to dogs (Greenfield 1988), but without the scoring made by the canine teeth of the carnivores, and those lacking scoring may have been chewed by pigs. Pigs were kept within the town until the 15th century, and ordinances were promulgated which attempted to enforce the owners to keep the pigs from scavenging in the streets. Some of the gnawed chicken bones and bones of young pigs which lack punctures and scoring may well have been chewed by humans.

Medieval hunting dogs were fed a diet of bread and bones (Cummins 1988), and there is every reason to suppose that the dogs belonging to all classes of the population were also fed bones as a major part of their supply of food. Gnawing is therefore to be expected on bones from households which kept dogs. Even otherwise very well-preserved bones have traces of gnawing; this of course implies that household bones were buried with other rubbish only after the dogs had been allowed their turn. The bones which lack traces of gnawing are those from industrial deposits, such as the cattle metapodials from the city defences in the Saxo-Norman period. Table 5.3 shows the proportion of mammal limb bones on which traces of gnawing were clearly seen. Deposits where the proportion is significantly lower or higher than the mean of 25 per cent are discussed in the text.

The material by context and period

The system of phasing used in Winchester has already been briefly explained (Chapter 1) and the site name or its code and phase number are the only stratigraphic references consistently given here. A full list of the contexts studied (c.) is available in the archive. References to property boundaries are after Keene (1985).

Saxo-Norman; 10th to 11th / early 12th centuries

Northern suburb

The Saxo-Norman activity represents an early phase of extra-mural development, predating the construction of Hyde Abbey to the east. The interpretation of the deposits of this period is made difficult by truncation in later times but there may have been a decline in the use of the area compared with the late Saxon period (see also Chapter 4). There are only traces of timber structures and the best groups of finds are from deep negative features, mostly pits. The animal bones, together with the other finds from the pits, can contribute to the interpretation of the nature of settlement in the area. Seven of the pits excavated at Victoria Road (VR) have large, well-preserved assemblages of animal bones: F957 (Phase 529), the intercutting pits, F758, F794, F798, and F803 (Phase 530), and F1021 and F1042 (Phase 532).

VR Phase 529

The pit (F957) contained two cat skeletons and around 600 further bones (Table 5.4), nearly all of which appear to be food remains. The only bones of commensal species are a corvid, a rook or crow, and amphibians. A horse tooth was found.

Bone survival was good, and recovery of small elements, such as the smaller cat bones, was excellent. The high number of unidentified fragments confirms the good recovery. Most of the fragmentation is a consequence of butchery and dog gnawing.

One of the two cat skeletons (from c.3891), is almost complete; the other (from c.3868), lacks the skull and mandibles. The first, an adult with all bones fully fused, has traces of cuts on the skull, a location often damaged by the knife when the cat is skinned. The second is immature. No cut marks were seen on the surviving parts of the skeleton.

Of the three main food species, sheep bones were most common, followed by cattle (Fig 5.1; *see* colour section). None was identified as goat. Fewer than 10 per cent of the identified bones were from pig. A high percentage of the sheep bones were from young lambs (Table A5.21). Many of the bones have been butchered, and a very high proportion (37 per cent) of the limb bones have clear traces of gnawing (Table 5.3). The elements from the head and lower leg are proportionately higher than those for the rest of the skeleton in both sheep (Fig 5.2) and cattle (Fig 5.3; see also Table A5.1).

Domestic fowl bones are not common, with only ten recovered; as this is not a consequence of unequal recovery, this reflects a real rarity in the food remains disposed of in the pit. Four of the ten goose bones, all from a single layer, (c.3836), are complete carpometacarpi, and one is a wing phalanx. This concentration of carpometacarpi may be bones discarded when the geese were dressed for the table, or may be from wings collected for the primary wing feathers.

Four fish bones were recovered by hand and a further 30 from the sieved samples. Most were from eel and herring, and one was from a larger fish, the conger eel.

VR Phase 530

The fills of a group of intercutting pits (F758, F794, F798, and F803) are included in Phase 530. Pit F758 was 1.4m in diameter and over 4m deep; the others were smaller.

The total assemblage of bones from these pits is a highly unusual one, and its deconstruction is more than usually complex. One layer (3174) from F803, recorded as including 'organic material', contained nearly 800 amphibian and over 100 rodent bones (Table 5.4). The former included both frog and toad, and the latter included both field mouse (*Apodemus* sp.) and water vole (*Arvicola terrestris*). The presence of frog bones strongly suggests that the lower levels contained standing water, which attracted the frogs, and the presence of all four species in such numbers indicates that the pit lay open acting as a pit fall trap for a period. At least two puppies were also disposed of in the pit.

The domestic fowl remains are enigmatic. All but

Table 5.4   Saxo-Norman: Victoria Road, Phases 529, 530, 532: NISP

	529		530		532			
	Hand	Sieve	Hand	Sieve	Hand	Sieve	Total	%
sheep + goat	120	2	297		331	13	**763**	58.6
goat			(4)		(1)			
cattle	68		150	2	191		**411**	31.6
pig	36		58	5	27	1	**127**	9.8
domestic fowl	10		154*	40	106*	1	**311**	
goose	10		0		3		**13**	
duck sp.			1		11		**12**	
hare					5		**5**	
cat	111*	1	3	15	151*	1	**282**	
dog			31*	9			**40**	
horse	1		116*			1	**118**	
Falconidae				1			**1**	
crow/rook	1						**1**	
Arvicola terrestris				(1)				
Apodemus sp.				(1)				
rodent				114			**114**	
toad *Bufo bufo*			x	x				
frog *Rana temporaria*			x	x				
amphibian	3	2	18	778	13		**814**	
Subtotal identified	**360**	**5**	**828**	**964**	**839**	**16**	**3012**	**66.8**
bird NFI	1		6	4	51	1	**63**	1.4
small mammal NFI	1			13	3	3	**20**	0.4
sheep/pig-size	120	2	134	5	131	11	**403**	8.9
cow-size	84		95		45		**224**	5.0
unidentified	142		327		318		**787**	17.5
Total	**708**	**7**	**1390**	**986**	**1387**	**31**	**4509**	
Fish								
skate/ray Rajidae			6			1	**7**	
herring *Clupea harengus*		9		15		7	**31**	
eel *Anguilla anguilla*		1		29		15	**45**	
conger eel *Conger conger*		2	1		5		**8**	
cod *Gadus morhua*						6	**6**	
cod family Gadidae			1		3	12	**16**	
mackerel *Scomber scombrus*						17	**17**	
turbot *Scophthalmus maximus*					14		**14**	
brill *Scophthalmus rhombus*					2		**2**	
flatfish Pleuronectidae		2				3	**5**	
fish NFI		21	3	2		109	**135**	
Total		**35**	**11**	**46**	**24**	**170**	**286**	

* includes skeletons
% per cent NISP; NFI not further identified
Note: numbers in brackets ( ) are not included in main totals
x present

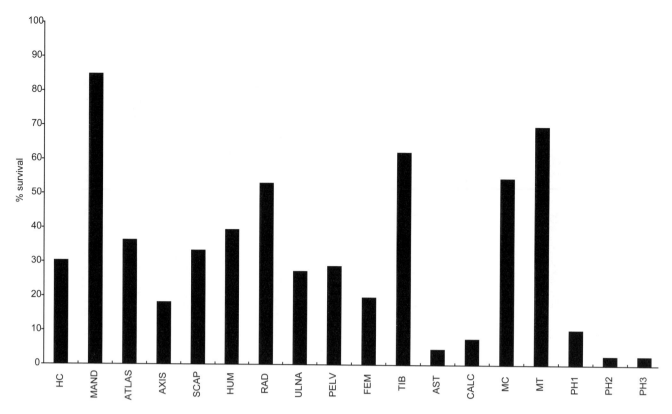

Figure 5.2   Saxo-Norman: Victoria Road, Phases 529, 530 and 532: anatomical distribution of sheep and goat. Key: HC horn core; MAND mandible; SCAP scapula; HUM humerus; RAD radius; PELV pelvis; FEM femur; TIB tibia; AST astragalus; CALC calcaneum; MC metacarpal; MT metatarsal; PH phalanx

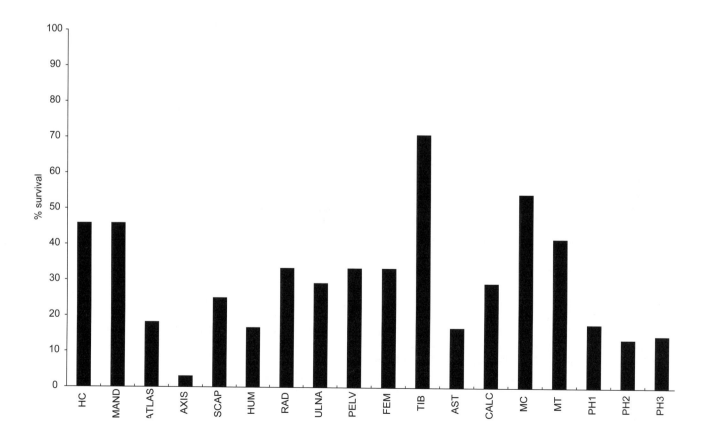

Figure 5.3   Saxo-Norman: Victoria Road, Phases 529, 530 and 532: anatomical distribution of cattle (Key as Fig 5.2)

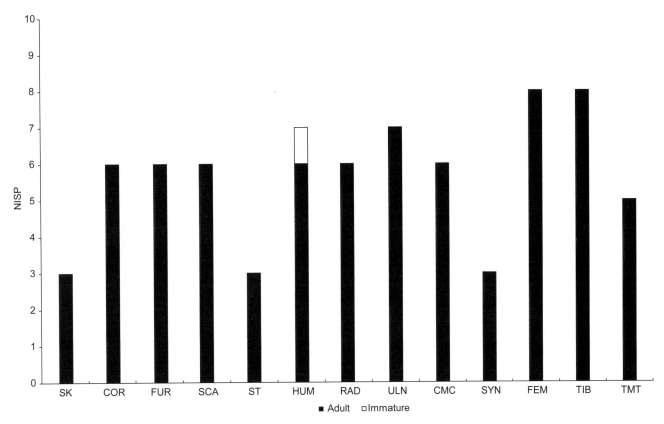

Figure 5.4 Saxo-Norman: Victoria Road, Phase 530: anatomical elements and age of domestic fowl. Key: SK dkull; COR coracoid; FUR furcula; SCA scapula; ST sternum; HUM humerus; RAD radius; ULN ulna; CMC carpometacarpus; SYN synsacrum; FEM femur; TIB tibiotarsus; TMT tarsometatarsus

eight of the bones are from three skeletons, as the unusually consistent representation of anatomical elements shows (Table A5.2). All were found in the same layer as the amphibians and rodents, in a remarkably complete condition, suggesting preservation in inert and anaerobic conditions. None has cut or chop marks, and the only breaks are recent, so rather than food remains these bones are of complete birds. They are adult birds (Fig 5.4) but lack spurs on the tarsometatarsi, so were probably hens. These may have been disposed of in the bottom of the pit after dying of disease, or, like the amphibians and rodents, they may have fallen victim to the pit full of water from which they could not escape.

A separate pit, F798, c.3136, in the western part of the trench, contained 106 bones from a horse skeleton. The bones were broken in the ground and during retrieval, but were not otherwise damaged by butchery or dog gnawing.

The pits also contained some bones of the main domestic food animals, some butchered and a very high proportion (37 per cent) of the limb bones gnawed (Table 5.3). The horn cores identified included four from goat (Table 5.26). The sheep included fewer lambs than in F957 (Phase 529, above) and only a single cattle bone was from a calf. The samples included a high proportion (85 per cent) of eel and herring.

The bone evidence points to pit F758 having been an open pit, well, or deep pond with standing water, in which some creatures drowned accidentally and in

which others were deliberately disposed of, possibly even, in the case of the puppies, deliberately drowned. Between them, the pits have a considerable component of bones from origins other than food remains.

VR Phase 532

The two pits, F1021 and F1042, were circular and just over 1m in diameter. F1021 was nearly 2m deep, and F1042 was between 0.3m and 0.6m deep. These contained nearly 1400 mammal and bird bones, including two cat skeletons, and a large collection of fish bones, of which 163 were recovered in samples (Table 5.4). Thirteen amphibian bones were also recovered, all from c.3979.

All except one of the 152 cat bones are from two skeletons from F1021, one in c.3978 and one in c.3979. Both were complete when buried and neither have cut marks on the skull, mandibles, or other bones. The disarticulated cat bone is the maxilla of a young kitten.

The large number of domestic fowl bones (106) were also from birds of which the skeletons have survived unusually complete (Fig 5.5). They were from a minimum of six skeletons from the two pits. Whether these were slaughtered for consumption is unclear. Four bones have cut marks, three on the distal articulation of tibiotarsi and one on the distal articulation of a femur, suggesting disarticulation of the leg bones. The carcass from c.3939 has been attacked by a carnivore,

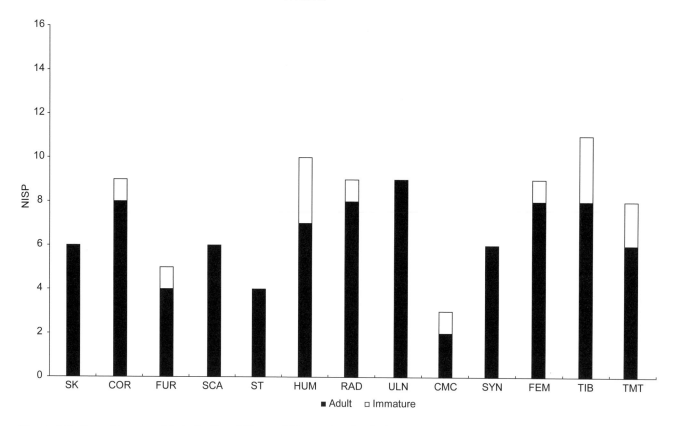

Figure 5.5 Saxo-Norman: Victoria Road, Phase 532: anatomical elements and age of domestic fowl (key as Fig 5.4)

with punctures in the skull, humerus, radius and ulna, more compatible with the small canine teeth of a cat than a dog. Relatively common in these pits, but rare elsewhere in Winchester, are bones of duck; eleven bones were found. All are from c.3939, but they are from at least three different ducks, one a large mallard, which from its size was probably domestic, the other the size of a wild female mallard, and a third from a smaller species.

The sheep bones (331) outnumbered those of cattle (191) by a considerable margin and pig remains were rare, with only 27 found. The only bones of a wild mammal were five of hare. The pits of this phase contained many fish bones, as 88 were recovered in the trench and a further 163 in the samples taken for sieving. As well as the species found in the pits already described, there was mackerel in this phase.

City Defences

HG Phase 29

Large and well-preserved groups of animal bone were recovered from eight Saxo-Norman pits (F170, F171, F172, F174, F179, F180, F183, and F184) of Phase 29 at Henly's Garage (HG) on the southern city defences. The area is within the late Saxon city but truncation of the deposits has precluded the survival of all but large cut features. However, this part of the site is believed to have been used for workshops and industrial activity, as a large quantity of iron smithing slag

was also recovered from the pits, and what appeared to be hearths and working surfaces were observed in the main sections of the excavated area. The animal bones can further test this hypothesis.

Bone surface condition was very good, and more than 90 per cent of the fragments were identified (Table 5.5). A small proportion (<1 per cent) were very eroded, raising the possibility that these lay on the surface before being buried or were reworked from Roman deposits on the site. The absence of sheep toe bones, astragali, carpals, and smaller tarsals (Table A5.3), bones of a size and shape which are easily be overlooked, may be a reflection of recovery problems. The two cat skeletons and some sheep vertebrae which articulate, suggest that disturbance was not great.

The sample of 1092 bones included seventeen species and incorporated food remains, animals kept for other reasons, and some isolated finds, of a passerine, a rodent, and an amphibian. The tibiotarsus of a herring or lesser black-backed gull (*Larus argentatus / fuscus*) is also more likely to be from a commensal species incidentally incorporated in the rubbish. Two partial cat skeletons were found, one from c.827 and the second from c.930, both immature. The bones were examined for cuts or other butchery but none was seen. Three disarticulated elements of horse were found: two teeth and a humerus, the last with sharp cuts marks on the shaft of a type made when the meat was removed. Four disarticulated dog bones from different contexts were also recovered. These have probably been incorporated incidentally with the other bones from food and craft remains.

Table 5.5   Saxo-Norman: city defences: Henly's Garage, Phase 29: NISP

	Hand	%	Sieve	Total
sheep + goat	218	41.1	9	227
(goat)	(4)			(4)
cattle	232	43.8		232
pig	80	15.1	1	81
domestic fowl	20		2	22
duck *Anas* sp.	1			1
cat	39		1	40
dog	4			4
horse	3			3
gull *Larus argentatus/fuscus*	1			1
Passeriformes NFI			1	1
rodent			1	1
amphibian *Rana/ Bufo*			1	1
Subtotal identified	**598**	**60.5**	**16**	**614**
bird NFI	4	0.4	2	6
small mammal NFI	1	0.1		1
sheep/pig-size	112	11.3	16	128
cow-size	187	18.9	1	188
unidentified	86	8.7		86
Total	**988**		**35**	**1023**
Fish				
herring *Clupea harengus*	7		39	46
cod *Gadus morhua*			1	1
conger eel *Conger conger*	1		1	2
garfish *Belone belone*			2	2
fish NFI	12		6	18
Total	**20**		**49**	**69**

Key as Table 5.4

Of the three main species, cattle are most numerous both by fragment numbers (43 per cent) and MNI, which is fourteen. A collection of cattle metapodials accounts for the relatively high proportion of cattle bones from this group, the highest proportion of all groups analysed. Sheep and goat bones are 41 per cent of the total by NISP, from an MNI of thirteen. Though goat horn cores were recognised, none of the post-cranial bones was of goat. The bones of sheep (Fig 5.6) are more evenly distributed between the upper and lower limbs than those of cattle. Foot bones of pig are lacking, but most other parts of the skeleton are present in small numbers (Fig 5.7). The proportion of gnawed limb bones (24 per cent) is typical of most of the groups studied.

Domestic fowl bones are a very small proportion of the identified bones, less than 4 per cent. Two of these were from the sieved samples. All but one were from adult fowl. This was one of the few groups studied from which goose bones were absent, despite the fact that the group was one of the larger groups studied. The single mallard bone, a humerus, was of a size which could be wild or domestic, but it was certainly of anthropogenic origin as there was a knife cut at the distal end.

Some herring bones and one conger eel bone were recovered in the trench, as well as twelve unidentified fish bones. The samples also yielded herring bones (39), as well as some of cod, conger eel, and garfish, but, in contrast to Victoria Road, no eels.

The most common part of the skeleton of cattle, whether calculated from NISP or MNE (Fig 5.8), were the metacarpals and metatarsals, with over 40 of each. The number and treatment of the bones distinguishes them from the other bones. Most have been smashed in half, but not further fragmented, and two only have

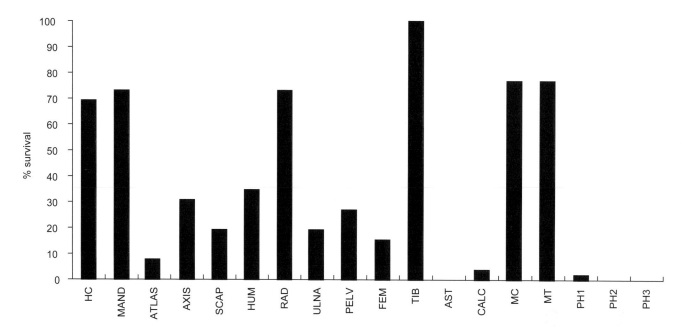

Figure 5.6 Saxo-Norman: Henly's Garage, Phase 29: anatomical distribution of sheep and goat (key as Fig 5.2)

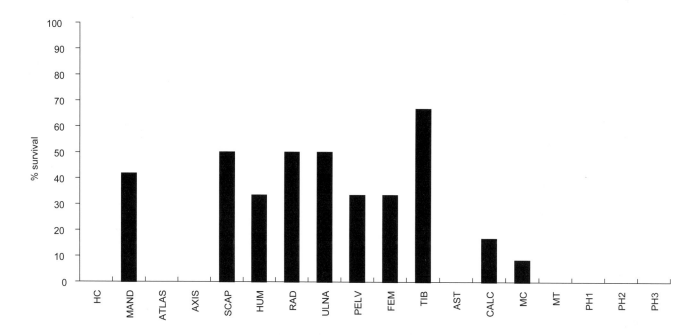

Figure 5.7 Saxo-Norman: Henly's Garage, Phase 29: anatomical distribution of pig (key as Fig 5.2)

been gnawed, compared with the other limb bones, which are more fragmented. The butchery, discussed below, is very distinctive, and unlike any seen in other deposits from the Winchester suburbs. With these were twelve phalanges, one of which was chopped. This is most probably debris from some industrial or craft process.

There were 24 horn core fragments from a minimum of twelve sheep and goats, of which at least four were from goats, and eight from sheep. Where the base of the horn has survived, it is clear that all from goat and most from sheep have been chopped from the skull, from which it may be inferred that these were used

for horn working. The three cattle horn cores from the pits have also been chopped. As the goat horn cores were not associated with post-cranial bones they are best interpreted as horn carried to the town, perhaps with skins, for craft use.

Discussion

The two areas with Saxo-Norman bone assemblages are quite contrasted. In the bones from food remains at Victoria Road, sheep are much more numerous, at 59 per cent, than cattle (32 per cent). Pig remains are sparse

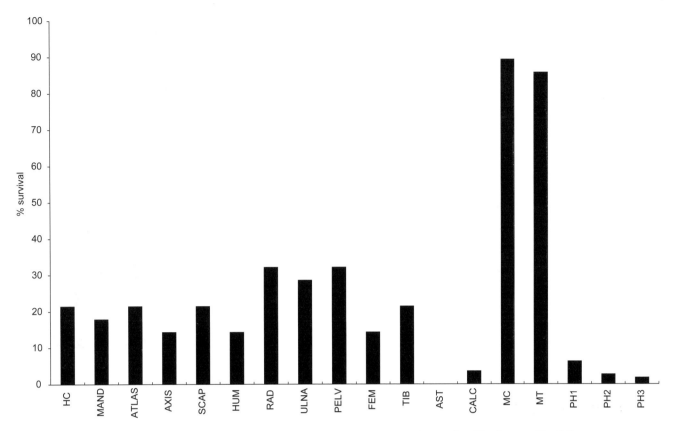

Figure 5.8   Saxo-Norman: Henly's Garage, Phase 29: anatomical distribution of cattle (key as Fig 5.2)

(10 per cent). Domestic fowl bones are numerous, but, as discussed, a high proportion of these appear to be from complete skeletons. Evidence in the food remains for species other than the main domestic food animals is notably scant, with the exception of fish. The good preservation and recovery from these pits allows a confident interpretation that herring and eel were commonly eaten. There is little or no evidence of species associated with high status.

The anatomical distribution of the sheep and goats, with mandibles the most common anatomical element, is compatible with whole sheep being slaughtered, butchered, and consumed at the site (Brain 1976). This distribution of body parts contrasts with most of the other groups studied. By contrast, the tibia and metacarpal are more frequent than the mandibles and horn cores of cattle. It is usually assumed that young lambs would not be taken from the farm where they were reared for sale, and therefore when bones are found, as here, it is evidence that a flock was maintained at the settlement.

More than one feature of the bones suggest that the area in this period may well have been a farming settlement or small-holding, where sheep, fowl, geese, and possibly ducks were raised.

There is also evidence which suggests collection of skins and horn for sale or processing. The animal bone evidence is not incompatible with preparation of tanning of small skins. The chopped horn cores also raise the possibility that horn working was carried out here, but this too would need confirmation from

other sources of evidence. A supply of water for these activities would have been provided by the Fulflood Stream to the north. Cat skins also appear to have been collected. Though only one skeleton has positive evidence for skinning, the number of cat skeletons is disproportionately large and the immaturity of all but one could suggest deliberate capture. The goose wing bones in Phase 529 hint at the collection of feathers.

The city defences assemblage contrasts with that from the northern suburb at this period by the proportions of the main species, the scarcity of domestic fowl, and the cattle butchery and anatomical parts. The proportion of cattle is notably higher than Victoria Road. The component which represents food remains shows that beef and mutton were the main animal foods, with pig and domestic fowl less common. This may reflect the 'plain diet' described in Chapter 4 for the late Saxon period, but in this context it may also reflect disposal practices. If bones were collected from elsewhere and then disposed of in these pits, smaller bones such as those of fowl would be lost.

More clearly than at Victoria Road and other later groups, these bones fall into two distinct components, with a strong craft component as well as food remains. The bones confirm the theory that this part of the city was a tradesmen's or craftsmen's quarter, where primary butchery and other industrial activities such as horn working were carried out, and possibly also where hides were collected and processed.

High Middle Ages: late 12th / 13th to early 14th centuries

Eastern suburb

Activity in the eastern suburb in the Middle Ages was dominated by St Giles Fair, held on the hill to the east of the town each year in August and September. Merchants came from all over Europe to buy and sell wool and other commodities. The properties in St John's Street and Chester Road were substantial tenements owned by major landowners. At St John's Street (SJS), deposits of the 12th and 13th centuries were, however, badly truncated and the bones analysed were from four pits which were stratigraphically earlier than the earliest building recovered from the site (occupying property 1031). The bones from Chester Road (CHR) were from a very large and deep feature of uncertain function, possibly a cellar, quarry or well-head.

SJS Phase 13

The earliest group comprises 229 bones from the late 12th- to 13th-century fill of a pit, F53, at St John's Street (Table 5.6). It is clear that the contents of the pit were carefully recovered, as small bones such as carpals and patellae of pig and sheep were collected. The proportion of bones identified is 50 per cent. A rodent bone and an amphibian bone were recovered from the lowest layer of fill.

There was a fragment of sheep horn core and four of goat, but as in the earlier, Saxo-Norman deposits from the city defences, no other goat bones were recognised among the metapodials or other post-cranial bones. The three undamaged horn cores were chopped from the skull. These can readily be interpreted as horns brought to Winchester for sale from the farm or estate where they were reared, possibly attached to skins. The pit as a place for disposal of waste from the collection or treatment of skins may be confirmed by the number of metapodials (9) and phalanges (7) in the total sample of 61 identified bones of sheep and goats (Table A5.4). Four of the metapodials are of sheep below the age of six months, as they are unfused and still relatively small and porous (Table A5.22), so cannot be from the same animals as the horn cores.

The proportion of bones interpreted as food remains is small, if the head and foot bones do not have this origin. The pig bones (9) include bones from the skull and limbs; and most of the cattle bones are from the trunk. The vertebrae and ribs proportions fit those of the identified bones, with over 90 per cent of these

Table 5.6   13th–14th: eastern suburb: St John's Street, Phase 13: NISP

	Hand	%
sheep + goat	49	67.1
(goat)	(4)	
cattle	16	21.9
pig	8	11.0
domestic fowl	18	
goose *Anser anser*	2	
rodent	2	
Subtotal identified	**95**	**44.8**
bird NFI	4	1.9
fish NFI	1	0.5
small mammal NFI	2	0.9
sheep/pig-size	64	30.2
cow-size	6	2.8
unidentified	40	18.9
Total	**212**	
Fish		
ling *Molva molva*	2	
conger eel *Conger conger*	1	
Total	**3**	

Key as Table 5.4

Table 5.7   13th–14th: eastern suburb: St John's Street, Phase 16: NISP

	Hand	%
sheep + goat	114	69.9
(goat)	(7)	
cattle	28	17.2
pig	21	12.9
domestic fowl	8	
goose	8	
cat	2	
horse	1	
Subtotal identified	**182**	**42.0**
bird NFI	4	0.9
fish NFI	1	0.2
sheep/pig-size	109	25.2
cow-size	45	10.4
unidentified	92	21.2
Total	**433**	
Fish		
ling *Molva molva*	1	
conger eel *Conger conger*	3	
Total	**4**	

Key as Table 5.4

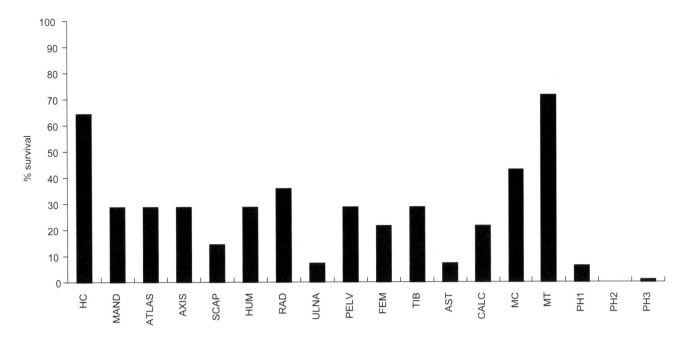

Figure 5.9 13th–14th century: St John's Street, Phase 16: anatomical distribution of sheep and goat (key as Fig 5.2)

identified as sheep- / pig-size, of which 34 (56 per cent) are rib fragments.

Chicken and goose bones comprise 17 per cent of the identified bones. The three tibiotarsi have knife cuts across the distal articulation, the normal method of separating the tarsometatarsus from the tibiotarsus either when the bird was dressed for cooking or when it was eaten. Two butchered goose bones were found, the humerus at least from a large robust bird which matches modern domestic geese in size. The only fish bones recovered were two vertebrae from a large ling (*Molva molva*) and the right dentary of a conger eel (*Conger conger*) – all recovered by hand.

SJS Phase 16

The contents of pit F47/55 are dated to the 13th to 14th centuries and are therefore probably slightly later than those from pit F53 nearby. Approximately 440 bones were recovered by hand (Table 5.7), including five of fish. The bones have preserved well, and the only notably worn and eroded fragments are three cattle-size limb bone splinters. They were carefully recovered, with sheep phalanges and many small fragments which could not be identified to species. A fairly high proportion (27 per cent) of the identified long bones have been chewed by carnivores. Two cat bones, a distal tibia and a metatarsal, were recovered, the tibia with a burnt patch on the bone indicating some contact with fire. The lateral metapodial of a horse was also found.

The high proportion of sheep bones, nearly 70 per cent, are mainly from the skeletons of three lambs (Table A5.5). These are in a fragmentary state, because of retrieval difficulties. Their identification as lambs rather than kids is based on the absence of any trace of a bovine

pillar on the four surviving DPM4s. The age at death of the lambs, as assessed from the mandibles (Table A5.21), suggests that all were below three months. One from c.199 has the two halves of the medial metacarpal unfused to each other, while the metacarpals of another suggest that they are slightly older. A jaw from c.174 is from a very young lamb, with lower DPM4 erupting through the bone but unworn, but here the two halves of the medial metacarpals are fused but porous. The absence of butchery traces makes it unlikely that these were cooked and served at table, but two proximal humeri appear to have been gnawed by a carnivore. The high proportion of fragments of sheep- / pig-size includes rib and vertebrae from these skeletons.

As in pit F53, both sheep and goat horn cores were found, ten of sheep and five of goat, all from adults. The goat horn cores with the base surviving have traces of where they were chopped from the skull, but this was clear on only four of the ten sheep horn cores; three others were still attached to the frontal bones. There were no fragments of cattle horn cores, and no evidence for skulls or maxillary teeth, other than a few small fragments.

The proportion of metapodials and phalanges of sheep is high (Fig 5.9). None of the metapodials is from goat. The seven first phalanges are from skeletally adult animals. The association of the metapodials (other than the ten which are certainly from the lambs) with the phalanges is unclear, as many have distal ends gnawed by carnivores, which has removed all trace of whether or not they were fused. If indeed the lamb skeletons are from lambs which were not eaten, then the number of bones from food remains is few; as well as the sheep bones, there are just 28 of cattle, and 21 of pig.

There are 16 identified bird bones, eight from domestic fowl and eight from geese, all of the latter

Table 5.8   13th–14th: eastern suburb: St John's Street, Phases 29 and 30: NISP

	SJS29 Hand		SJS30 Hand		Sieve	Total
	n	%	n	%		
sheep + goat	17	50.0	107	39.2		**107**
(goat)	(1)		(4)			
cattle	10	29.4	95	34.8		**95**
pig	7	20.6	71	26.0	1	**72**
domestic fowl	2		61			**61**
goose	1		14			**14**
duck ?domestic			1			**1**
fish			(1)			
fallow deer			1			**1**
rabbit			2			**2**
hare			11			**11**
cat*	1		237			**237**
dog			1			**1**
horse	1		7			**7**
gull *Larus canus*			2			**2**
jackdaw *Corvus monedula*			1			**1**
amphibian spp			6		2	**8**
Subtotal identified	**39**	**32.8**	**617**	**57.4**	**3**	**620**
bird NFI	1	0.8	19	1.8		**19**
sheep/pig-size	19	16.0	134	12.5	3	**137**
cow-size	27	22.7	126	11.7		**126**
unidentified	33	27.7	178	16.6		**178**
Total	**119**		**1074**		**6**	**1080**

* 6 skeletons. Key as Table 5.4

compatible in size with domestic greylag geese. These could be from a single goose, of which the wing at least was disarticulated with a sharp knife, leaving cut marks below the head of the radii and ulna and on the carpometacarpus.

SJS Phases 29 and 30

The small sample of 119 bones from pit F39 (Phase 29) and the larger sample of 1080 from pit F214A (Phase 30) are dated to the 13th and 14th centuries. The pottery assemblages suggest that, within this date range, F214A may have been filled at a slightly later dater than F39.

The bones were well-preserved and carefully retrieved; 32 per cent were identified to species from pit F39, and 58 per cent from pit F214A (Table 5.8). The second pit contained six cat skeletons and the fact that the elements of these were included in the count contributes to the high proportion of identified bones; if the cats are omitted from the count, it falls to 46 per cent. Some bones have encrusted sediment character-istic of a waterlogged pit or cess pit. The proportion of gnawed bones is low. Few fowl bones have been gnawed, but five of the fourteen goose bones have suffered carnivore damage.

Two distinctive pieces of worked bone were recovered from pit F214A. These are two horse mandibles which have been chopped in such a way as to produce plates for the production of worked bone artefacts.

Four of the cats skeletons were between one and four months of age and one was fully adult with all epiphyses fused. The four surviving skulls and six of the eight mandibles have cut marks from skinning (see below). Pit F39 has one tibia of a cat. As well as the chopped mandibles, four other isolated horse bones were found.

These pits too contained both sheep and goat horn cores. Four from pit F214A and one from pit F39 are from goat, and five fragments are from sheep. No post-cranial bones from either pit were recognised from goat. No cattle horn core was found, but metapo-dial fragments, phalanges, and jaws and teeth are as numerous as other parts of the skeleton (Table A5.6) in pit F214A.

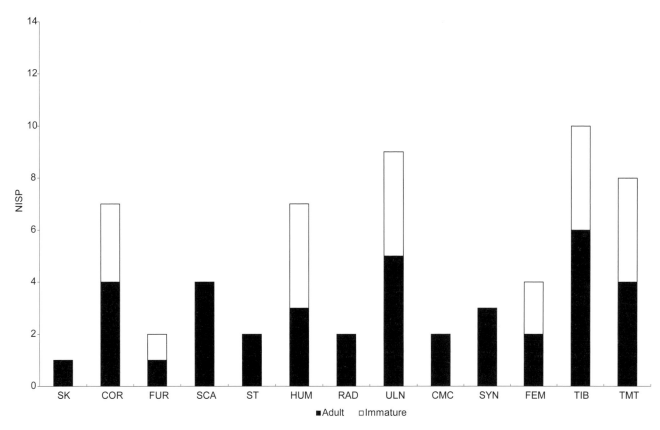

Figure 5.10   13th–14th century: St John's Street, Phase 30: anatomical elements and age of domestic fowl (key as Fig 5.4)

Unusually, this group has three bird bones from non-domestic species: the tarsometatarsus of an immature jackdaw, a fledging casualty or the victim of a cat, and two wing bones of a gull, a close match with the common gull *(Larus canus)*. Though gulls were eaten on northern coastal settlements at this time (Serjeant-son 1988), these few finds are more likely to be casual inclusions of birds visiting the outskirts of the town to scavenge than from food remains.

Sheep bones (with goat) were rather more numerous (at 38 per cent) in Phase 30 than cattle (35 per cent). Seven (7 per cent) of the cattle bones were from calves, and these included one frontal bone with horn core buds in the earliest stage of development. The five pig jaws (Table A5.38) were from older animals than in contemporary deposits at Victoria Road. This pit, with 25 per cent of the bones of the three main species being from pig, has one of the highest percentages of pig bones from the suburbs, particularly as some of the sheep and goat, and possibly some of the cattle, may be from industrial activity rather than food.

The pit contained a good sample (61) of domestic fowl (Table A5.12), and fourteen goose bones, 12 per cent of identified bones. Up to half of the fowl bones could be from two part skeletons, one with a spur, so probably male, and one without. One third of the bones, all disarticulated (Fig 5.10), were from immature birds (Table 5.29). The goose bones were from all parts of the carcass, and following the common pattern, none is immature. Three have knife cuts.

There are a further four food species in the sample:

hare, rabbit, fallow deer, and mallard, though the single fragment of fallow deer is an isolated molar tooth. The eleven hare bones include an enigmatic group of two right- and four left-hand distal radii (but no ulnae), all snapped or chopped midshaft. One at least of the two tibias has been treated in the same fashion. This appears to have been deliberate. This provides evidence for how hares were dressed for the table.

CHR Phase 53

A large sample of over 2200 bones (Table 5.9) was recovered from the fill of F15, a large cut feature, the contents of which are 13th- to 14th-century in date.

The high number of small unidentified fragments of bird bones (56) and the relatively high proportion (29 per cent) of unidentified fragments show that bones were recovered with care from this feature. The proportions of species and anatomical parts can therefore be considered a good reflection of what was disposed of in the feature. One sample was taken which contained no fish and only three fragments, that could be identified to anatomical element. A single amphibian bone was recovered.

Four bones were identified as goat: three horn cores and a distal metacarpal (Table 5.25). These have been included with the sheep in the anatomical distribution (Table A5.7). The percentages of the main species are: 35 per cent sheep, 40 per cent cattle, and 25 per cent

Table 5.9   13th–14th century: eastern suburb: Chester Road, Phase 53: NISP

	Hand		Sieve	Total
	n	%	n	
sheep + goat	290	34.6	3	**293**
goat	(3)		(1)	-
cattle	335	39.9		**335**
pig	214	25.5		**214**
domestic fowl	73			**73**
goose	26			**26**
rabbit	4			**4**
hare	7			**7**
hare/rabbit	1			**1**
fallow deer	14			**14**
red deer	6			**6**
roe deer	2			**2**
pigeon *Columba* sp.	2			**2**
duck spp.	2			**2**
cat	16			**16**
horse	9			**9**
amphibian	1			**1**
Subtotal identified	**1002**	**40.3**	**3**	**1005**
bird NFI	56	2.2	1	**57**
cat/rabbit-size	5	0.2		**5**
sheep/pig-size	348	14.0	4	**352**
cow-size	356	14.3	1	**357**
unidentified	722	29.0		**722**
Total	**2489**		**9**	**2498**
Fish				
ray *Raja* sp.	1			**1**
conger eel *Conger conger*	10			**10**
cod family Gadidae	1			**1**
ling *Molva molva*	1			**1**
unidentified fish	1			**1**
Total	**14**			**14**

Key as Table 5.4

pig. Of the elements not identified to species, 38 per cent are cattle-size and 62 per cent sheep- and pig-size, compatible with the figures for the identified bones.

The bones of sheep found in the highest numbers were the tibia (MNI=13), the humerus, and the metatarsal, followed by the radius, metacarpal and astragalus (Fig 5.11). Fewer mandibles (30 per cent only) were present than would be expected if relative survival was based on bone density alone. This is a typical distribution for cases in which whole animals were consumed, but heads are lacking.

As well as the bones of the trunk and limbs, heads and foot bones of cattle were found (Fig 5.12). There were 27 mandible fragments and 20 loose lower teeth, skull, horn core, and maxilla fragments. The most numerous bone was the calcaneum, of which eleven right-hand bones were recovered, but other bones with 30 per cent or more of what would be expected if the whole carcass had been present and survived were the mandible, scapula, humerus, radius, tibia, metacarpal and, unusually, first phalanx.

The most common pig bone was also the tibia (Fig 5.13), and the only other parts of the skeleton common were the humerus (88 per cent), radius (81 per cent),

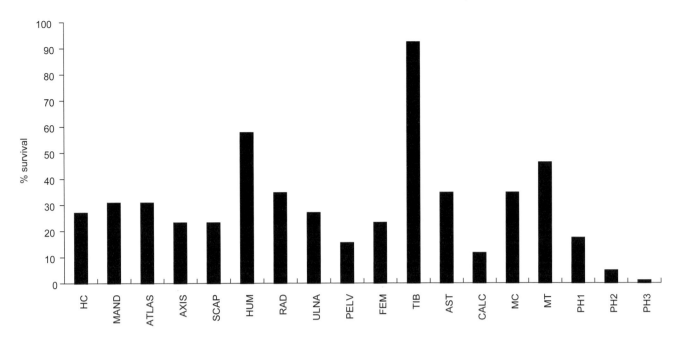

Figure 5.11   13th–14th century: Chester Road, Phase 53: anatomical distribution of sheep and goat (key as Fig. 5.2)

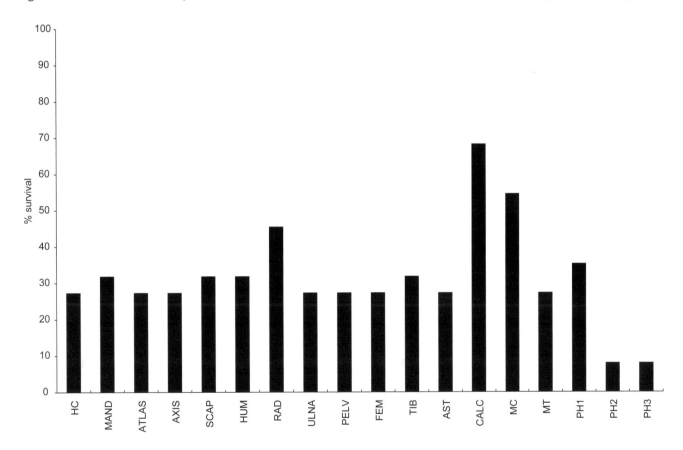

Figure 5.12   13th–14th century: Chester Road, Phase 53: anatomical distribution of cattle (key as Fig 5.2)

and ulna (56 per cent). Skull fragments, jaws and teeth, and foot bones were present in relatively small numbers. The anatomical parts present and the high percentage of gnawed limb bones (29 per cent) suggest that these are mostly from food remains.

Bones of domestic birds represent approximately 10 per cent of identified bones, fewer than in most groups

studied. Over 70 bones of fowl were recovered, from all parts of the skeleton except the skull (Fig 5.14), but including a few vertebrae and toes which were not identified to species. The percentage of immature fowl bones is 19 per cent (Table 5.29), low compared with other groups. There are 26 goose bones, mostly fragmented and from the more robust bones of the wing

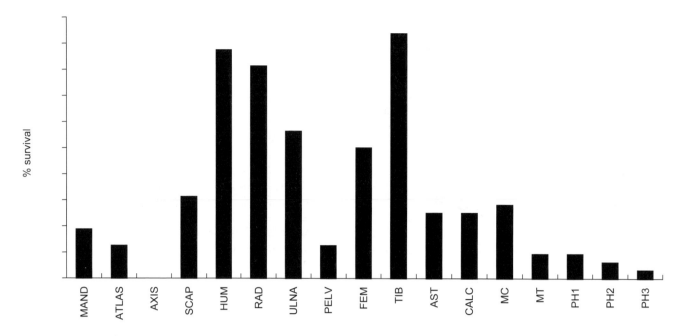

Figure 5.13   13th–14th century: Chester Road, Phase 53: anatomical distribution of pig (key as Fig 5.2)

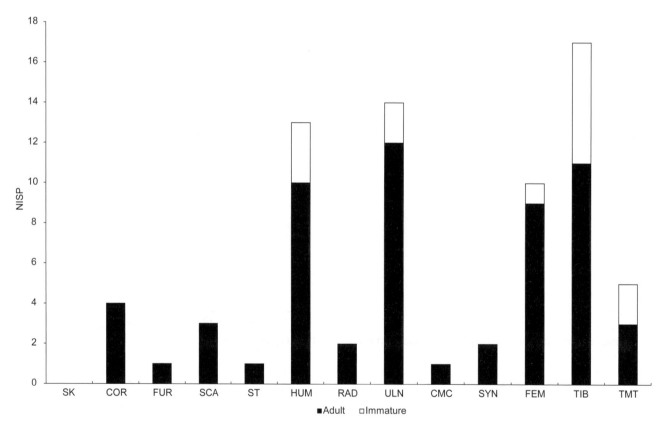

Figure 5.14   13th–14th century: Chester Road, Phase 53: anatomical elements and age of domestic fowl (key as Fig 5.4)

and leg (Table 5.30) and all compatible with domestic greylag, but not outside the size range for wild geese. Only three other bird species were identified: two pigeon bones from context 105, one from a medium-sized duck (*Anas* sp.) the size of a wigeon, and an ulna of a teal (*Anas crecca*). This is one of the few phases in which pigeon bones were found.

Of the 22 deer bones identified, two were from roe, fourteen from fallow and six from red deer, of which two were fragments of chopped antler. Other than the last, no skull fragments or teeth were found, but one of the roe deer bones is a second phalanx and seven of the fallow deer bones metapodials or phalanges. When the carcass was distributed following the hunt, the hide would have been removed (Cummins 1988), often leaving the feet remaining, and these last may have come into the town on hides. However, enough other parts of the skeleton survive to show that some deer were eaten in the eastern suburb.

Most of the fourteen fish bones recovered were from four species, conger eel, ling, cod or cod family (Gadidae), and ray (Rajidae). The ten bones of conger were from large specimens. No fish bones were present in the small samples which were sieved.

Sixteen disarticulated cat bones and teeth, from at least three different cats (Table 5.35), were found in eight different contexts. Five have cut marks: a skull, two of the three mandibles, a metacarpal, and an ulna.

There were three horse teeth and six disarticulated bones, including a metacarpal shaft which was smashed in a manner which could be interpreted as a deliberate butchery chop. They are from at least two horses, one very old, to judge from a lower incisor in which the infundibulum is no longer present, and one less than three years, as suggested by an upper M3 with the molar roots still open. All fragments come from the skull or feet, with the exception of a right radius. A distal metacarpal has probably been chopped through the shaft and the radius has been gnawed by a carnivore.

Discussion

The 13th- to 14th-century animal bone finds are again from a mixture of deposit types. Those from St John's Street, Phases 13 and 16, fit the interpretation of the eastern suburb as an area where commodities like horn and skins were collected, treated or traded, as well as being food remains. The range of species present does not include any of the rarer high status food animals that are found later in this part of the city. The contents of the two other pits from St John's Street also suggest that the occupants of the properties were involved either in primary butchery or in collection of skins. The cats, with cut marks on at least one bone of each skeleton, suggest collection of pelts. This and the residue from bone working suggest that the area had some use for industrial purposes. Some elements in the food remains, however, such as the hare and the high proportion of pig, suggest a relatively high status for the property, compared to most of the other suburban samples analysed.

The bones from the property at Chester Road at this time, as with the other groups, are mixed; with 'carrion' and butchery or craft waste as well as food remains. These include the widest range of food species of any group analysed, with at least sixteen including four of fish. Both hare and rabbit are present, and all three deer species, consumption of which was restricted to households of high status (R Grant 1991). The carcasses of these were either the perks of the hunters themselves or were donated to those whom they wished to honour or impress. The other wild species from which bones were found

– the hare, rabbit, and wild ducks – may have been provided by hunters but equally could have been purchased from the butchers.

Northern suburb

The 13th to 14th centuries witnessed the development of buildings along the eastern edge of the site at Victoria Road (VR), which respected an alignment corresponding to the present Hyde Street. This ran from the north gate northwards to Hyde Abbey and from there to points north and east, including London. The excavations exposed features at the back of the properties on Hyde Street including a large number of pits, some of which produced good groups of animal bone.

None of the many pit groups was closely dated from structural evidence, as their association with the individual buildings recovered during the excavations or even with documented property boundaries is not always clear. The pits were dated from the pottery, which was not undergoing rapid change in the 13th and 14th centuries, so at the present time they cannot be dated more closely within this period. The features were probably cut as wells or cess pits, which were filled with rubbish when they fell out of use. The bones in the fill of each appears to have been deposited fairly rapidly, as they are in good condition, with little erosion of the bone surface and little fragmentation other than from butchery and gnawing.

VR Phase 616

Two intercutting pits, F179 and F274, one circular and one subrectangular, were selected for analysis because among the 139 bones recovered (Table 5.10) were 26 bones of geese, most of these carpometacarpi. These are two of a number of pits within the boundary of property 935.

Some of the bone cannot be other than food remains: the sheep, cattle, and pig bones are fragmented, some are butchered and a comparatively high proportion (32 per cent) show evidence of gnawing. Of the two types of bone selected for distinction, none was of goat. Though limb bones were the most common anatomical elements recovered (Table A5.8), some, teeth, vertebrae, and ribs were also found. The three fowl bones, and some of those of goose are also food remains. There were two bones of wild animals: a proximal humerus of roe deer, with cut marks on the trochanter; and a fragment of metatarsal shaft which may have been worked, and which, like much of the other bone from these pits was heavily gnawed with punctures and scoring of the bone surface. The only bone from a non-food animal is a horse metapodial fragment, unmodified by butchery.

The most interesting finds in the pits are the thirteen carpometacarpi and eleven wing digits of goose. Two other pits studied have disproportionately high numbers of carpometacarpi of geese (Phases 635 and 792). The

Table 5.10   13th–14th: northern suburb: Victoria Road, Phase 616: NISP

	Hand		Sieve	Total
	n	%	n	
sheep + goat	31	47.7		31
cattle	23	35.4		23
pig	11	16.9	1	12
domestic fowl	3			3
goose	16		10	26
roe deer	2			2
horse	1			1
Subtotal identified	**87**	**69.6**	**11**	**98**
bird NFI	3	2.4		3
sheep/pig-size	10	8.0		10
cow-size	22	17.6		22
unidentified	3	2.4		3
Total	**125**		**11**	**136**
Fish				
ray Rajidae			1	1
fish NFI	1		2	3
Total	**1**		**3**	**4**

Key as Table 5.4

carpometacarpi, ten right and three left, are complete, and are undamaged by chopping or gnawing. One has a cut made with a metal knife on the proximal extremity – see Figure 5.46. The high proportion of distal wing bones strongly suggests that they were deliberately collected. The alternative, that they were discarded when the geese were dressed for cooking, is less likely because foot bones, which were also discarded when geese were dressed, were not found.

VR Phase 635

Over 1000 bones (Table 5.11) were recovered from a pit, F960, 1.8m in diameter and 2.30m deep, from one of the five pit groups within the bounds of property 936. Nearly all are from food remains, and the contents of this pit make a very important contribution to the interpretation of the diet of the period. The mandible of a field mouse (*Apodemus sp.*) and some frog bones are likely to be unconnected with the rubbish disposal by the occupants of the property, but probably come from creatures that fell into the pit accidentally. This group is of particular value because the samples taken for sieving contained a large quantity of fish bones, including seven species not present in the unsieved material. The bones were carefully recovered in the trench, as the high proportion of small unidentified fragments (24 per cent) and the high number of bird bones

shows. A moderate proportion (19 per cent) of limb bones had been chewed by carnivores.

Most of the identified bones (64 per cent) of the three main domestic mammals were from sheep. Neither of the horn cores was from goat, and no post-cranial bones were recognised as goat. Twenty percent were from pigs and only 16 per cent from cattle. This balance is reflected in the fragments: 15 per cent of identified fragments are of sheep-/pig-size, and only 4.5 per cent of cattle-size. The main limb bones outnumber fragments of skull and feet in sheep (Table A5.9), with the tibia and radius being the most common bones with nineteen and fifteen fragments respectively. This is reflected in the percentages present based on MNE, 81 per cent and 75 per cent. Cattle bones are few, and from all parts of the skeleton; and all parts of the carcass of pig are present, including thirteen fragments from the head. The sheep- / pig-size fragments include 62 ribs, of which 44 have clearly been chopped, and 37 fragments of vertebrae from all parts of the vertebral column of which 24 have been chopped through the mid line.

Domestic fowl and goose fragments were more common than cattle and pig. While the parts of the skeleton of chicken (Fig. 5.15; Table 5.29) suggest that these were food remains, the most common parts of the goose skeleton found were the carpometacarpus and wing phalanges (Table 5.30), as in Phase 616. Two of the three duck bones, a complete skull and a carpometacarpus, were identified as mallard, but these

Table 5.11 13th–14th: northern suburb: Victoria Road, Phase 635: NISP

	Hand		Sieve	Total
	n	%	n	
sheep + goat	119	64.3	2	121
cattle	29	15.7	1	30
pig	37	20.0		37
domestic fowl	75			75
goose	60			60
duck *Anas* sp.	1			1
hare	113		1	114
fallow deer	8			8
duck cf domestic	2			2
Turdidae	1			1
horse	11			11
mouse *Apodemus* sp.	1			1
frog *Rana* sp	1			1
Subtotal identified	**458**	**52.7**	**4**	**462**
bird NFI	35	4.0	1	36
cat/rabbit-size		0.0	3	3
sheep/pig-size	127	14.6	2	129
cow-size	39	4.5		39
unidentified	210	24.2		210
Total	**869**		**10**	**879**
Fish				
ray *Raja* sp.			1	1
eel *Anguilla anguilla*			2	2
conger eel *Conger conger*	10		1	11
herring *Clupea harengus*			31	31
haddock *Melanogrammus aeglefinus*			4	4
lythe *Pollachius pollachius*			1	1
ling *Molva molva*	2			2
cod family Gadidae			1	1
mackerel *Scomber scombrus*			1	1
flatfish NFI Pleuronectidae			5	5
unidentified	8		65	73
Total	**20**		**111**	**131**

Key as Table 5.4

are larger than the bones of wild mallards, and are therefore probably domestic. An ulna was from a middle-size wild duck.

The deposit is exceptional in having over 100 bones of hare, all except two from one context (3886). The bones were from at least five hares, as shown by the five right and five left tibias recovered. Fragment numbers distort the importance of hare because the 22 vertebrae and seven ribs found were identified to species, and large numbers of metapodials (34) and phalanges (24) were found. Other bones from hunted species were eight of fallow deer: a proximal tibia and a distal metatarsal with six associated phalanges.

The species of fish represented were ray, freshwater eel, conger eel, herring, haddock, lythe, ling, mackerel, and a flatfish not identified to species. The larger fish, the ling and conger eel, were not unexpectedly the species recovered in the trench.

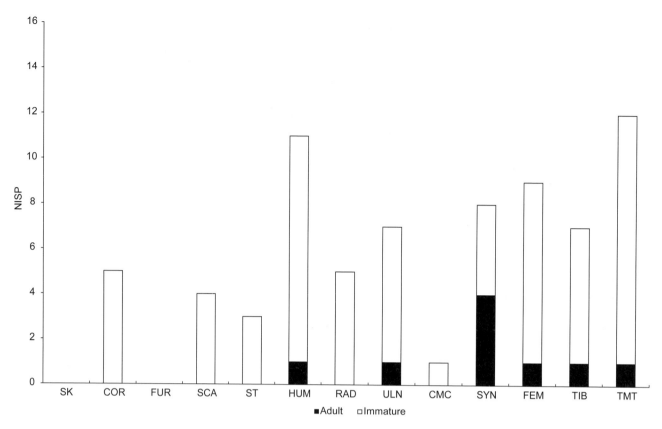

Figure 5.15   13th–14th century: Victoria Road, Phase 635: anatomical elements and age of domestic fowl (key as Fig 5.4)

VR Phase 637

Over 600 bones were recovered from a group of pits (F1018, F1049, F1065, and F1114), including 125 fish bones from samples. They were also asscociated with property 936. The finds (Table 5.12) of amphibian bones, both frogs and toads, suggest that the pit stood open, probably with standing water, for a time. In the same layer (c.4189) as the amphibians was a cat skeleton, much of two skeletons of young chickens, and part of the wing of a jackdaw (*Corvus monedula*). The cat was immature. There was a knife cut on the right mandible below P1, a skinning mark. Both domestic fowl were very immature, with very porous unformed bones and the tibiotarsi and tarsometatarsus elements unfused, whereas others from this phase were mostly mature (Fig 5.16). There were no traces of butchery or carnivore gnawing on either.

This combination of species is reminiscent of the finds from pits of the Saxo-Norman period. The amphibians enter the pit or well and become trapped, but the other articulated skeletons are typical of animals disposed of in a well: the skinned cat carcass, a dead jackdaw, and fowl not taken for the pot, no doubt because they died of disease or accidents.

The percentages of fragments of sheep (55 per cent), cattle (29 per cent), and pig (16 per cent) are similar to those from other pits of the period. No goat horn cores or bones were identified. Most regions of the pig and cattle skeleton were identified (Table A5.10). The

most frequent anatomical elements of sheep, calculated from MNE as well as NISP, were the metatarsal and metacarpal, and mandibles were relatively rare (Fig 5.17). A very high proportion, 27 per cent, of the limb bones were gnawed. Only four domestic fowl bones other than the two skeletons were recovered, and five goose bones. Unlike those of the skeletons, these were mostly fragmented, cut marks are present on some, and one at least was gnawed. While most goose bones from Winchester exceed those of the wild female greylag in size, this matches the wild goose well. It was certainly eaten, as there is a small nick below the femoral head, as described by Coy (1988), a trace of filleting. No food remains of wild species were present; the single red deer find was a piece of worked antler tine.

The fish assemblage from the sieved samples like that from Phase 635 is also a representative one on which to base an interpretation of fish consumption. All but eight of the 67 identified fish bones were from eel, herring, and the cod family. Others were from mackerel (6), conger eel (1), and flatfish (1). The cod family species included saithe and whiting, the former at least traded dried and salted.

VR Phase 743

The main deposit in this pit, F1022 (property 936), was the skeleton of a horse; only 226 further mammal

Table 5.12   13th–14th: northern suburb: Victoria Road, Phase 637: NISP

	Hand		Sieve	Total
	n	%	n	
sheep + goat	108	55.4		**108**
cattle	56	28.7		**56**
pig	31	15.9		**31**
domestic fowl	29			**29**
goose	5			**5**
red deer (1)	1			**1**
cat (2)	20			**20**
dog	1			**1**
horse	3			**3**
gull *Larus* sp.	1			**1**
jackdaw *Corvus monedula* (3)	3			**3**
Rana			X	
Bufo			X	
amphibian	3		20	**23**
Subtotal identified	**261**	**50.3**	**20**	**281**
bird NFI	12	2.3		**12**
cat/rabbit-size	1	0.2		**1**
sheep/pig-size	82	15.8	1	**83**
cow-size	61	11.8		**61**
unidentified	102	19.7		**102**
Total	**519**		**21**	**540**
Fish				
eel *Anguilla anguilla*			17	**17**
herring *Clupea harengus*			27	**27**
conger eel *Conger conger*	1		1	**2**
cod family Gadidae			12	**12**
whiting *Merlangius merlangius*			3	**3**
flatfish NFI Pleuronectidae			1	**1**
mackerel *Scomber scombrus*			6	**6**
unidentified	1		58	**59**
Total	**2**		**125**	**127**

Key as Table 5.4
(1) worked antler
(2) 18 bones from part skeleton
(3) same bird

bones, 28 fish bones, and no bird bones were recovered (Table 5.13). There were no samples with bone.

The horse, an animal about eight years at death, was substantially complete, but knife marks on the proximal femur suggest that some disarticulation had taken place, if only to reduce the carcass so that it would fit in the pit. No cuts indicating skinning were seen. Other evidence for the removal of the hide, a valuable resource after the horse had died, can be the absence of phalanges removed with the hide. The recovered bones include a single phalanx only, inconclusive evidence either way.

Sheep bones were most numerous after those of horse. Most were from the head and feet (Table A5.11), including three phalanges. The only fish bones were recovered in the trench; there were none from samples. The identifiable bones were from plaice and cod.

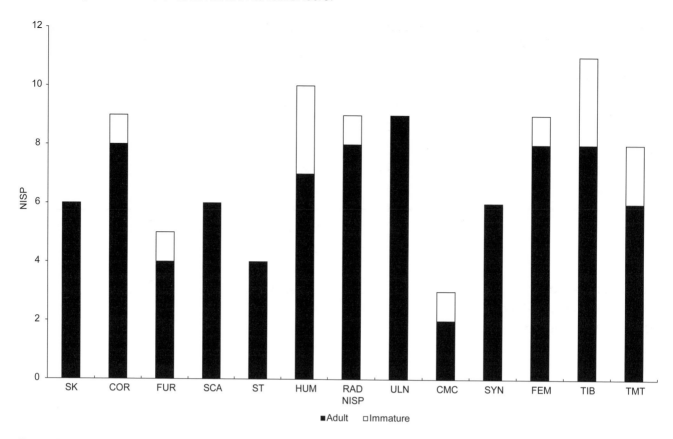

Figure 5.16   13th–14th century: Victoria Road, Phase 637: anatomical elements and age of domestic fowl (key as Fig 5.4)

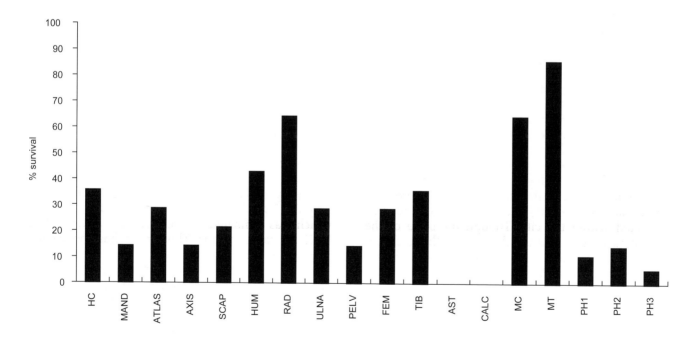

Figure 5.17   13th–14th century: Victoria Road, Phase 637: anatomical distribution of sheep and goat (key as Fig 5.2)

VR Phase 783

The contents of pit F413 were selected for analysis because of the large group (118) of cattle horn cores recovered. These can provide important data for the study of changes in size and conformation of cattle.

Though it was not appreciated at the time of the assessment, the archive records of the excavation show that a sample only of the horn cores, 60 per cent, and approximately 10 per cent of the other bones were kept. This group (Table 5.14) cannot therefore be used for comparisons of species, but the individual elements

Table 5.13 13th–14th century: northern suburb: Victoria Road, Phase 743: NISP

	NISP	%
sheep + goat	36	78.3
cattle	6	13.0
pig	4	8.7
horse	47*	
Subtotal identified	**93**	**34.1**
sheep/pig-size	37	13.6
cow-size	8	2.9
unidentified	135	49.5
Total	**273**	
cod *Gadus morhua*	1	
plaice *Pleuronectes platessa*	4	
flatfish NFI Pleuronectidae	1	
fish NFI	22	
Total	**28**	

Key as Table 5.4
* part skeleton

Table 5.14 13th–14th century: northern suburb: Victoria Road, Phase 783: NISP (selected sample)

	Hand	Sieve	Total
sheep + goat	13		**13**
cattle*	146		**146**
pig	2		**2**
domestic fowl	6		**6**
goose	2		**2**
dog	1		**1**
horse	34		**34**
Subtotal identified	**204**		**204**
sheep/pig-size	19		**19**
cow-size	40		**40**
unidentified	21		**21**
Total	**284**		**284**
Fish			
eel *Anguilla anguilla*		1	**1**
herring *Clupea harengus*		2	**2**
Total		**3**	**3**

Key as Table 5.4
* Horn cores

can provide information on the species in question, and the horn cores, horse bones, and dog skull are all discussed below.

Collections of cattle horn cores represent the waste product from butchery or horn working. Most have been chopped from the skull. If they were butchery waste, from which the butcher had removed the horn, we should expect more of the skull, and possibly foot bones, to be present. As recovery was partial here, the anatomical parts found cannot suggest the origin, but as the horn cores were chopped or broken from the skull they were probably horner's waste.

The most likely explanation for their presence is that horn working was being carried out in the vicinity, but the alternative is that the land within property 935 was at this time being used for disposal of rubbish generated within the city. Though the scale of the deposit makes this possible, there is no other archaeological evidence that leads one to suppose the rubbish was brought in from elsewhere.

VR Phase 975

The large cut feature, F28, was a cellar or possibly a quarry, later filled with bone and other rubbish. Unlike most of the features whose bone assemblages are discussed here, F28 was in the area occupied by property 937, fronting on to Swan Lane.

Over 1000 bones were recovered (Table 5.15). A few (five of the identified bones) have a flaky texture, so may have been exposed on the ground surface or reworked before incorporation in the deposits, but

others are well preserved. There were no deposits with anaerobic preservation such as those which preserved the fish in Phases 635 and 637, and no fish were recovered in the samples.

The proportion of bones of animals not usually part of the diet is low; there were isolated finds of cat (an ulna and an axis vertebra), dog (a pelvis fragment and a large carnassial), and one horse tooth. An incidental find was the ulna of a gull.

Of the three main food animals, cattle fragments, unusually, were most frequent, and pig almost as frequent as sheep and cattle. The estimated MNI of eight pigs, based on the most frequent bone, the scapula (Fig 5.18), is the same as the MNI of sheep, which was estimated on the distal tibia shaft, while MNI for cattle is four. This group has the second highest proportion of pig among those studied. The sheep remains, whilst predominantly the main meat bearing elements, also included seven mandibles and a horn core (Fig 5.19; Table A5.13). The cattle remains (Fig 5.20) were mostly the upper limb bones but included metapodials and some phalanges, but few bones from the head. There was a high proportion of unidentified fragments, most of which were rib and vertebra.

The proportion of bird bones and fish was low, and fish bones were absent in the sieved samples. Geese (NISP=37) were almost as numerous as domestic fowl (NISP=39). No articulated bones were found and all parts of the carcass were present for both fowl (Table 5.29) and geese (Table 5.30). Some cuts and chop

Table 5.15 13th–14th century: northern suburb: Victoria Road, Phase 975: NISP

	Hand	%	Sieve	Total
sheep + goat	104	32.3		**104**
goat	(1)			
cattle	116	36.0		**116**
pig	102	31.7		**102**
domestic fowl	39			**39**
goose	37			**37**
hare			1	**1**
rabbit			2	**2**
mallard *Anas platyrhynchos*	2			**2**
swan *Cygnus* sp.	2			**2**
cat			2	**2**
dog	1		1	**2**
horse	1			**1**
common? gull *Larus* cf *canus*	1			**1**
rodent	2			**2**
Subtotal identified	**407**	**31.9**	**6**	**413**
bird NFI	19	1.5		**19**
cat/rabbit-size	4	0.3		**4**
sheep/pig-size	227	17.8	2	**229**
cow-size	211	16.5	1	**212**
unidentified	408	32.0		**408**
Total	**1276**		**9**	**1285**
Fish				
conger eel *Conger conger*	5			
haddock *Melanogrammus aeglefinus*	5			
fish NFI	10			
Total	**20**			

Key as Table 5.4

marks were noted on both species: six on the geese bones and two on the domestic fowl bones. Like the food mammals, punctures on some bones of each species indicate the attention of cats or small dogs: ten goose bones and five of chicken were affected. Two bones of a swan were found: a cervical vertebra and a foot phalanx. (These anatomical elements cannot be reliably distinguished between the mute and whooper swan.) Though the swan is usually associated with households of high status, these are from parts of the skeleton removed when the bird was dressed, unless, of course, it was served with the head and neck in place for display.

These features together suggest that the group mainly represents food remains, but with an element of waste from primary butchery in the kitchen or by the butcher, as with skulls that were disposed of together in pit F413 (Phase 783). Only 17 per cent of the limb bones are gnawed, damage more common on table waste and less common on more specialised bone waste. Bird bone numbers would be expected to be higher if this were mainly table waste.

Discussion

The contents of the 13th- to 14th-century pits in the northern suburb were varied. As in other areas, all contained both food remains and some bones from other sources, but in some pits, food remains predominated and in others craft working debris. The immature chicks in Phase 637 suggest that fowl at least were raised on the premises.

Generalisations about the proportions of food from the different animals have to take into account the fact that the three groups with good assemblages of food remains give widely differing proportions of the main species, and of birds to mammal. The high pro-

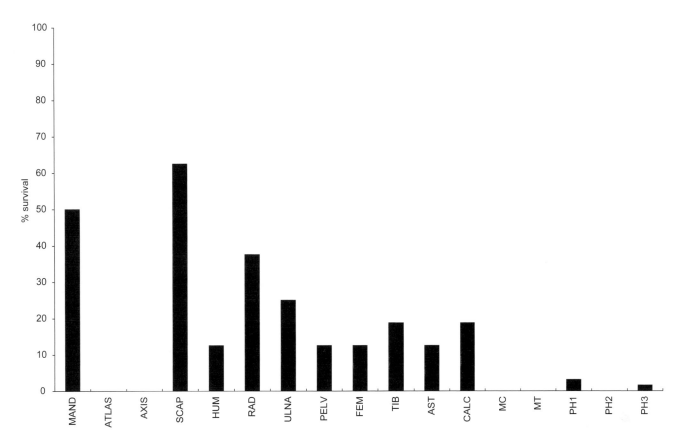

Figure 5.18   13th–14th century: Victoria Road, Phase 975: anatomical distribution of pig (key as Fig 5.2)

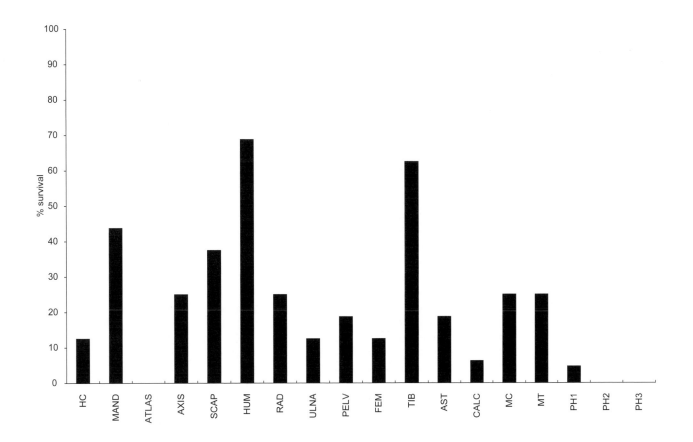

Figure 5.19   13th–14th century: Victoria Road, Phase 975: anatomical distribution of sheep and goat (key as Fig 5.2)

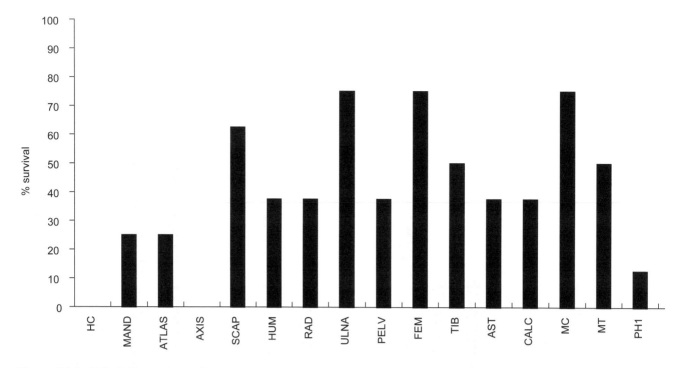

Figure 5.20   13th–14th century: Victoria Road, Phase 975: anatomical distribution of cattle (key as Fig 5.2)

portion of cattle and the low proportion of bird bones in Phase 975 is likely to be a function of the type of deposit. While the fish finds from Phase 975 are not a representative sample of fish eaten, as small species are missing, herring are the most numerous fishes in Phases 635 and 637, and eel are also numerous in Phase 637.

Of the two groups of food remains which are mainly table waste, the range of food species in Phase 637 is limited, while that from Phase 635 which included hare, deer, and at least nine species of fish is more varied, and suggests greater wealth or status in the occupants of the property (936) at the time of its deposition. The sheep included a higher proportion of bones of younger sheep than other deposits, which also tends to confirm greater wealth or status. There is also variety in the species from Phase 975, with swan, duck, hare, and rabbit, though in low proportions. This pit had an unusually high proportion of pig, a more desirable source of meat than mutton, particularly when eaten fresh.

The evidence of craft activity is strong. Unless the properties were being used for disposal of waste from the town, which on other archaeological grounds is unlikely, the horn cores are evidence either that one of the activities on the property was either large-scale cattle butchery, or, more likely, horn working. Skulls of sheep and goat are also present, but more dispersed among the pits. The horse carcasses which were disposed of in pits F1022 (Phase 743) and F413 (Phase 783) raise the possibility that the premises were a knackers, a trade which would have operated close to others dealing with hide working and utilisation of animal products. These appear to have included collection of goose wing feathers.

The later medieval period: late 14th to 15th centuries

Northern suburb

Occupation of properties 935 and 936 at Victoria Road (VR) continued into the later 14th and 15th centuries. The bones from the fill of a large stone-lined feature, four pits, and a linear feature suggest some changes in the use of the site in the later medieval period.

VR Phase 700

Over a thousand bones (Table 5.16) have been analysed from a large rectangular feature (F131), 3m deep, partly lined with masonry; a smaller pit F111, cut by F131; and a linear feature, F121 – all dated from the pottery to the 14th century. The bones are well-preserved, with the exception of fewer than half a dozen fragments more eroded than the rest, which may be residual.

The large numbers of bones of pig, sheep, cattle and domestic fowl, and the preponderance of limb bones over skull in the sheep (Fig. 5.21) and pig (Fig. 5.22), suggest that the three features contained mainly food remains, but a cat skeleton, and some disarticulated dog and horse bones were also present, and incidental species were also recovered. Context 477 contained three piglet skeletons and one of a young chicken.

These features contained one of the highest proportions of pig remains (38 per cent) of all groups from the suburbs – higher than that for sheep. The minimum number of individuals has been put at eight sheep, estimated from the metatarsal, and seven pigs, estimated from the humerus (Table A5.14). These

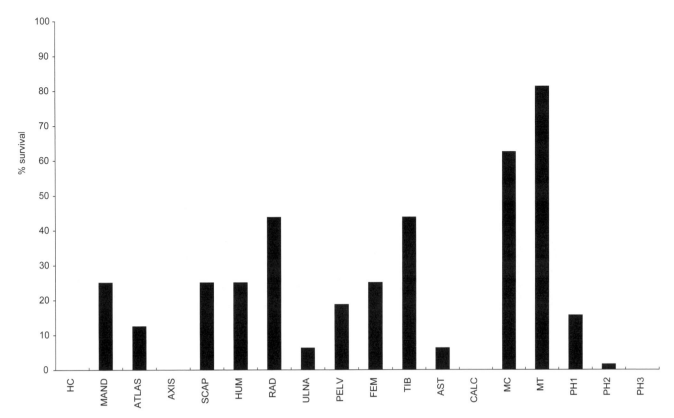

Figure 5.21   14th century: Victoria Road, Phase 700: anatomical distribution of sheep and goat (key as Fig 5.2)

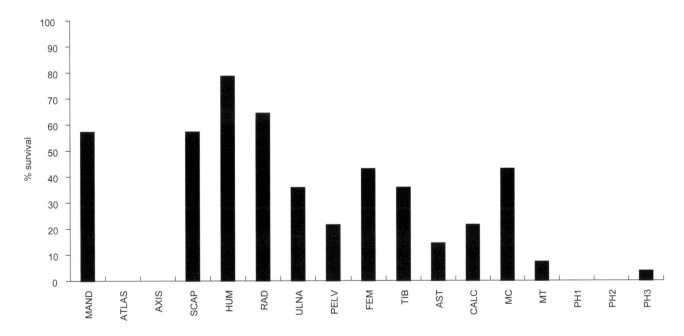

Figure 5.22   14th century: Victoria Road, Phase 700: anatomical distribution of pig (key as Fig 5.2)

proportions do not necessarily suggest increased consumption of pork and ham during this period, as some of the bones were from piglet skeletons. These were unbutchered and fairly complete, so appear to be from casualties rather than bones from joints of meat. A robust thick-walled tibia is probably from a large adult male domestic pig or a wild boar.

Domestic fowl (Fig 5.23; Table A5.15) bones were more common than goose, and the range of fish was similar to that from earlier groups. The range of food species was increased by the presence of bones of fallow deer, roe deer, rabbit, and hare.

Two dog and two horse bones were found disarticulated, and part of a cat skeleton. Two of the sieved contexts, 375 and 477, contained bones of incidental species, including rodents and amphibians. The

Table 5.16   14th century: northern suburb: Victoria Road, Phase 700: NISP

	Hand	%	Sieve	Total
sheep + goat	102	35.4	7	**109**
cattle	89	30.9		**89**
pig (1)	97	33.7		**97**
domestic fowl (2)	57			**57**
goose *Anser* spp.	7			**7**
duck ?domestic	1			**1**
rabbit *Oryctolagus cuniculus*	3			**3**
hare *Lepus* sp.	4		1	**5**
fallow deer *Dama dama*	9			**9**
roe deer *Capreolus capreolus* (3)	4			**4**
cat (4)	12		2	**14**
dog	2			**2**
horse	2			**2**
common gull *Larus canus*	1			**1**
mouse *Mus musculus*			X	
black rat *Rattus rattus* (4)	10			**10**
rodent			6	**6**
amphibian Rana/ Bufo			28	**28**
Subtotal identified	**400**	**47.5**	**44**	**444**
bird NFI	5	0.6		**5**
small mammal NFI	3	0.4		**3**
sheep/pig-size	171	20.3	2	**173**
cow-size	95	11.3		**95**
unidentified	168	20.0		**168**
Total	**842**		**46**	**888**
Fish				
dogfish *Scyliorhinus* sp			1	**1**
herring *Clupea harengus*			18	**18**
eel *Anguilla anguilla*			3	**3**
conger eel *Conger conger*	3			**3**
haddock *Melanogrammus aeglefinus*	1			**1**
ling *Molva molva*	1			**1**
cod family Gadidae			2	**2**
stickleback *Gasterosteus aculeatus*			1	**1**
fish NFI	4		19	**23**
Total	**9**		**44**	**53**

Key as Table 5.4
(1) includes 3 skeletons
(2) including part skeleton
(3) includes 1 antler fragment
(4) part skeleton

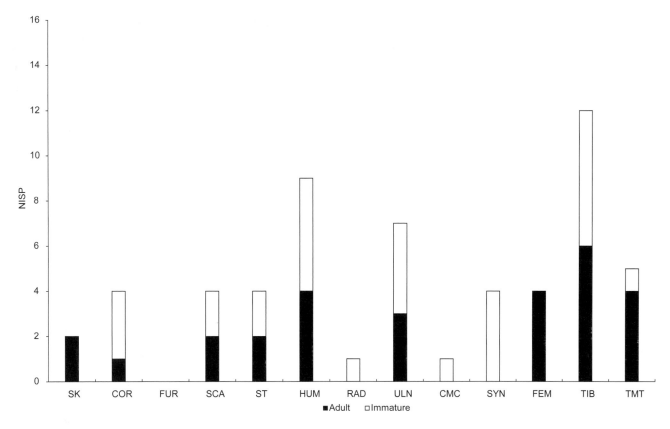

Figure 5.23 14th century: Victoria Road, Phase 700: anatomical elements and age of domestic fowl (key as Fig 5.4)

rodent remains included the mandible of a house mouse *(Mus musculus)* and the skeleton of a black rat *(Rattus rattus).* Also probably an incidental find was the distal humerus of a common gull. The amphibians, and the stickleback, of which a single bone was identified, suggest that the pit c.477 was originally an open pond or tank containing fresh water.

VR Phase 685

The second group of bones from the 14th to 15th centuries at Victoria Road was from two neighbouring features, pit F48/49 and a circular feature 1m to the south, F35. The pit was of irregular shape, *c* 1.70m deep and 1.40m at its widest diameter. Following the assessment, the dating of some of the layers was reassigned, and the sample which can be reliably dated therefore contains only 183 bones (Table 5.17).

As in Phase 700, the species most common among the main domesticates was the pig, but at least seven of the 33 bones were from a young piglet, with no evidence for butchery or breakage other than in excavation. An ulna from hare was recovered. The sample is small, but proportions of the main domesticates are similar to those in Phase 700.

VR Phase 792

The bones analysed (Table 5.18) date to the 14th and 15th centuries and were from a small subcircular pit,

Table 5.17 14th–15th century: northern suburb: Victoria Road, Phase 685: NISP

	NISP	%
sheep + goat	25	30.1
cattle	25	30.1
pig	33	39.8
domestic fowl	3	
goose *Anser* spp	1	
duck ?domestic	1	
hare	1	
Subtotal identified	**89**	**48.6**
bird NFI	3	1.6
sheep-size	47	
cow-size	14	7.7
unidentified	30	16.4
Total	**183**	

Key as Table 5.4

F117, still within the probable boundary of property 935. A large proportion of the bones were from the samples taken for sieving. Nearly 60 per cent of the 1100 bones comprise cat remains; at least two lamb skeletons were also recovered. The proportion of gnawed limb bones was very small, only 2 per cent, because it was based on totals which included the cat and lamb bones.

Table 5.18   14th–15th century: northern suburb: Victoria Road, Phase 792: NISP

	Hand		Sieve	Total
	n	%	n	
sheep + goat (1)	99	59.3	157	256
cattle	22	13.2		22
pig	46	27.5	3	49
domestic fowl	11			11
goose	5			5
duck ?domestic	1			1
hare	1		1	2
cat (2)	451		65	516
horse	7			7
gull Laridae			1	1
amphibian			5	5
Subtotal identified	**643**	**75.2**	**232**	**875**
bird NFI	1	0.1	1	2
cat/rabbit-size	2	0.2	40	42
sheep/pig-size	81	9.5		81
cow-size	77	9.0		77
unidentified	51	6.0		51
Total	**855**		**273**	**1128**
Fish				
herring *Clupea harengus*			1	1
cod *Gadus morhua*	2			2
haddock *Melanogrammus aeglefinus*	1			1
fish NFI	3		11	12
Total	**6**		**12**	**16**

Key as Table 5.4
(1) includes lamb skeletons (MNI = 2)
(2) includes skeletons (MNI = 33)

This pit contained the largest sample of cat bones from the suburbs of medieval Winchester. The bones were recovered in the trench (451) and also in samples (65). The identified bones included ribs and vertebrae. The Minimum Number represented by the surviving bones was 33, calculated from the 33 left tibias (Table 5.35). Altogether, seventeen of the bones have cut marks, most on the mandibles and skull, but four on other bones: humerus, radius, and femur. Such a large number of cats must have been collected specially, and the cuts on four out of the 24 mandibles show that some were skinned.

A high proportion of the sheep bones comprised skulls, mandibles, metapodials, and phalanges (Fig 5.24; Table A5.16). None of these were gnawed, and many were from immature animals. These may have been bones discarded after butchery, or be from skins collected for treatment; furs made of lambskins were sold as budge (Serjeantson 1989). This activity would complement the collection of cat

skins. If the lambs have an origin other than in food remains, then the proportion of sheep, nearly 60 per cent, probably overestimates the relative proportion in the diet.

The eleven domestic fowl bones were from all parts of the carcass, and from birds of different ages and both sexes, but the goose remains were more selected, with three of the five being carpometacarpi, two with cuts. One bone only of duck was found, the femur of a large duck. Another bone from hare links this pit to the others of the period. Of the seven horse bones from the pit, five were complete and undamaged.

Discussion

The use of the northern suburb for crafts as well as domestic activity continued in the 14th and 15th centuries. The most notable craft debris in this period is the cat bones; the most likely explanation of these

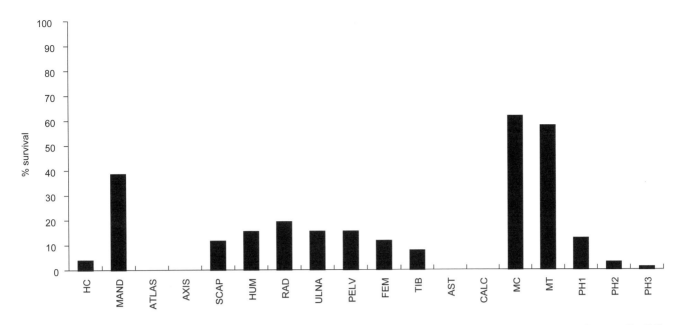

Figure 5.24 14th–15th century: Victoria Road, Phase 792: anatomical distribution of sheep and goat (key as Fig 5.2)

is that one of the buildings was being used as a centre for the collection of cats and lambs for skinning. The bones from the utilisation of goose wing feathers are fewer in this period than earlier.

The food remains, especially from Phase 700, include a wide range of mammals, though as in all the deposits from the suburbs, the three main domestic food mammals, together with domestic fowl, predominate over wild foods. The range of fish species is limited mainly to those species which have already made their appearance as part of the diet. Proportions of bones of the three main food species are similar in Phase 700 and Phase 685, but in both cases the high proportion of pig is enhanced by the number of partial skeletons recovered.

If skeletons of young animals represent evidence that these were reared on the site, the three part skeletons in Phase 700 and one in Phase 685 provide good evidence for pig keeping at this time. On this criterion, chickens too were kept.

If wealth and status at this period is judged from the craft activities, the occupants of the site appear to have been involved with crafts of a lowly nature, though perhaps less noisome than horn working of the earlier period. The food remains on the other hand include some evidence of species associated with wealth or higher status. Resolution of the apparent inconsistency may lie in the fact that a variety of individuals – and activities – were found on the site.

The post-medieval period: later 15th to 17th century

The latest assemblages analysed include two from Victoria Road (VR), Phases 756 and 763; and two from the eastern suburb, St John's Street (SJS), Phase 49, and Chester Road (CHR), Phase 56. The first three belong

to the later 15th and 16th centuries, and the last to the 17th century.

Northern suburb

This period sees a general decline in the fortunes of the area, as the medieval buildings were demolished and not replaced. However, pits continued to be dug, although their purpose is less clear than that of the 13th- to 15th-century pits.

VR Phase 756

The assemblage is from two intercutting pits F313 and F320, which may be associated with the destruction of the building occupying property 936. The 826 bones, of which over 40 per cent were identified to species (Table 5.19), included only three other than from food species. These were the distal femur of a dog, and the ulna of a cat, neither humanly modified, and an amphibian bone from the sieved sample from c.952 (F313). The condition of the bone surface was good, and none was noted as unusually eroded. This suggests little residuality or mixing. The relative infrequency of the smaller bones of pig and sheep, and of small unidentifiable fragments, suggests that recovery was of an average standard. The proportion gnawed, 23 per cent, is close to the mean for all sites.

The proportions of sheep, cattle and pig are typical of those from the Winchester suburbs, with identified bones of sheep most numerous (42 per cent). The pit is distinctive in being one of the few in which pig remains (33 per cent) are more frequent than those of cattle (25 per cent). If MNI is calculated, both sheep and pig bones were from a minimum of six animals. No bones were recognised as from goat.

Table 5.19   Later 15th–16th century: northern suburb: Victoria Road, Phase 756: NISP

	Hand	Sieve	Total	%
sheep + goat	125	1	**126**	41.9
cattle	75		**75**	24.9
pig	99	1	**100**	33.2
domestic fowl	46		**46**	
goose	11		**11**	
rabbit	2	5	7	
fallow deer	1		1	
cat		1	1	
dog	1		1	
pigeon *Columba* cf *livia*	1		1	
partridge *Perdix perdix*	1		1	
amphibian		1	1	
Subtotal identified	**362**	**9**	**371**	**46.1**
bird NFI	5		**5**	0.6
small mammal NFI	1		**1**	0.1
sheep/pig-size	209		**209**	26.0
cow-size	105		**105**	13.1
unidentified	113		**113**	14.1
Total	**795**	**9**	**804**	
Fish				
conger eel *Conger conger*	8		**8**	
ling *Molva molva*	2		**2**	
fish NFI	12		**12**	
Total	**22**		**22**	

Key as Table 5.4

The anatomical distribution of sheep and pig is similar (Table A5.17); percentage survival places mandibles as the most frequent element of sheep, and humerus that of pig (Fig 5.25), but NISP of jaws and teeth is similar for the two species. Only three sheep horn core fragments were found, and few metapodials and phalanges. Cattle remains were also mostly from the main meat bearing elements, but included some jaws and loose teeth. Horn cores were absent, and metapodial fragments and phalanges were few. The many ribs and vertebrae present, included in the totals of cattle- and sheep-size fragments, had been heavily butchered. Two sheep heads had been chopped sagitally. Though the proportion of cattle limb bones which have clearly been chopped is low, at least one mandible had been chopped in a manner which exposes the marrow cavity below the teeth, as have the pig mandibles. This evidence that the heads were used as a source of food reinforces the interpretation of this context as food remains.

Nearly 80 per cent of the bones of domestic birds were from fowls; goose bones, all compatible in size with domestic geese, make up just under 20 per cent of bones of domestic birds. The domestic fowl (Table 5.29) and goose bones (Table 5.30) were from all parts of the skeleton, with no articulated bones found. Fish bones recovered in the trench were exclusively those of large marine fish which have been found in other contexts, conger eel and ling.

Other food species were pigeon, rabbit, and partridge. Finds of seven rabbit bones are a reminder that this species became more widely available by the 15th and 16th centuries. A humerus of the native grey partridge (*Perdix perdix*) was the only bone of a species certainly wild.

VR Phase 763

An assemblage of over 1400 mammal bones and *c.* 30 fish bones (Table 5.20) was recovered from a group of pits occupying the area where buildings had formerly stood (F751/759, F763, F770, F779, F776). The largest, F770, was irregular or sub-rectangular in shape and

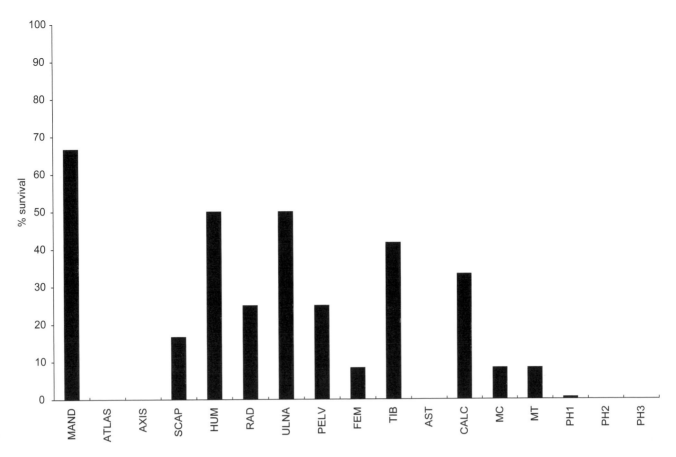

Figure 5.25   Late 15th–16th century: Victoria Road, Phase 756: anatomical distribution of pig (key as Fig 5.2)

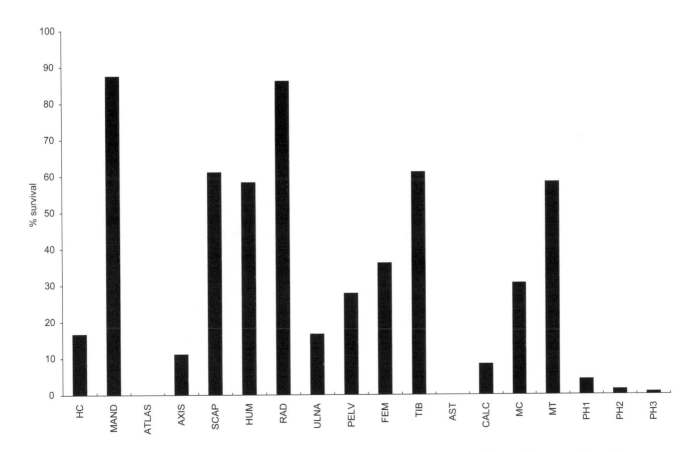

Figure 5.26   Late 15th–16th century: Victoria Road, Phase 763: anatomical distribution of sheep and goat (key as Fig 5.2)

Table 5.20 Later 15th–16th century: northern suburb: Victoria Road, Phase 763: NISP

	Hand	%	Sieve	Total
sheep + goat	290	49.1		**290**
cattle	192	32.5		**192**
pig	109	18.4	1	**110**
domestic fowl	XXX			**XXX**
goose	X			**X**
rabbit	4			**4**
fallow deer	7			**7**
red deer	1			**1**
cat	4			**4**
dog	6			**6**
horse	1			**1**
pigeon *Columba* cf *livia*	X			**X**
toad *Bufo bufo*	X			**X**
Subtotal identified	**614**	**41.7**	**1**	**615**
sheep/pig size	209	14.2		**209**
cow size	180	12.2		**180**
unidentified	469	31.9		**469**
Total	**1472**		**1**	**1473**
Fish				
dogfish *Scyliorhinus canicula*			6	**6**
Lamniform NFI	1			**1**
conger eel *Conger conger*	7			**7**
cod *Gadus morhua*	2			**2**
ling *Molva molva*	2			**2**
herring *Clupea harengus*			2	**2**
flounder *Platichthys flesus*	1			**1**
fish NFI	2		8	**10**
Total	**15**		**16**	**31**

Key as Table 5.4
XXX common X present

more than 5m wide in the largest dimension and at least 0.50m deep.

For two reasons the bones from Phase 763 are unsatisfactory as a coherent assemblage. Firstly, the site records leave some uncertainty about whether all the pits were fully excavated. Secondly, the bird bones have not been analysed, as the bags into which they were sorted at the time of the assessment have since been mislaid. It is clear from the assessment that the birds were potentially very important to complete the picture of the food remains, so it is unfortunate that detailed evidence is lacking. The sieved samples from contexts 3072, 3018, and 3111 produced sixteen fish bones and one other identified bone.

The proportion of identified fragments is high, in view of the fact that no skeletons and part skeletons were found. The percentage of gnawed limb bones is close to the mean, and typical for food remains (Table 5.3).

The proportions of the three main species, with sheep at 49 per cent, cattle at 32 per cent, and pig at 19 per cent, is typical of the medieval bone assemblages. Calculation of MNI gives eighteen sheep, nine cattle, and seven pigs. No goat horn cores or other bones were recognised, but the figure for sheep may include some goat bones. The anatomical distributions (Table A5.18), whether based on NISP or MNE, show that most parts of the skeleton are present for all three species (Figs. 5.26–5.28). The strongest contrast between the species is the skull. Cattle horn cores are lacking and skull fragments and mandibles are rare, while pig and sheep mandibles are more common. The smaller bones such as astragali and sheep and pig phalanges, easy to miss in excavation, are also

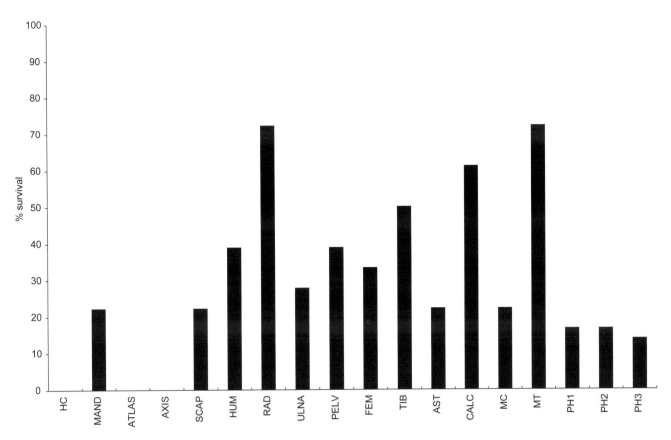

Figure 5.27 Late 15th–16th century: Victoria Road, Phase 763: anatomical distribution of cattle (key as Fig 5.2)

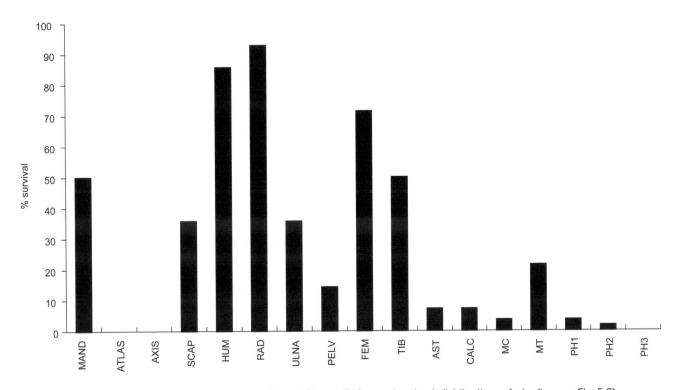

Figure 5.28 Late 15th–16th century: Victoria Road, Phase 763: anatomical distribution of pig (key as Fig 5.2)

low in number. The cattle bones include those of calf (Table A5.34). Butchery was heavy, with chops used to separate the upper leg from the lower, and to smash long bones through the shaft.

In the assessment domestic fowl was noted as the fourth most frequent species after sheep, cattle, and pig. Goose and pigeon bones were also found. The fish bones recovered by hand were from conger eel, cod, ling, and flounder. The sieved sample included vertebrae of dogfish (*Scyliorhinus canicula*) and herring. An operculum of cod has been chopped through. This fairly narrow range of fish species is similar to that from other groups.

There is some evidence of hunted species: fallow deer, rare or absent from most groups, here are 1 per cent of the identified bones, the seven bones, from four contexts, are from both the front and back legs. One humerus and one femur were chopped midshaft. The single red deer find is a fragment of unworked antler. Rabbit, a species which becomes more common in food remains in the late Middle Ages, is represented by four bones from three different contexts.

Disarticulated dog bones were found in three contexts; a humerus has a clean midshaft break which may be a chop. A cat mandible and three limb bones were found, all from adult cats. The mandible is broken, but no cut marks were seen on the jaw where it survived below the molar tooth row. A horse skull had been buried in pit F751/759 (c.3002) and a fragment of horse tibia was found, also apparently chopped.

Discussion

The bones from these late and post-medieval deposits at Victoria Road are clearly from domestic food remains. The contents of the pit have been less mixed with bones from other sources than most of the other groups studied. The unmixed character of the pit contents suggests that the rubbish was generated close to where it was disposed of. There was no longer evidence of craft activity or of backyard stock raising.

The meat component of the diet was less restricted than in previous centuries. The possible domesticates have been augmented by rabbit and pigeon, and two wild species were found. Consumption included the less favoured parts of the carcass as well as the main joints. Together these suggest a moderate status or wealth in the households which generated the rubbish. The relative scarcity of fish remains is a phenomenon of deposition and survival.

Eastern suburb

SJS Phase 49

The group of six features (F312/319, F313, F305, F307, and F308) which make up Phase 49 are dated, from the abundant pottery recovered, to the 16th century. The properties with which the pits were associated were not certainly exposed in the course of the excavation, and their status and function is not known. They were near St John's Church in the eastern suburb, which at this time had declined in relative importance, as the annual fair no longer took place on St Giles Hill.

The contents of the features are similar to each other, with the same range of species, mostly sheep, cattle, and pig, but also rabbit, hare, fallow deer (in four of the six pits), fowl, and goose. The *c* 2000 bones have

Table 5.21   Later 15th–16th century: eastern suburb: St John's Street, Phase 49: NISP

	NISP	%
sheep + goat	378	46.9
goat	(1)	
cattle	267	33.1
pig	161	20.0
domestic fowl	76	
goose	50	
mallard ?domestic	6	
rabbit	71	
hare	3	
fallow deer	9	
duck NFI wild	2	
horse	2	
jackdaw *Corvus monedula* (1)	4	
crow/rook	1	
Subtotal identified	**1030**	**51.5**
unidentified bird	40	2.0
cat/rabbit-size	3	0.1
sheep/pig-size	423	20.7
cow-size	199	9.7
unidentified	327	16.0
Total	**2022**	
Fish		
tope *Galeorhinus galeus*	1	
conger *Conger conger*	2	
cod *Gadus morhus*	3	
ling *Molva molva*	3	
cod family NFI Gadidae	5	
fish NFI	10	
Total	**23**	

Key as Table 5.4
(1) part skeleton

been analysed here as a single group (Table 5.21). Bones from the domestic animals not usually eaten are an incisor tooth and a hoof of horse, four bones from a jackdaw, and one of a rook or crow, the former certainly, and the last probably incidental inclusions.

The proportions of sheep and goat, cattle and pig are 47 per cent, 33 per cent and 20 per cent. This falls within the typical range of the groups studied from earlier centuries. The MNIs, twenty sheep, seven cattle, and eight pigs, show that more cattle bones survive, or are identified from each skeleton (Fig 5.29), a common finding. None of the sheep or goat limb bones examined appeared to be from goat, but a single mandible with DPM$_4$ with the characteristic pillar indicated that at

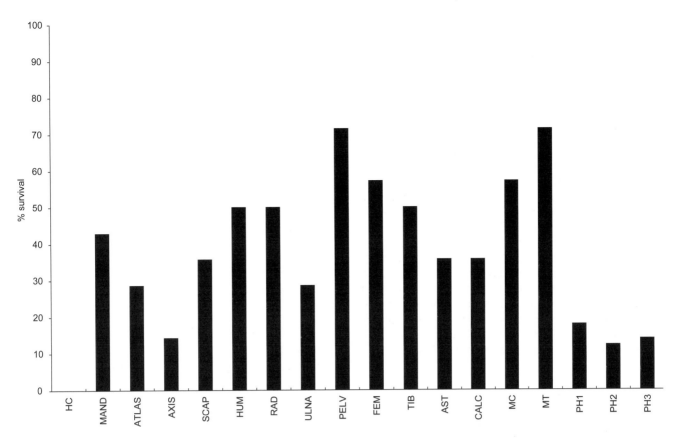

Figure 5.29 Late 15th–16th century: St John's Street, Phase 49: anatomical distribution of cattle (key as Fig 5.2)

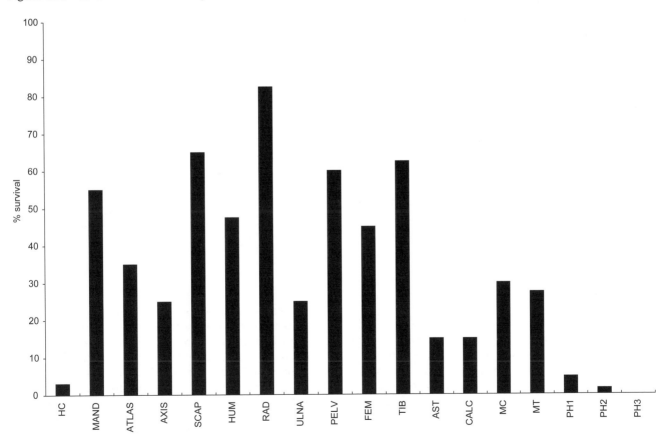

Figure 5.30 Late 15th–16th century: St John's Street, Phase 49: anatomical distribution of sheep and goat (key as Fig 5.2)

least one goat bone was present. There were few horn cores, none from goat.

Nearly all parts of the carcass of sheep (Fig 5.30) and pig (Fig 5.31) were present, with the parts of the

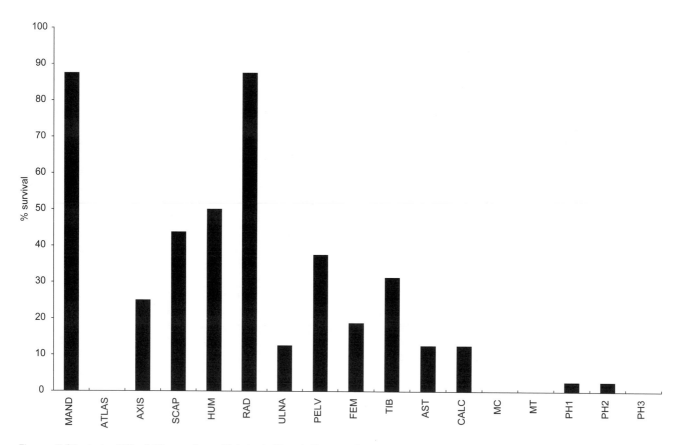

Figure 5.31 Late 15th–16th century: St John's Street, Phase 49: anatomical distribution of pig (key as Fig 5.2)

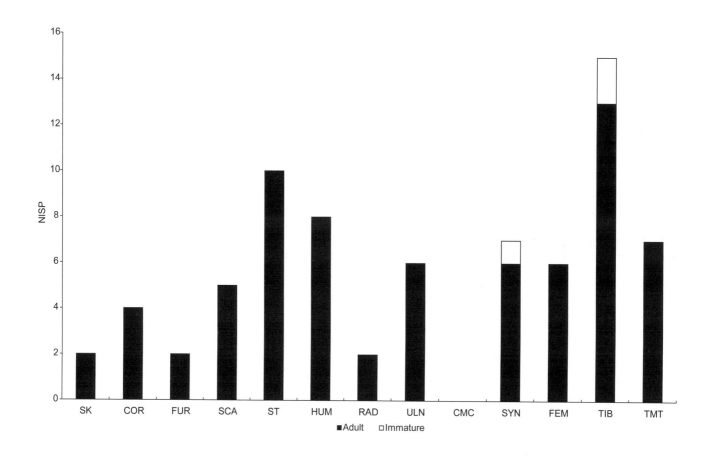

Figure 5.32 Late 15th–16th century: St John's Street, Phase 49: anatomical elements and age of domestic fowl (key as Fig 5.4)

carcass served at the table, the front and back upper leg, the vertebrae and the ribs (recorded as sheep/pig-size) most common for sheep and high proportions of bones from the head as well for pig (Table A5.19). Metapodials were less common (30 per cent and 28 per cent) than bones from the upper limb, and unlike the other limb bones were much less fragmented. Most have been chopped in half, but only one of the metatarsals was less than half complete. Five sheep skulls have the horns chopped off, and there were very few horn cores (3 per cent); these appear to have been taken elsewhere for use. There seems no reason to suggest here that the heads and feet of pigs and sheep were waste; the evidence can equally be interpreted here that they were eaten.

Cattle bone survival contrasts with the other two main species. The MNI for cattle is seven, and bones have survived in more equal numbers over the skeleton than in the other two main species (Fig 5.29). Of the ten mandibles, six have been chopped either through the diastema or behind the third molar, apparently to expose the marrow, so were clearly used for food before being discarded. Fragments of skull and maxillary teeth were very rare, and horn cores were absent.

The proportion of first phalanges was nearly 18 per cent, fewer than expected for the number of limbs present, but a higher proportion than was found in other phases, and more than is usually found. Metapodials are also among the most frequent bones. Second and third phalanges were also quite common, and some articulate. Two metapodials were complete, all the others were broken or chopped midshaft. All but two of the phalanges were complete and unbutchered. The high proportion of metapodials and phalanges has been interpreted as butchery waste or alternatively waste from hide treatment (Serjeantson *et al* 1986, 1989). These bones were commonly left attached to the hide when it was removed ready to be delivered to the tanner. If the deposits were of butchery waste, more evidence for skulls would be expected, so the interpretation of foot bones attached to hides is more likely.

Nearly 9 per cent of the bones were from birds, mostly domestic fowl, but also duck and other species. The 76 bones of domestic fowl originate from at least five fowls. All parts of the carcass were present (Fig 5.32). A very small proportion of fowl bones (<4 per cent) are immature, fewer than from any other feature with a good sample of fowl bones. One tarsometatarsus out of the seven recovered was from a fowl which was prepared for the table by chopping through the shaft.

This deposit has more goose remains (50) than any other from the Winchester suburbs; the remains are almost as numerous as those of domestic fowl. The bones come from a minimum of five geese. One scapula matches the wild female greylag in size, but most of the rest match domestic goose in size and robustness. All parts of the carcass were found, with tarsometatarsals and carpometacarpals most numerous. The normal method of dressing a goose today is to chop off the head and remove the feet by chopping through the middle of the tarsometatarsus. Four of the eight tarsometatarsals from these 16th-century pits have

been chopped in this fashion. Unusually, there were bones (24 per cent) of immature geese, some of adult-size and others smaller. The finds of immature goose bones here strongly suggest that geese were raised in the property. Six bones of mallard were found, and two of other ducks smaller than the wild mallard, one of which matches only the teal, and the other of which matches the middle-size ducks.

Rabbit bones were the fourth most numerous in fragment numbers (71), after sheep, cattle, and pigs, from a minimum of seven animals (Table 5.34). Many of the bones from this group were noted to be bigger than those of wild rabbits today. All parts of the skeleton were present, including mandibles and one maxilla. Nearly 10 per cent had been gnawed, at least one with punctures so small that the carnivore must have been a cat or a very small dog.

Nine fallow deer bones were positively identified, from five different contexts, all from the front or back leg, and some showing butchery (see below). These were from at least two deer, one fully adult and one immature. Two fragments of antler were found, one of which was a tine chopped from the beam. A mandible, scapula, and femur of hare were recovered, the last with cut marks at the attachment for the muscles on the proximal shaft. The scapula had been partly eaten by a dog.

Twenty-four fish bones were recovered by hand, all from quite large fish. Both cod and ling were found, as well as the conger eel, which was almost ubiquitous in the Winchester samples. One dogfish vertebra was recovered.

Discussion

Other than butchery or collection of cattle skins, little evidence was found for crafts in this post-medieval deposit from the eastern suburb. The most common parts of the carcass of the sheep and pig and the very high number of rabbits and birds strongly support the hypothesis that the remains were mainly household rubbish, but some waste from butchery or collection of cattle hides was also present. The food species were even more varied than that from Victoria Road. It is clear that by the 16th century, rabbit and perhaps fallow deer, were more available for consumption in towns. The numbers of geese, and the presence of immature geese, suggest these may have been raised on the property. If so, the high proportion will reflect local abundance, rather than reflect city-wide consumption patterns in the 16th century.

Eastern suburb (17th century)

CHR Phase 56

This collection of over 1400 animal bones (Table 5.22) is exclusively from the 17th century. The bones were recovered from the general site layer (primarily c.19) which covered the entire excavated trench.

Table 5.22   17th century: eastern suburb: Chester Road, Phase 56: NISP

	NISP	%
sheep + goat	334	49.4
cattle	218	32.2
pig	124	18.3
domestic fowl	18	
goose	10	
rabbit	5	
hare	5	
fallow deer	6	
roe deer	2	
red deer	1	
cat	3	
dog	22*	
horse	4	
Subtotal identified	**752**	**52.7**
bird NFI	12	0.8
cat/rabbit-size	1	0.1
sheep/pig-size	197	13.8
cow-size	205	14.4
unidentified	260	18.2
Total	**1427**	
Fish		
conger eel *Conger conger*	6	
fish NFI	1	
Total	**7**	

Key as Table 5.4
* includes part skeleton

Most bones were from the large domestic animals, cattle, sheep, and pig, but nine deer bones were also present. Birds and fish were scarce. An exceptionally high proportion, 42 per cent, of the limb bones have evidence for dog gnawing. A dog skeleton was recovered, but otherwise the only bones from other domestic animals were three of cat and four of horse. The horse bones were a jaw, two loose teeth, and a phalanx with sharp knife cuts midshaft. Preservation of all bones was good. The dog bones have a darker stain and lighter texture than the rest of the assemblage, consistent with this as a separate dog burial.

Smaller bones of the large mammals were few (Table A5.20), as were birds and fish, in contrast with the St John's Street pits. This is not the result of differential survival, which was good, and it is difficult to differentiate from internal evidence what was originally in the deposit, but not recovered, as opposed to what was never there. Recovery tends to be less good when bones are sparsely distributed in a soil deposit than when they fill a pit more densely. Analysis of the

sieved samples was therefore highly useful. These were scanned, and contained fragments of bones of the larger mammals, but no bones of fish and birds. This suggests that the small proportion (3 per cent) of bird bones is a real reflection of what was in the deposits. Rabbit, like birds, were much less common in these deposits than in the St John's Street pits. Only seven fish bones were recovered in the trench and the samples which were scanned did not contain further fish bones. All those identified were from large conger eels.

The proportions of the main species were as follows: 50 per cent sheep, 32 per cent cattle, and 18 per cent pig. Though larger bones predominate in this assemblage, cattle fragments are in proportions typical for the earlier centuries. If the phalanges were omitted from the fragment comparisons, the proportion of cattle would be lower. The anatomical distribution of sheep, cattle, and pig is similar in many respects (Figs 5.33–5.35). No bones of goat were recognised. Horn cores were few; there were two each of sheep and cattle, both the latter from calves. Mandibles were few in all three species. The main bones of the upper limbs, the distal humerus and distal tibia, were high in all three species, but metapodials were common in sheep and rare in cattle. This pattern of finds fits well with the bones being from food remains.

One component of the finds does not derive from food remains: 21 first phalanges of cattle. The humerus and calcaneus each show that the bones were from a minimum of five cattle. Though not so numerous as to give the MNI for cattle, percentage survival is over 50 per cent of the expected number present, an unusually high proportion, and notably higher than from any other group analysed. As with those from St John's Street, these are likely to be waste from butchery or hides. Two have clear cut marks, one at ligament insertions. The horse phalanx, by contrast, has cut marks around the shaft.

Goose bones made up 35 per cent of the bird bones; all were compatible with domestic geese. All were from skeletally adult birds, while a few fowl bones were from immature birds (Table 5.29). One of the two carpometacarpi of goose has knife cuts.

Discussion

At present this is the only group which can provide a picture of activity and diet in the 17th century, but it has deficiencies. The possibility has to be considered that the bone remains were rubbish removed from within the town and disposed of on the outskirts. The character of this deposit, with its dearth of bones of the small species, makes this a possible interpretation, but if this is the case, the deposit will not reflect the activities in the suburb. Whether the rubbish was generated close to the site or from within the town, it is only a partial reflection of the meat in the 17th-century diet, lacking as it does the smaller bones. Domestic fowl, scarce here, continued as an important part of everyday daily food, and there is no reason to suppose that the

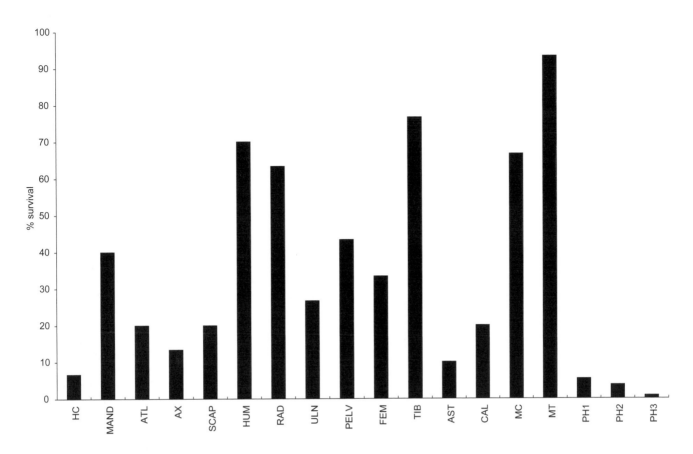

Figure 5.33   16th century: Chester Road, Phase 56: anatomical distribution of sheep and goat (key as Fig 5.2)

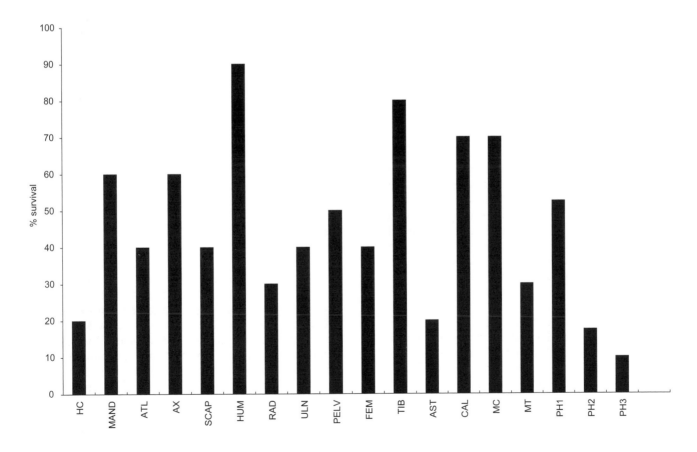

Figure 5.34   16th century: Chester Road, Phase 56: anatomical distribution of cattle (key as Fig 5.2)

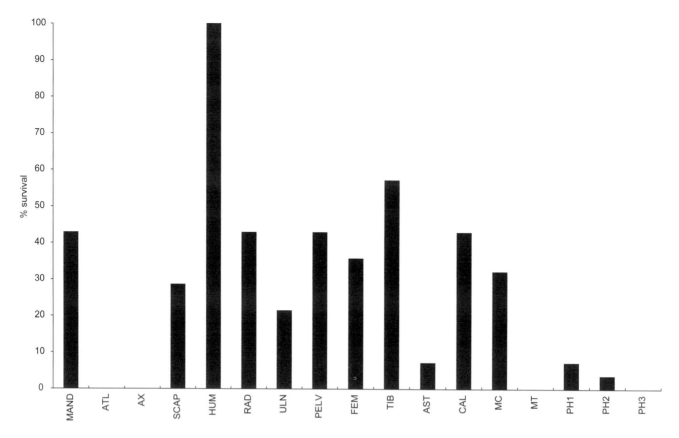

Figure 5.35   16th century: Chester Road, Phase 56: anatomical distribution of pig (key as Fig 5.2)

increased consumption of rabbit, seen in the previous century, did not continue. Historical sources suggest that fish consumption diminished after the Dissolution, but not to the extent suggested by the absence of finds from the Chester Road deposit.

Animals and fish and the diet

Sheep

In every group which consisted predominantly of food remains except one, sheep bones were more frequent than those of other species. Wool was the single most important source of wealth in medieval England (Postan 1975, 205) and the demand for English wool – the most sought-after in Europe – encouraged small farmers and larger landowners to raise sheep for export. Study of the bones can amplify the knowledge of sheep husbandry by providing evidence of the composition of flocks and the type of sheep kept. Disease and sub-clinical changes in the skeleton in the sheep populations and their implications for sheep husbandry are discussed in the Chapter 6.

The proportion recognised as goats from the mandibles and metapodials stands at less than 5 per cent, and no goat was recognised among the other post-cranial material from the northern and eastern suburbs, though a few were noted from the western suburb. (The role of goats is discussed below). The mandibles, loose teeth, and unfused post-cranial bones

used in the estimation of the age at death of the sheep may therefore include a proportion of unrecognised goat bones and teeth, but, based on the proportion in other parts of the skeleton, this will not exceed about 5 per cent.

It has been argued above that most of the bones were from sheep brought to the city for consumption, but some finds, such as the horn cores and metapodials from St John's Street, Phases 13 and 16, and Victoria Road, Phase 792, may be from skins or pelts carried to the town for sale. The lamb bones from the Saxo-Norman deposits at Victoria Road and some from St John's Street (Phase 16) may be from sheep raised on the periphery of the town.

Age at death

Mandibles with all or most molar teeth, and loose molars which could be certainly ascribed to their position in the tooth row have been used in the estimation of age at death. Tooth wear stages have been defined using the notation of Ewbank *et al* (1964) and Grant (1982), and the jaws and teeth have been grouped into age classes following the classification of Payne (1973). All records are listed in the Appendix (Table A5.21). Where the full dentition is lacking, assignment to an age class uses internal evidence from the asssemblage and Payne's illustrations. The numbers dead in each age stage are compared for each period (Table 5.23) and the cumulative percentages are compared

Table 5.23 Tooth eruption and wear in sheep and goat

Payne stage	11th	13th–14th (ES)	13th–14th (NS)	14th–15th	16th	17th
A	3	3	1			
B	6	1			1	1
C	1	1	1		2	
D	8	7			1	1
E	9	1	1	1	-	-
F	25	2	3	3	5	3
G	9	12	3	5	15	7
H	5	2			4	
I					2	1
Total	66	29	9	9	30	13

Key: ES eastern suburb; NS northern suburb
Stages A to I after Payne 1973

for the Saxo-Norman period, the 13th to 14th centuries in the eastern suburb, the 16th century, and the 17th century (Fig 5.36, *see* colour section).

The Saxo-Norman bone assemblage includes 66 jaws and teeth from Victoria Road in the northern suburb and from Henly's Garage on the southern city defences, which give fairly consistent results. All but two of the eleven jaws from Henly's Garage were at stage F, and half of those from the Victoria Road were slaughtered at the same stage. These were young adult sheep, between 3 and 4 years. Nearly 14 per cent (including a single jaw from Henly's Garage) were dead by stage B, at the time of, or shortly after weaning towards the end of the summer, if births were in spring. The proportion in stages A and B is similar (14 per cent and 11 per cent) in 13th- to 14th-century samples from both Victoria Road and from the sites at Chester Road and St John's Street in the eastern suburb, though the Victoria Road sample size is small. However, the eastern suburb has the high proportions in stage D, when M2 comes into wear at one to two years of age, and stage G, fully adult sheep, whilst at Victoria Road most are stages F and G. Some mandibles from the eastern suburb (SJS 16) may be from whole skeletons. There are nine ageable mandibles from later 14th- and 15-century contexts at Victoria Road. None of the jaws is from a sheep younger than the stage E, when M3 comes into wear but none is old. These sheep were eaten as mutton, but the age at which they were brought to the town for slaughter is a good compromise between a wool crop and saleable meat. By the 16th and 17th centuries, the jaws and teeth suggest that sheep were not brought into town for sale until a greater age, in contrast to a rather earlier age of slaughter in the preceding four centuries. The proportion of older adult sheep is greater, and fewer jaws are from animals below two years. Two from the 16th century are in the oldest age stage (I), with M3 in heavy wear, and one third molar from the 17th-century deposits also has a very worn third molar, indicating an animal perhaps as much as eight years.

Bone fusion has been analysed for each phase in which NISP of sheep bones is greater than *c* 100. Each

of the main limb bones is listed in fusion order, with the number of bones very young, unfused, fusing, and fused shown separately. These were grouped into three main age classes, early, middle ('mid'), and late fusing. The data from the separate groups are then summed. Fusion evidence for each phase is shown separately, as different phases in the same period do not always give a consistent pattern, partly no doubt because sample sizes are small, but also because of the diverse nature of the deposits.

Fusion evidence on sheep of the Saxo-Norman period varies between groups (Table A5.22). The smallest proportion (13 per cent) of bones from animals dead before about one year is from Henly's Garage, while, at Victoria Road, it is as high as 65 per cent in Phase 532, whereas in Phase 529 it is 35 per cent, and 25 per cent in Phase 530. The mean figure is 32 per cent. Overall, however, the fusion data matches the dental data and both suggest a high proportion of sheep slaughtered before the later fusing bones are fully fused, at two to three years. In the 13th- to 14th-century groups from the eastern suburb sites (Table A5.23) overall nearly 70 per cent of bones are from animals dead before the bones are fully fused, and 33 per cent in the earliest age group, that is, killed before one year. This fits the dental evidence. Both sources of evidence together suggest that young and older sheep were brought in for slaughter and consumption, but that few were kept for over about five years. For the same period in the northern suburb at Victoria Road (Table A5.24) there is more evidence of age at death from bone fusion than from mandibles and teeth. The fusion data show proportions similar to the eastern suburb of bones of the oldest fusion group still unfused, 64 per cent, compared to 68 per cent. The proportion of lambs is lower at less than 20 per cent, but varies between deposits, being highest in Phase 635. The small sample from the later 14th and 15th centuries (Table A5.25) has similar proportions. The 16th- and 17th-century fusion data (Tables A5.26 and A5.27) confirms the dental evidence in showing the trend towards keeping sheep until a greater age, with low overall percentages for early (2.5 per cent) and middle (7 per cent) fusing bones. The proportion still fused of late fusing bones is over 73 per cent, but this fluctuates between the 100 per cent of the small sample from Victoria Road (Phase 756) and just over 60 per cent of that from the 17th-century material recovered from Chester Road. There is likely to be some bias towards preservation of bones from older animals in this, as the sample is from a general soil deposit, whereas most of the material from earlier centuries is from pits.

Sex ratio and size

Medieval wool flocks included wethers, as well as intact rams and ewes. The part of the skeleton which shows most dimorphism between ewes and rams is the horn core, but recognition of the horn cores of wethers is not straightforward. These are discussed below (Chapter 6) in the context of the pathology of the sheep. Bivariate plots of the horn core base of the measurable specimens show that four have a notably greater breadth and depth than the majority of the specimens, and these are interpreted as rams. The large group, the horn cores intermediate in size, appears to include both ewes and wethers, as discussed below.

Discussion of sheep husbandry

Some very broad trends can be observed at Winchester, despite the heterogenous nature of the deposits examined. The age to which sheep were kept increased in the 16th and 17th century onwards. The proportion of lambs is high in the Saxo-Norman deposits, and also in some of those of the 13th to 14th centuries. A high proportion of lambs in the cull should be a typical reflection of exploitation of sheep for milk (Payne 1973), for which there is evidence in Domesday. The overall trend of the dental and fusion evidence, even in the Saxo-Norman period is not very strong, but high proportions of juveniles in individual groups may be the result of raising – and milking – sheep on some of the properties from which bones were excavated. No general increase in size is seen in this material before the 17th century. By this period the relative dominance of wool in the economy of England had diminished, and there was also a requirement for a carcass which provided good fat mutton.

Goat

Goats are listed with the main food animals in the tables, but it is difficult to assess how common the consumption of goat flesh in medieval Winchester really was. Establishing the proportion of goats among the sheep and goat bones is a greater problem on urban sites than on rural sites, because the bones found on urban sites are not necessarily from whole animals that were slaughtered and eaten in the town. The different parts of the skeleton are not likely to be present in the numbers which would be expected when whole animals are represented. Goat horn cores have been found in higher numbers than indicated by the other parts of the skeleton at other sites, including Hamwic (Bourdillon & Coy 1980).

The following skeletal elements were distinguished between sheep and goat: horn cores, skull fragments where the fronto-parietal suture was present, proximal radius, distal humerus, distal metacarpal and distal metatarsal (Boessneck *et al* 1964; Prummel and Frisch, 1986), and lower deciduous fourth molar (Payne 1985).

Altogether 28 horn cores and four other elements, three DPM4s and a distal metacarpal, were recognised as goat (Table 5.24). DPM$_4$s have been ascribed to goat when the bovine pillar, even in vestigial form, was present. No proximal radii or distal humeri from the northern and eastern suburbs, or from the city defences were recognised as goat, but a few were recognised at this period in the bones from the western suburb.

The results from Winchester support findings from other towns that there are few goat bones among the food remains, and that the highest proportion are among the horn cores. Though no unmixed deposits of sheep and goat horn cores have been studied here, several pit groups included material that seemed to be horns collected for craft use. Notable were the Saxo-Norman groups from Henly's Garage on the southern city defences, from Victoria Road in the northern suburb (HG 29, VR 530, and VR 532), and the 13th- to 14th-century groups from St John's Street in the eastern suburb (SJS 13, SJS 16, and SJS 30).

Possible evidence of size change in the goats comes from the horn cores complete enough to show the full size and shape: three from the 10th to 11th centuries are larger than all from later periods.

Discussion

The disparate evidence from the Winchester suburbs shows the presence of goat in the Saxo-Norman period and into the 13th and 14th centuries. Only one horn core, from the 16th-century pits in the eastern suburb, is later than this date. This may reflect a decreasing role for goats in the rural economy, but this would need confirmation from other sources.

The relative dearth of evidence for bones from the rest of the carcass does suggest that goat horns, still attached to the horn cores, were brought to Winchester for sale. The great majority are from adult animals, which provide the biggest and therefore most useful horn. The goat, largely missing from the documented records and from post-cranial animal bone finds, must have been kept in small numbers on farms and smallholdings, where it had a role as provider of milk, and sometimes as leader of the sheep flock. Though it cannot be ruled out that skins with attached horns were being imported from overseas, it is more likely that those found at Winchester are from goats kept in the wider hinterland of Winchester.

Table 5.24 Horn cores and fourth deciduous premolar (DPM4) in sheep and goat (the % of goat is shown)

Date	Phase	Horn cores			DPM4		
		goat	sheep	goat	goat	sheep	goat
		N	N	%	N	N	%
10th–11th	VR529		2	0.0		1	0.0
10th–11th	VR530	3	9	25.0	1	3	25.0
10th–11th	VR532		11	0.0		7	0.0
10th–11th	HG29	4	20	16.7		1	0.0
13th	SJS13	4	1	80.0			
13th	SJS16	7	8	46.7		3	0.0
13th–14th	VR616		–				
13th–14th	VR635		2	0.0		1	0.0
13th–14th	VR637		6	0.0			
13th–14th	VR743		–			1	0.0
13th–14th	VR783		1	0.0			
13th–14th	VR975	1	1	50.0			
13th–14th	SJS29	1	1	50.0			
13th–14th	CHR53	3	6	33.3		1	0.0
14th	SJS30	4	5	44.4		1	0.0
late 14th	VR700						
14th–15th	VR685						
14th–15th	VR792		1	0.0			
14th–15th	VR756	0	3	0.0			
16th	VR763	0	7	0.0			
16th	SJS49	0	5	0.0	1	1	50.0
17th	CHR56	0	2	0.0	0	0	
Total		**27**	**91**	**22.9**	**2**	**19**	**9.5**

Cattle

The questions with which the study of medieval cattle husbandry are concerned are the numbers and proportions of draft oxen and cows kept, and the extent to which cattle were raised for meat and dairying for the growing urban markets, as well as for the plough. These are only partly answered by documentary records, in which draft animals feature more prominently than those kept for breeding and provision of dairy products (Langdon 1986). Archaeological findings can supplement the evidence, but the discussions above of individual groups have made it clear firstly that the parts of the cattle skeleton were disposed of differently, and secondly that there is no reason to assume that any one phase group will contain the complete age range of the population of cattle brought into the town.

Age at death

Age at death has been estimated from tooth eruption and wear and bone fusion. A sample of horn cores from the 13th to 14th centuries provides complementary evidence. The samples of mandibles and ageable teeth are no more than ten for any period, and the bone fusion evidence, for which there are larger samples, may be a more reliable guide to the age classes selected for slaughter. The teeth were recorded using the notation of Grant (1982) (Table A5.28) and have been assigned to four broad age groups. These are: calves, immature, adult, and old. Teeth are interpreted as from calves below three months when DP_4 is unworn or in very early wear (up to Grant stage c), from immature cattle between that time until M_3 is worn to stage 'g', as adult while M_3 is at 'g', and from old animals when M_3 is very worn (Grant stages h–m) (Table 5.25). Bone fusion has been shown for the ten groups for which there are more than 20 skeletal elements with fusion data. The bones are listed in the order in which they fuse in modern cattle, with subtotals for epiphyses which are fused by approximately one, two, and three years (Tables A5.29–A5.34). The tables also show the total number of bones recognised as from calves below approximately three months (VJU).

In the urban context, consumption of veal of calves at about three months of age is associated

Table 5.25 Tooth eruption and wear in cattle

Stage	11th	13th–14th (ES)	14th–15th	16th	17th
Calf		2	1	4	1
Immature		1	3		2
Adult	1	5	1		2
Old	3	2		1	1
Total	**4**	**10**	**5**	**5**	**6**

Key to stages: 1 calf below c 3 months; 2 immature; 3 adult; 4 old adult. ES eastern suburb

Table 5.26 Summary of ages at death of cattle, based on horn cores from Victoria Road, Phase 783: 13th–14th centuries

	Left	Right	Total	Per cent
Young adult	10	9	19	16
Adult	29	33	62	52
Old adult	21	17	38	32
Total	**60**	**59**	**119**	**100**

with exploitation of cattle for milk and other dairy products (Serjeantson *et al* 1986), and the archaeological evidence for this is the presence of mandibles from stage 1 and of bones recognised as porous and juvenile (VJU). In the Saxo-Norman period there are no jaws at this stage, no porous bones from Victoria Road, and fewer than 5 per cent from Henly's Garage. If cattle dairying was taking place in the farms and manors in the hinterland of Winchester, few of the surplus calves were finding their way to the town. By the 13th and 14th centuries between 10 per cent and 20 per cent of the jaws are from calves; bones from this age class are lacking from some groups, but are as high as 9 per cent in the substantial sample from the eastern suburb sites, suggesting some increase in dairying and veal consumption. The increase is greatest in the 16th century, where the proportion of jaws is highest, and the more substantial number of bones from two groups have proportions of 14 per cent and 23 per cent from calves. The proportion in the 17th century is also higher (14 per cent).

The evidence for the age to which beef cattle were kept is inconsistent. From the 13th century onwards there are more jaws of younger adults (stage 3) and immature animals (stage 2). This fits with the increase in the market for beef from about the 13th century, for which younger adult animals were selected. The proportion of very old animals can be estimated from the proportion of latest fusing bones that are fused. This is highest (70 per cent) in the sample from Saxo-Norman Victoria Road, but in later centuries it is inconsistent between groups, ranging from *c* 30 per cent to *c* 64 per cent, and the material does not show a consistent trend towards consumption of younger or older animals through time.

The horn cores from Phase 783 at Victoria Road were measured (Tables A5.35 and A5.36) and assigned to age classes following the definitions of Armitage (1982). The ages at death (Table 5.26) suggest that in

the 13th and 14th centuries just over half of the cattle were killed as adults, one third as old adults and the remainder as young adults.

There are none from calves in this sample, the presence of which is otherwise attested by the mandibles, and this is no doubt because the skulls with horn buds or undeveloped horns were not collected for processing by the hornworker. Otherwise the distribution between young adult, adult, and old adult reflects the age composition seen in the bones and teeth.

Sex ratio and size

Measurements (Table A5.37) confirm the findings that in Britain and the rest of Europe cattle remained small before the 17th century (Audouin-Rouzeau 1991b). Other dimensions studied provide a wider picture. The distal metacarpal, of which 23 measurements are available, shows both large and small animals in each period (Fig 5.37, *see* colour section). As this epiphysis has been shown to be sexually dimorphic (Higham & Message 1969), this result may distinguish females and males. However, with such a small sample, the measurements obtained cannot do more than suggest a hypothesis to be tested further. It is not certain whether oxen used for the plough were castrated or intact males (Langdon 1986), and this sample is too small to clarify this question. The proximal metacarpal dimensions (Fig 5.38, *see* colour section) show a simpler picture, with the single 14th-century bone at the smaller end of the range and the largest in the 16th century.

The 13th- to 14th-century horn cores are of several different types. Seven examples are shown in Figure 5.39. These show the mark of the chop which detached the horn from the rest of the skull. The length of the outer curve, measured in 53 horn cores which survived

Figure 5.39 Cattle horn cores from Victoria Road, Phase 783, F413 (Photograph by J Crook)

intact, ranges from 172mm to 340mm (Fig 5.40), but as only a sub-sample of those present was recovered, it is likely that the larger ones were preferentially collected, so the minimum size may have little significance. The shape variation, which bears little relation to the size variation, includes some with forward and backward curves, and some with upward and downward tips.

Selection of cattle by the size and shape of the horns is a tradition found in the earliest written records of cattle husbandry in Europe (Lucas 1982), and throughout the cattle herding world (eg Evans-Pritchard 1940). If it can be assumed that different parts of the country favoured different types, the variation in this sample may indicate that the horn cores are from disparate sources, as would be expected in a central place such as Winchester.

Discussion of cattle husbandry

The limited evidence from this sample from Winchester tends to confirm work from elsewhere that veal was eaten mainly by the wealthy (Gidney 1991; Harvey 1993) and that there was little production of surplus calves for sale as veal in the towns before the 17th century (O'Connor 1989, 15). Driving cattle to markets originated as a means of supplying meat for towns, but it also supplemented the breeding stock in the arable counties that raised fewer of their own cattle, and the young adult component seen in the horn cores may be of these beasts as well as more local beasts not selected for breeding or draft. There is scant evidence for cattle killed at what in modern terms is the prime age for beef (mandible stage 2) in any period except the 14th century. In the main, cattle were kept until fully adult before slaughter, but only a small proportion of those kept beyond this age were brought to the town for consumption. This fits the later documented records that cattle were fattened for slaughter before they were very old, so that the meat would still have a sale value. The size classes of metapodials indicate an even balance of sexes in the cull, which tends to support the view that both males and females were used for the plough. The disparate nature of the finds from the Winchester suburbs has limited the conclusions that can be drawn on cattle husbandry.

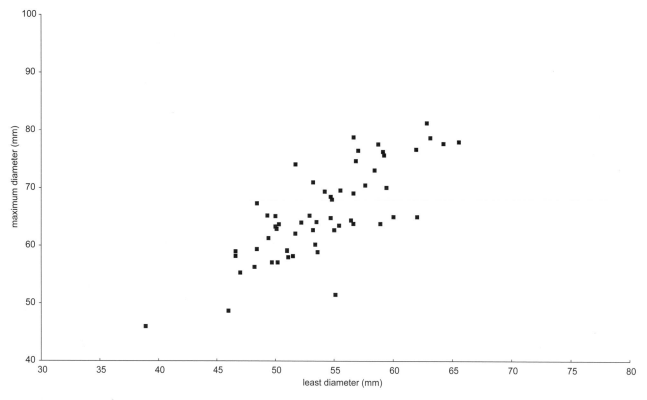

Figure 5.40 Cattle horn cores from Victoria Road, Phase 783, F413: scatter plot of greatest (maximum) x least diameter horn core base, left side only

Pig

Most of the pig bones have been interpreted as from food remains, with the exception of skeletons from Victoria Road (Phases 685 and 700) which were sufficiently complete to seem to be from casualties.

In each group studied except Phase 700 at Victoria Road, pigs provided fewer identified bones than sheep and cattle, but the MNI for pigs is as high as that for sheep in some groups. The age at slaughter, estimated from the dentition, allows us to consider preferred age of consumption, and taken together with the context of the bones provides evidence of whether pigs were raised around the city. Unlike sheep and cattle, the secondary products produced by the pig are unimportant, so both sows and boars are kept to maturity only when required for breeding. The age at death will therefore be interpreted differently from the other two species. There are three hypotheses which may explain the presence of high proportions in an assemblage of piglets dead before or at the time of weaning: that they were weaning casualties, that sucking pig was a luxury food, or they were surplus to the available resources of space and food for raising further. If they were weaning casualties, the remains would suggest that pigs were bred locally. Evidence for old pigs may have a similar interpretation, since these were breeding stock. Bacon and ham (most, but not all from pig meat) was eaten even by those who could afford little other meat, but other than an overwhelming bias in the remains towards the upper limb and leg bones, there is still

no means of distinguishing ham bones from pork in archaeological finds.

Age at death

The eruption and wear stage of each mandible and molar tooth which could be assigned to a position in the tooth row has been recorded using Grant (Table A5.38) and each has been assigned to one of seven stages of eruption and wear as defined by Maltby (1993) (Table 5.27). Where a mandible could belong to one of two stages, they were allotted to the earlier or late of the two *pro rata*. The ages suggested are those defined for domestic and wild pig by Bull & Payne (1986). The proportions of fused bones have been calculated from each group with over c. 20 pig bones, and the proportion from animals dead by one year, two years, and over two years is shown (Tables A5.39–A5.44). The fusion ages used are those for modern pigs (Habermehl 1975), so may underestimate the ages of the more slow-growing older type of pig.

The nine jaws and teeth from the Saxo-Norman deposits at Victoria Road and Henly's Garage are all from stages 5–7, that is from older immature or mature pigs and the fusion evidence (Table A5.39) shows that the proportion of unfused epiphyses from animals interpreted as dead by two years is lower at this time than in later periods. While the presence of old animals could indicate breeding at this time, there was no evidence for piglets.

From the 13th century onwards, the dentition

Table 5.27 Tooth eruption and wear in pig

Stage		S-N	13th–14th C E suburb	13th–14th C N suburb	L14th–15th C	16th C	17th C
1	DPM4 unworn			2	5	8	2
2	DPM4 in wear; M1 not in wear		1		1		
3	M1 in wear; M2 not in wear		9	2		2	3
4	M2 in wear; PM4 not in wear		1			3	
5	P4 in wear; M3 not in wear	2	4	1	6	2	
6	M3 early wear	6		1	2	5	
7	M1–2 heavy wear (Grant j–n); M3 in full wear	1					
Total		9	15	6	14	20	5

suggests an increasingly younger age at death of the pigs, whether or not the probable casualties in the late 14th-century deposits are included. Fusion evidence from these periods (Tables A5.40–A5.42) supports the dental evidence. The 16th-century groups have high proportions of jaws in the youngest age classes, and in two groups over 50 per cent of the bone which could be aged were from piglets. The five ageable jaws and teeth from the 17th-century soil deposit at Chester Road included two jaws of sucking pigs; the remainder were from older but still immature animals. As the material is biased in favour of larger animals and more complete bones, the proportion of very young pigs will be under, rather than over-estimated. The bones from the 16th- and 17th-century deposits (Tables A5.43–5.44) included the smallest proportion, less than 2 per cent, from animals alive beyond two years.

Size and sex ratio

As most bones were immature, few measurements of articulations were possible. One astragalus with a lateral length of 46.7mm was large enough to be from wild boar, but it was from a 16th-century deposit, by which time the wild boar was extinct in England, and so it is more likely to be from a large old domestic boar.

Discussion

As is the common pattern with pigs, most were slaughtered while still immature, the optimum age for slaughter for an animal raised for meat rather than any by-product. While the youngest were probably consumed as fresh pork rather than bacon, both immature and adult pigs were killed for bacon. The bones from these suburban deposits include few from adult boars.

If the piglet skeletons from the 13th- to 14th-century phases at Victoria Road represent casualties, this suggests that pigs were being raised in the northern suburb in the later Middle Ages. Documentary records make it clear that pigs were indeed raised in backyards in towns, as their presence scavenging in the streets was considered a nuisance requiring legislation to control. The First Book of Ordinances of Winchester (Victoria County History 1912 , 31) includes the regulation of 1558 that 'hogs and weanling pigs were not to be allowed in the streets'.

Domestic fowl

Bones of domestic fowl were present in all but one of the phases (Table 5.28). The only feature from which they are absent is pit F1022 at Victoria Road (Phase 743), in which most of the bones were from a horse skeleton. None of the tarsometatarsi or femurs has the characteristics of the pheasant; from this it has been inferred that all chicken-size galliform bones are in fact from domestic fowl.

The proportions in which domestic fowl bones are present in the other phase groups vary for several reasons, not by any means relating to the numbers of domestic fowls eaten. Many of the pits of the Saxo-Norman period and the 13th and 14th centuries in both the northern and eastern suburbs contained what appear to be complete skeletons of immature fowls. In these groups (Victoria Road, Phases 530, 532, 635, and 637; St John's Street, Phase 30) the bones were unbutchered, but were not necessarily recovered complete, as they suffered damage in the ground and during recovery. Bones from all parts of the carcass were found and smaller bones such as phalanges and fibulae ('other') bones were frequent (Table 5.29, where the number of skeletons is indicated in brackets). That from Phase 530 at Victoria Road was retrieved with exemplary care; as well as the 157 bones from hand recovery, 40 were recovered in sieves, mostly phalanges and ribs. In all groups disarticulated fowl bones were also found.

Relative numbers of fowl bones are high in some groups where all fowl bones are disarticulated and butchered: the largest samples are from Victoria Road, Phase 700 (n=57), Chester Road, Phase 53 (73) and St John's Street, Phase 49 (76). In these pits the more dense skeletal elements, the tibiotarsus, humerus, and ulna, are most common, having survived the

Table 5.28   Bird bones: domestic fowl, goose, and other birds: NISP and %

Date	Phase	Total	Domestic fowl	Goose	Other birds
		n	%	%	%
10th–11th	VR529	20	50.0	50.0	0.0
10th–11th	VR530	195	99.5	0.0	0.5
10th–11th	VR532	121	88.4	2.5	9.1
10th–11th	HG29	23	95.7	0.0	4.3
13th	SJS13	20	90.0	10.0	0.0
13th	SJS16	16	50.0	50.0	0.0
13th–14th	SJS29	3	66.7	33.3	0.0
13th–14th	CHR53	103	70.9	25.2	3.9
13th–14th	VR616	29	10.3	89.7	0.0
13th–14th	VR635	138	54.3	43.5	2.2
13th–14th	VR637	34	85.3	14.7	0.0
13th–14th	VR975	80	48.8	46.3	5.0
14th	SJS30	76	80.3	18.4	1.3
Late 14th	VR700	65	87.7	10.8	1.5
14th–15th	VR685	5	60.0	20.0	20.0
14th–15th	VR792	17	64.7	29.4	5.9
15th–16th	VR756	59	78.0	18.6	3.4
16th	SJS49	134	56.7	37.3	6.0
17th	CHR56	28	64.3	35.7	0.0
Total		**1166**			

processes of butchery, consumption, and the attentions of carnivores better than the more fragile bones of the skeleton. These groups better reflect typical consumption patterns of fowl and the proportions best reflect the importance in the diet of the suburban inhabitants of Winchester.

Proportions of fowl bones are low in the pits from 13th- and 14th-century contexts at Victoria Road which were repositories for industrial waste as well as food remains. They are also low in the 17th-century soil deposit at Chester Road (Phase 56), but for different reasons. The context of the finds suggests that the bones which found their way into the CHR soil deposit were predominantly those of the large domestic animals, disposed of at a distance from where they were consumed. It would be therefore be wrong to infer from this deposit that fewer chickens were eaten in the 17th century. The remains can assist in answering the question of whether fowl were raised in the town, and of whether their importance for egg production was higher than that for meat. The birds which were served at table (Woolgar 1995) or offered for sale were mainly pullets and capons. Pullets today are hens in their first laying season, below about nine months, and the term capon is used strictly to refer to cocks castrated for fattening. In the past these terms may have been used more loosely, the first for birds killed for the pot at the age at which they are first worth eating, and the second for any older

bird, cock or hen, fattened for consumption. As well as the context of the finds, the proportions of adult and immature birds and the incidence of spurred tarsometatarsi can help to answer these questions. Size change over time is also considered.

Age

The adult and immature skeletal elements are shown separately. Immaturity can be readily recognised in the tibiotarsus and tarsometatarsus, and in other bones by the porous quality of the bone and unformed articulations. In most contexts the proportion of immature bones is under about 25 per cent. Numbers of immature bones exceed those of mature birds only in Phases 635, 637, and 700 at Victoria Road, but in these phases, part skeletons of immature birds were found, so may not reflect the proportions of young and old birds eaten. In general, there was more consumption of older rather than younger fowl in the medieval suburbs.

Size and sex

The most useful guide to the proportions of cocks and hens among the adult birds is the presence of a spur or spur scar on the tarsometatarsus of the male bird. This is not a universal distinction, as any poultry keeper will

Table 5.29   Domestic fowl: anatomical distribution (adult and immature are also shown)

Saxo-Norman

Phase	VR529	VR530 (3)		VR532 (?5)		HG29		Total	Total
Age	AD	AD	IMM	AD	IMM	AD	IMM	AD	IMM
skull		3		6					
coracoid		6		8	1	2			
furcula		6		4	1				
scapula		6		6		1			
sternum	1	3		4		1			
humerus	2	6	1	7	3				
radius		6		8	1	1			
ulna		7		9		1			
carpomc		6		2	1				
synsacrum	1	3		6		2			
femur	2	8		8	1	5	1		
tibiotarsus	3	8		8	3	5			
tarsomt	1	5		6	2	1			
other		83		10	1				
Total	10	156	1	92	14	19	1	277	16
TMTs with spur	0	0		3		0			
% with spur	0	0		50		0		% IMM	5.5

13th–14th century: northern suburb

Phase	VR616	VR635		VR637		VR783	VR975		Total	Total
Age	ALL	AD	IMM	AD (2)	IMM (2)	ALL	AD	IMM	AD	IMM
skull							1			
coracoid			5	2	3		4	1		
furcula					1					
scapula			4		2					
sternum			3		2		3			
humerus		1	10		3		10	1		
radius			5		1		4			
ulna		1	6	1	5	1	1	1		
carpomc			1				2			
synsacrum		4	4		1		1			
femur	1	1	8		3	1	3			
tibiotarsus	1	1	6	1	2	1	2			
tarsomt	1	1	11		2	3	3	1		
other		1	2				1			
Total	3	10	65	4	25	6	35	4	58	94
TMTs with spur	0	1				1	0			
% with spur	0	100				33	0		% IMM	61.8

Table 5.29 (*cont.*) Domestic fowl: anatomical distribution (adult and immature are also shown)

13th–14th century: eastern suburb and city defences

Phase	SJS29	HG20	CHR53		SJS30 (2)		SJS13	SJS16	Total	Total
Age	AD	ALL	AD	IMM	AD	IMM	AD	AD	AD	IMM
skull					1		0			
coracoid			4		4	3	2	1		
furcula			1		1	1	1			
scapula			3		4		3			
sternum			1		2		0			
humerus			10	3	3	4	3	1		
radius			2		2			1		
ulna		1	12	2	5	4	2			
carpomc			1		2					
synsacrum			2		3		1	1		
femur			9	1	2	2	2	1		
tibiotarsus		1	11	6	6	4	3	1		
tarsomt	1		3	2	4	4		1		
other							1	1		
Total	**1**	**2**	**59**	**14**	**39**	**22**	**18**	**8**	**127**	**36**
TMTs with spur	0		2		2			0		
% with spur	0		67		50				% IMM	22.1

Late 14th–17th century

Phase	VR700		VR685	VR792		VR756		SJS49		CHR56		Total	Total
Age	AD	IMM	AD	AD	IMM	AD	IMM	AD	IMM	AD	IMM	AD	IMM
skull	2							2					
coracoid	1	3		1		4		4		1			
furcula								2		1			
scapula	2	2				3	2	5		1			
sternum	2	2				1		10					
humerus	4	5		1	1	4	1	8					
radius		1				4	1	2					
ulna	3	4				7	1	6		1			
carpomc		1								1			
synsacrum		4				4		6	1	1			
femur	4			1	1	5	2	6		3	3		
tibiotarsus	6	6		3		2	3	13	2	3			
tarsomt	4	1	3	2	1	2		7		3			
other								2					
Total	**28**	**29**	**3**	**8**	**3**	**36**	**10**	**73**	**3**	**15**	**3**	**163**	**48**
TMTs with spur	1		1	1		1		3		0			
% with spur	25		33	50		50		43		0		% IMM	22.7

Note: Number of skeletons in brackets ( )

Key: AD adult; IMM immature; CARPOMC carpometacarpus; TARSOMT, TMT tarsometarsus hasten to point out that a proportion of females also have spurs, but has been used here as an approximate guide. By this criterion hens exceed cocks in twelve of the eighteen groups, and they are equal in number in a further four. As absolute numbers in individual groups are low, and as many of the features contain atypical assemblages, it is difficult to draw general conclusions, but the proportion of cocks among the adult birds therefore appears to be fewer than 30 per cent.

Size may also show a useful distinction between the sexes, though the presence of different breeds or types can mask this distinction. The tarsometatarsus falls into two distinct size classes (Fig 5.41, *see* colour section), even when all periods are considered together. Each specimen in the group of larger bones has a spur, but two spurred bones, from 14th- to 15th-century contexts, fall into the group of smaller bones. These may be hens with spurs or cocks of a smaller breed. Where samples from a single time period are large enough, it is also clear that the humerus (Fig 5.42, *see* colour section) and the femur (Fig 5.43, *see* colour section) also show two size groups, but this is masked when all are considered together by the generally larger size of the 16th- to 17th-century specimens. Where the specimens suggest two groups, they suggest that approximately 20–30 per cent are males in each period, which fits the composition of a domestic or barnyard flock.

None of the elements considered shows an absolute increase in size between the 10th and 14th century (Tables A5.45–A5.49), and indeed the mean length of the tarsometatarsus shows a decrease between the 10th and the 14th centuries, but from the 16th century onwards the measurements of the humerus and femur all fall into the upper part of the size range, showing that fowls increased in size from that time.

Discussion

The small proportion of immature birds in typical contexts suggests that the proportion of pullets or young fowl of either sex consumed was low in all periods; rather, most birds consumed were adult. Elsewhere, finds from towns have suggested that domestic fowl were kept to a greater age in the medieval period than they were in Roman times (Maltby 1993). The conclusion must be that most of the fowls were adult hens, kept primarily for their eggs, and slaughtered for the pot (whether or not after a period of deliberate fattening) as their capabilities for laying were superseded by younger and more prolific birds. The sex ratio confirms this. The immature fowls found in the pits and wells at Victoria Road are best interpreted as casualties, probably of disease, and, following the argument proposed for the pigs, the presence of these skeletons suggests that fowls were reared in the properties at Victoria Road in the northern suburb throughout the Middle Ages. Some size increase is seen, possibly at an earlier date than the increase in the other domestic animals.

Goose

Though fewer than domestic fowls in all phases but one, goose bones are remarkably common in medieval Winchester, being absent only from three groups, two Saxo-Norman (Table 5.28) and one 13th- to 14th-century (Victoria Road, Phase 743, an industrial deposit which also lacked other bird bones). They are most numerous in Phase 635 at Victoria Road, where specialised exploitation is likely, and they are relatively more common than domestic fowl only in the related group from Phase 616. The proportion relative to fowl bones does not show a consistent increase or decrease during the Middle Ages (Fig 5.44).

It seems likely that most if not all of the geese are the domestic form of *Anser anser*. The presence of domestic geese was commonly described in the records of the city. Domestic geese mostly exceed wild geese in size, but since males and females are dimorphic, and sizes overlap with wild geese, (Bacher 1967), absolute distinctions are difficult. The thickness of the tarsometatarsus shaft of the King's Lynn geese suggested that most of these were domestic. The small sample from Winchester which could be measured (Table A5.50) shows little variation in shaft thickness. Most lengths (GL) of the main wing and leg bones are within the range for domestic geese, but the mean length of the carpometacarpi in all periods is smaller than that in the modern domestic geese studied by Bacher (Table 5.30). It is implausible that most of the remains are from other than domestic geese, and an alternative explanation for the notably short examples of this bone are that there was selection for a bird with short wings. If the measurements of modern geese are appropriate for comparison with those from Winchester in the 13th and 14th centuries it appears that the sample may include some white-fronted geese, the smallest of the grey geese. White-fronted geese used to winter on the stubble of Hampshire until the 19th century (Victoria County History V, 1912).

Goose bones were mostly found with other food remains, disarticulated, with cuts and chop marks, and quite frequently with punctures from carnivore gnawing. The proportion with cut marks is high. Domestic or wild, they ended up in the pot. According to the King's *Art of Cookery* of the 16th century, geese for the table were a seasonal food, eaten either as 'green goose' – killed in May after feeding on fresh grass, or 'stubble-goose', eaten at Michaelmas after feeding on stubble:

> So stubble-geese at Michaelmas are seen
> Upon the spit; next May produces green

> (Harting 1864)

The immature bones from SJS49 are the only ones to which a season of death can be assigned. They are birds in their first summer or autumn. The fully mature bones cannot be assigned to a season of slaughter.

The products which geese can provide are meat, eggs, and feathers. The relative importance of these products can be inferred from the age at death, and the treatment of the skeleton.

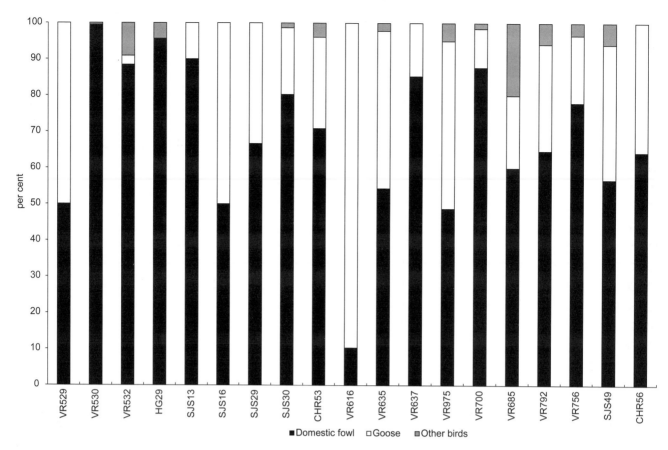

Figure 5.44   Relative numbers of domestic fowl, goose, and other birds

**Table 5.30   Goose: greatest length (GL) of carpometacarpus:
medieval Winchester compared with recent goose measurements quoted by Bacher (1967, 67–92)**

	Min	Max	x	n
Winchester				
10th–11th	83.2	98	89.5	4
13th–14th	76.5	94.6	87.7	27
15th	85.2			1
16th–17th	80	95.9	87.3	5
Bacher				
Domestic goose M+F	87.7	103.9	95.9	?
Anser anser wild M	90.8	103.3	95.1	9
Anser anser wild F	86.7	95.9	90.9	9
Anser fabalis M	88.8	101.5	96.4	13
Anser fabalis F	86.7	95.2	89.3	7
Anser brachyrhynchus M	82.2	91.2	88.2	9
Anser brachyrhynchus F	84	91.2		5
Anser albifrons M	80.4	90.1	85.9	9
Anser albifrons F	80.3	84	81	7

Key: min minimum; max maximum; x mean; n number; ? not known

Table 5.31 Anatomical distribution in goose

Phase	SC	COR	HUM	RAD	ULN	CMC	AP	SYN	FEM	TIB	TMT	PP	FUR	MA	ST	Total
VR529		1	1			4	1		1		1	1				10
VR532		1				1	1									3
SJS13			1												1	2
SJS16		1	1	2	1	1				1	1					8
VR616	1					13	11				1					26
VR635	2	2	1	4	5	11	13	1	2	2	4	4	2	3	2	58
VR637	1					1	1		1	1						5
VR783						2										2
VR975	2	2	1	15		4	2	1	1	4	1	1	2			36
SJS29														1		1
CHR53			2		1	4	1		3	5		2		2		20
SJS30		1	3		3	1			2	1				1	1	13
VR700	1					1					2		1	1	1	7
VR685						1										1
VR792			1			3									1	5
VR756		1	2		1	1		2			2			1	1	11
SJS49	5	1	1	1	3	5	3	2	1	6	6		1	1	3	39
CHR56		1	1		1	2				2	2					9
Total	**12**	**11**	**14**	**23**	**15**	**55**	**33**	**6**	**11**	**22**	**20**	**8**	**6**	**10**	**10**	**256**

Key: SC scapula; COR coracoid; HU humerus; RAD radius; ULN ulna; CMC carpometacarpus; AP wing phalanx; SYN synsacrum; FEM femur; TIB tibiotarsus; TMT tarsometatarsus; PP foot phalanx; MA mandible; ST sternum. Also 1 fibula and 1 maxilla in VR635

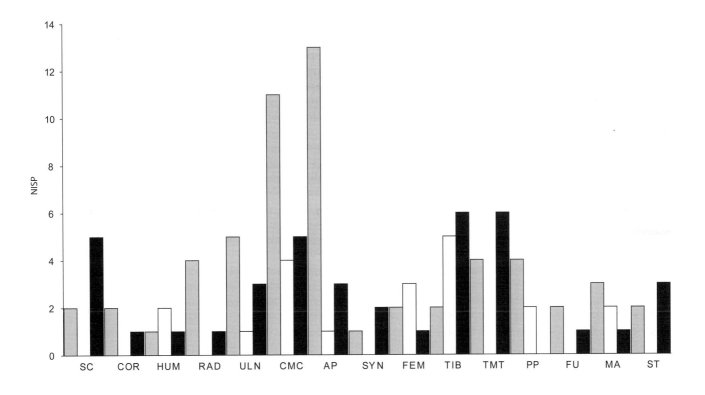

□Victoria Road 635 □Chester Road 53 ■St John's Street 49

Figure 5.45 Anatomical elements of goose: Victoria Road, Phase 635; St John's Street, Phase 49; and Chester Road, Phase 53 (key as Fig 5.4)

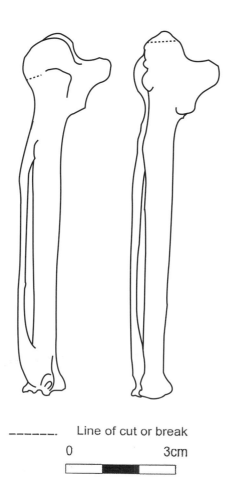

- - - - - - -.   Line of cut or break

0   3cm

Figure 5.46   Goose carpometacarpus from Victoria Road, Phase 616, showing typical cut marks (dotted lines) (Drawing by M Barden and P Copeland)

Bones of immature goose are absent from all contexts except the 16th-century pits in the eastern suburb (St John's Street), where 24 per cent of the goose bones are immature. If the hypothesis is accepted that immature birds are selected when meat is the most important end product, then birds other than those from St John's Street appear to have been reared predominantly for other purposes. Unlike domestic fowl, we should not expect much evidence of medullary bone, as geese remain in lay for a shorter time than fowls, and in fact, no medullary bone was seen. The shorter laying season means that geese are rarely kept principally for eggs.

Geese moult naturally twice a year, and the feathers, both the downy feathers of the body and the longer quills on the wing, have a long history of use. They can be plucked repeatedly, so, rather like sheep, there is every advantage in keeping geese into maturity. Throughout the Middle Ages goose quills were the most common writing implement. Those who dealt in feather or 'plumes' were known as 'plumers', one of the 21 trades listed carried out in Winchester in 1437 (Victoria County History 1912, 41).

The anatomical distribution (Table 5.31) shows that two different types of assemblages of goose bones were found in the Winchester deposits. These are exemplified by Phase 635 at Victoria Road, where carpometacarpi and wing digits are more numerous than other elements, and St John's Street, Phase 49 and Chester Road, Phase 53, where distribution is more even, and the tibiotarsus and tarsometatarsus are more common than the carpometacarpus (Fig 5.45).

In the deposits from the eastern suburb sites, the even pattern of survival of skeletal elements suggests that these are food remains, while those from the northern suburb, Victoria Road, Phases 635 and 616, and possibly also Phase 792, where three of the five goose bones are carpometacarpi, include restricted range of elements. These may be collections of bones discarded after having been disarticulated from birds to be served at the table, or they may have been deliberately collected. A high proportion of the carpometacarpi have cut marks, either on the pollical facet or on the nose where the extensor ligament attaches. Some were seen on the carpal trochleas where the external ligament from the distal ulna attaches. Examples are shown in Figure 5.46. These were made when the bones were disarticulated from the distal radius and ulna, or possibly when removing feathers. Ulnas and a radius from VR 792, c.860 are damaged where they have been snapped from the carpometacarpus (Fig 5.47).

The reason why the wing bones were collected is clear if we consider the plumage of geese. The carpometacarpus and wing digits are the bones to which the primary wing feathers attach (Fig 5.48), the largest feathers on the wing and those used for quills. A pen was also found in pit F117 (Phase 792) at VR (Rees *et al* 2008, 285–6, catalogue no 1988).

The presence of the skeletons of immature animals has been taken to indicate that they were raised in the locality. The immature bones from St John's Street are from at least two birds, not necessarily casualties. This locality is probably the only one with a possible claim to rearing geese. The absence elsewhere of bones of immature birds points to the fact that geese were mainly raised outside the city.

There are records of varying status confirming that flocks of geese were raised in the Wessex hinterland. One of the writers who referred to the local flocks of geese was Shakespeare:

> Goose, if I had you upon Sarum plain,
> I'd drive you cackling home to Camelot
>
> *King Lear* (Act II, Sc II)

A popular history of King Arthur, in print in the 16th century when Shakespeare was writing, descibes Winchester as the site of Camelot (Harting 1864, 199). Shakespeare in his metaphor drew on the common knowledge that in the 16th-century geese were raised on Salisbury plain, and driven from there to the markets at Winchester and elsewhere for sale.

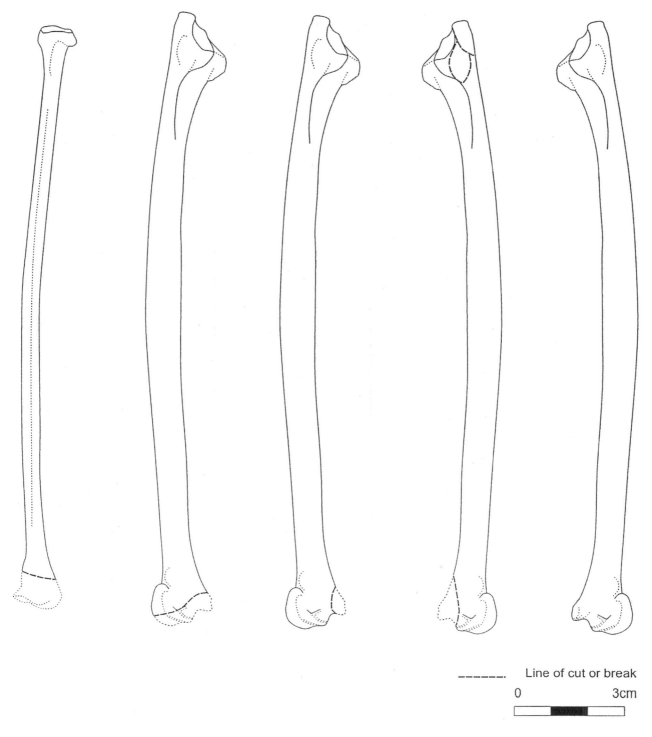

Line of cut or break

0   3cm

Figure 5.47 Goose radius and ulnas, with broken distal articulation where snapped apart from carpometacarpus, from Victoria Road, Phase 792, c.860 (Drawing by P Copeland)

Discussion

Geese were raised in the hinterland of Winchester, including Salisbury Plain, to provide feathers (and probably eggs) while still alive, and feathers and meat after death. Some may also have been raised in the city and suburbs, but it is only in the 16th century that there is possible evidence for this. It seems very likely that one of the occupations carried out at the Victoria Road properties in the 13th and 14th centuries was to collect feathers from goose wings for the provision of quills.

Duck

The only phase in which duck bones, including both wild and domestic, are frequent is in the Saxo-Norman period at Victoria Road. Otherwise ducks are present in small numbers in each period. Most are from mallard, but other species are also present.

The mallard bones were identified by comparison with modern wild specimens. Where they were within the size ranges for wild mallard quoted by Woelfle (1967) they have been listed as wild or domestic;

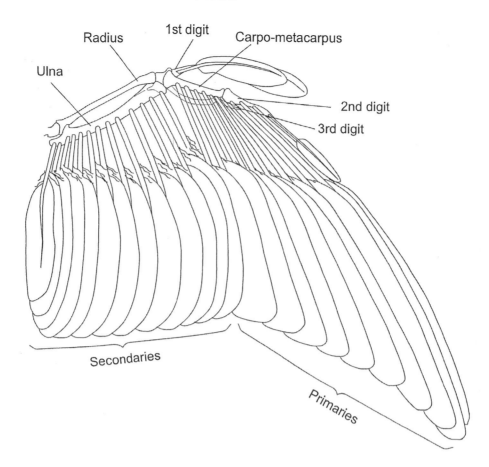

Figure 5.48 *Wing of bird, showing radius, ulna, and carpometacarpus, the bones to which the quill feathers (primaries) attach (Drawing by P Copeland)*

some outside the range, which compare in size with 19th-century domestic ducks in the collections of the Natural History Museum were listed as probably domestic. A scapula, humerus, and coracoid – perhaps from the same bird, from Saxo-Norman Victoria Road; a skull and carpometacarpus from Phase 635; and a femur from Phase 792 fulfil these criteria. No elements from immature birds were found.

Smaller duck species were also identified. Teal (*Anas crecca*), the smallest of the dabbling ducks, was found in deposits in the medieval eastern suburb (Chester Road Phase 53), and in the late medieval period in the same suburb, at St John's Street. Some bones have traces of butchery. Measurements are in Table A5.51.

Compared with geese, it appears that ducks were not kept in large numbers, but the few finds of duck which from size are probably domestic, do suggest they may have been kept in small numbers. If the features excavated at Victoria Road are associated with a farming settlement outside the town, as is suggested by other archaeological evidence, as well as some of the bone finds, the duck bones may be from ducks raised there. Until the 19th century, teal and other wild duck were common 'in the river valleys' (Victoria County History, Vol 1, 1912, 209). Wild ducks were caught in nets or by falcons, birds reserved for the nobility. There is a very fine carving on a miseri-cord in Winchester College chapel with a carving of

a gyrfalcon carrying a mallard in its beak (see frontis-piece). It is not surprising therefore that the mallards rarely found a place in the diet of those living in the northern and eastern suburbs.

Fish

Fish played an important part in the diet of both rich and poor in the Middle Ages. The Benedictine regulation that meat could be consumed only on four days of the week and feast days was obeyed by religious and laity alike. These rules could scarcely have been adhered to without the flourishing trade in herring and stockfish which allowed fish to be consumed by communities living at a distance from the coast. The herring fishery of the North Sea and the Baltic was already being carried out in the mid-1st millennium AD (Postan 1975, 209) with the product, dried or pickled, traded all over Europe. The deep sea fisheries for cod and related species developed soon after. Fresh fish was eaten in towns and villages near the coast, and Winchester was accessible by boat up the Itchen and was within one day's journey by land from the port at Southamp-ton, so the inhabitants also had the opportunity to obtain fresh fish. One species only, the eel, among those for which there is evidence in these samples,

Table 5.32 Fish: summary of species by phase (see phase tables for distinction between bones recovered from sieved samples and by hand)

	VR 529	VR 530	VR 532	HG 29	SJS 13	SJS 16	CHR 53	VR 616	VR 635	VR 637	VR 743	VR 783	VR 975	VR 700	VR 792	VR 756	VR 763	SJS 49	CHR 56	Total
skate/ray		1						1	1								7			10
Lamniform spp.		6	1											1				1		9
herring *Clupea harengus*	9	15	7	46					31	27		2		18	2		2			159
eel *Anguilla anguilla*	1	29	15						2	17		1		3						68
conger eel *Conger conger*	2		5	2	1	3	10		11	2	1		5	3		8	7	2	6	68
garfish *Belone belone*				2																2
cod *Gadus morhua*			6	1			1								2		2	3		15
haddock *Melanogrammus aeglefinus*									4				5	1	1					11
pollack *Pollachius pollachius*									1											1
saithe *Pollachius virens*		1								2										3
whiting *Merlangius merlangius*										3										3
ling *Molva molva*					2	1	1		2					1		2	2	3		14
cod family Gadidae			15				1		1	10				2				5		34
stickleback *Gasterosteus aculeatus*														1						1
plaice *Pleuronectes platessa*											1									1
flounder *Platichthys flesus*																	1			1
turbot *Scophthalmus maximus*			14																	14
brill *Scophthalmus rhombus*			2																	2
flatfish NFI Pleuronectidae	2		3						5	1	4									15
mackerel *Scomber scomber*			17						1	6	22									46
unidentified	21	5	109	18			1	3	73	59			10	23	13	12	10	9	1	367
Total	**35**	**57**	**194**	**69**	**3**	**4**	**14**	**4**	**132**	**127**	**28**	**3**	**20**	**53**	**18**	**22**	**31**	**23**	**7**	**844**

could have been caught in the Itchen or smaller rivers in the vicinity of the city.

Fish bones were found in most of the groups; where these were not sieved the species were almost exclusively the larger ones. Bones of smaller fish such as herring and eel were found in deposits with good preservation which were sieved, for instance Phases 635 and 637 at Victoria Road (Tables 5.11, 5.12). Most of these were contexts with waterlogged or strongly organic sediments, typically wells or cess pits. The summary table (Table 5.32) shows the scientific name, the number of identified elements of each species, and the tables for the separate phase groups distinguishes those recovered in the sieves from those recovered by hand. Details of elements identified and relative size are in the archives.

Some of the fish bones are from cess pits, and some of the eel, and a few of herring, have the damage characteristic of fish bones which have passed through the human gut (Wheeler & Jones 1989). The records from when these samples were excavated in the 1970s do not allow this question to be examined more rigorously. If this is indeed the origin of the bones from the smaller species, numerical comparisons with the larger species have little meaning. Any hypotheses as to relative quantities in the discussions which follow therefore take into account absolute numbers, the numbers of samples in which a species is present, and conditions of preservation.

The most common species is the herring, found in all phases from which samples were taken for sieving, though not recovered from other contexts. It is the most common species in the samples from the 13th century onwards. Among the fish bones recovered from the samples from the Victoria Road (13th to 14th centuries), herring are more numerous than all other species put together. If indeed it was herring which 'supplied most of the normal fish requirements of western Europe' (Bridbury 1955, xvi), this assemblage must best reflect the importance of this species in the diet of medieval England. Fewer bones were recovered in contexts from the 16th century onwards, but this was at least in part a consequence of the fact that the pit groups examined were from larger pits which lacked the layers of organic preservation of many of those from the northern suburb in earlier centuries. Herring were a more important part of the diet of the poor than the rich. They were mainly caught in the North Sea and the Baltic, and were sold both fresh and preserved (red), and were widely traded.

The second most common species, and the second of the smaller species found in any number, is the freshwater eel. It is more common than herring in the samples from the 10th century, but thereafter was only found in any number in one of the pits analysed in the northern suburb (Victoria Road Phase 637) in the 13th to 14th centuries. Eels can be transported fresh more readily than other fishes, but trade in eels was mainly in preserved fish (Cutting 1953). The relative importance followed by a decline broadly reflects the importance of the eel in the late Saxon and early Norman period – eel fisheries are an important source

of income in Domesday – and its relative decline as the sea fisheries developed throughout the Middle Ages.

As its bones were often recovered by hand as well as in the sieves, the species found in the greatest number of groups, fifteen out of nineteen, was conger eel, of which many bones identified were from fish of a metre or more in length. Unlike the large cod family species, the conger eel is caught close to the shore, and the relative numbers in sites on or near the south coast suggest that it was abundant in the Channel and round the south-west coast. While conger could have been imported fresh to Winchester up the Itchen if caught in the Solent or the Channel, it was also usual for these to be preserved by salting or salting and drying. Mackerel were numerous in two deposits, one from the 10th to 11th centuries and one from the 13th to 14th centuries, and present in two others. These too are a species of the fisheries of the south-west.

Bones identified as from cod were found in six groups from all periods, and many of those which were not distinguished between cod and the skeletally similar saithe were probably also from this species. Most from Winchester were from big fish, and these, with saithe and ling, present from the 13th century onwards, probably originate with the commercial offshore fisheries of the northern North Sea and the Atlantic. They were traded under a variety of names in many dried and preserved forms. The smaller fish of the cod family, the whiting and pollack, are a species caught on shore, and are as likely to be from the channel fisheries.

Flatfish were not common in any deposit, but were most numerous in Phase 532 at Victoria Road. These were usually, but not invariably, sold and consumed fresh. This group included fourteen elements of turbot, one of the largest of the flatfish, which was a fish restricted to the more important members of the community and eaten on special occasions (Harvey 1993). This is the only group for which the fish remains suggest high status. Otherwise, flatfish were found in five other groups.

Discussion

The relatively high numbers of conger eel among the larger fish strongly suggest that Winchester's fish supplies were to a considerable degree supplied from the Solent and the Channel, but also included preserved fish traded from farther afield. While it is not possible to compare relative quantities of larger and smaller species, the relatively fewer herring than eel at the beginning of our period, and more frequent finds in the 13th- to 14th-century deposits, fit the documented evidence for the fish trade in the Middle Ages.

There is a single deposit in which the fish remains suggest wealth or status, but it is less easy to use the fish evidence to confirm the low status suggested in most of the suburban groups studied, as even the cheap and lowly herring was eaten by rich and poor alike.

Wild mammals

Relative numbers of wild mammals are few in every phase (finds are summarised in Table 5.33). The tables include the antler fragments which were not removed for study with the small finds.

Red deer (*Cervus elaphus*), other than one antler fragment from Victoria Road, Phase 637, was identified only from the eastern suburb, where it was found in 13th- to 14th-century and 17th-century deposits. Roe deer (*Capreolus capreolus*) finds are almost as sparse: there are some from the eastern suburb in the same phases as the red deer, and four from the medieval deposits at Victoria Road. A pair of antlers from VR (Phase 616) were from an old male deer; they had an irregular pedicel and no tines. These were chopped from the skull but showed no other signs of modification. Fallow deer (*Dama dama*) was absent from the Saxo-Norman deposits but rather more common thereafter: bones were present in small numbers in eight phases both at Victoria Road and in the eastern suburb. Even in the 16th century, butchery of the large game was carried out using knives as well as the heavier chopping implements, as the humerus from SJS 49 illustrates (Fig 5.49).

Hare bones were found in ten of the 22 groups studied, but were only common in Phase 635 at Victoria Road. All bones identified are compatible with the common hare (*Lepus europaeus*). In VR Phase 635 altogether 113 bones were recovered from an MNI of five hares. The best examples of butchery are the limb bones from St John's Street, Phase 30. More than half of the tibias and radii have been chopped or snapped midshaft. The most likely reason for snapping these distal limb bones is to prepare the carcass for cooking and serving, but breaking open these bones also serves

Figure 5.49 Fallow deer humerus from St John's Street, Phase 49, butchered using both cut marks and chops (Photograph by J Crook)

the purpose of exposing the marrow. Some hare bones, such as the femur from SJS 49, also have knife cuts made in filleting the meat.

The bones of rabbit (*Oryctolagus cuniculus*) listed are all from deeply cut features where the possibility

Table 5.33 Red deer, roe deer, fallow deer, hare, and rabbit: NISP

Date	Phase	Red deer	Roe deer	Fallow deer	Hare	Rabbit	Total
10th–11th	VR532				5		**5**
13th–14th	CHR53	6	2	14	7	4	**33**
13th–14th	VR616		2				**2**
13th–14th	VR635			8	113		**121**
13th–14th	VR637	1*					**1**
13th–14th	VR975				1	2	**3**
14th	SJS30			1	11	2	**14**
late 14th	VR700		4*	9	4	3	**20**
14th–15th	VR685				1		**1**
14th–15th	VR792				2		**2**
15th–16th	VR756			1		7	**8**
16th	VR763			7		4	**11**
16th	SJS49			9	3	71	**83**
17th	CHR56	1	2	6	5	5	**19**
Total		**8**	**10**	**55**	**152**	**98**	**323**

* includes antler fragment

Table 5.34 Rabbit: anatomical distribution and butchery: 16th century: eastern suburb (St John's Street, Phase 49)

	NISP	MNE L	MNE R	Mid	Chopped midshaft	Knife cuts
cranium	1			1		
mandible	12	6	5			
scapula	5	3	3			
humerus	10	3	6			
radius	1	1			1	
ulna	5	3	2		2	
pelvis	10	3	7			2
femur	12	7	5		1	1
tibia	10	3	6		7	
metapodials	2	1	1			
sacrum	1			1		
ribs	2			1		
Total	**71**	**7**	**7**		**11**	**3**

Key: Mid midline

of recent burrowing can be ruled out. Like the fallow deer, there is little evidence for the introduction of the rabbit until the 12th century. No bones were found in the Saxo-Norman deposits at Winchester, but some were recovered in small numbers from four of the 13th- to 14th-century deposits, and some were found in all the post-medieval groups. The largest number (71) was recovered from the 16th-century features at St John's Street (SJS 49). These are from an minimum of seven animals (Table 5.34). The butchery on these was similar to that seen on the hares, with the majority of the lower limb bones chopped or snapped midshaft, and cut marks on some bones. Of the ten tibias, eight have been chopped or broken midshaft or across the shaft above the distal epiphysis. The radii and ulnas were also apparently chopped or snapped immediately above the distal end; of the six recovered, three have apparent chop marks, and the same part of the bone survives of the other three, though no chops were noted.

During the Middle Ages, the capture of all three deer species, and of the hare, the animals of the chase, was governed by the hunting laws, which had been strengthened and codified by the Norman kings, and enforced throughout the period. There was a degree of control over the fallow deer, which were kept in parks, and more over rabbits, which were confined to warrens, but they were regarded as game. The consumption of these animals was therefore mainly confined to households of high status, and indeed abundant finds have been made at some rich sites (Sadler 1990; Serjeantson 1991). The lack of finds from the Winchester sites serves to confirm the identification of these areas as of low status, as has been argued above for many of the individual groups. By the early 16th century at Westminster Abbey 'cony' made up as much as 2 per cent by weight of meat served per annum (Harvey 1993, 53), and the rabbit finds here reflect what appears to be a genuine trend towards more widespread availabil-

ity of this species for consumption in the late Middle Ages.

Cat

Cat bones were uncommon in late Saxon deposits, as noted in Chapter 4, but in the later Middle Ages they were so common – over 1000 were recovered – that it is apparent that Winchester had a large cat population. Bones were found in fifteen out of the twenty groups studied (Table 5.35), and complete or part skeletons were found in at least nine. These provide illuminating evidence concerning the increase in the numbers of cats kept and the treatment of the cats before and after death.

In the Saxo-Norman period, at least seven part skeletons were found, two from pits near the Henly's Garage on the southern city defences and the other five from the Victoria Road in the northern suburb (Fig 5.50). In the 13th and 14th centuries, part skeletons were found in groups studied from the eastern suburb and two from Victoria Road. A 14th- to 15th-century pit (Phase 792) there contained twelve skulls and at least 24 mandibles, but more than 30 left tibias and 28 right-hand bones show that the total was originally many more. In the 16th- and 17th-century deposits, eight disarticulated bones were found but no skeletons. Cat skeletons as well as disarticulated bones were also found in the medieval deposits in the western suburb, as discussed in Chapter 3 above. The proportion of skeletons to disarticulated bones is higher than for instance at Lincoln (O'Connor 1982) or Schleswig Schild, in north Germany (Spahn 1986), but this may be because there was a greater degree of selection of the features studied from Winchester.

The fusion of the main limb bones has been used as a guide to the age at which the cats died. A very high proportion in both the Saxo-Norman period and the

Table 5.35 Cats: skeletons and part skeletons (MN SKELS) and disarticulated bones (N DISART)

Date	Phase	CAT n	CAT %	MN SKELS	N DISART
10th–11th	VR529	112	15.7	2	
10th–11th	VR530	18	0.8	1	3
10th–11th	VR532	152	10.7	4	2
10th–11th	HG29	40	3.8	2	2
13th	SJS16	2	0.5		2
13th–14th	VR637	20	3.7	1	2
13th–14th	VR975	2	0.2		2
13th–14th	SJS29	1	0.8		1
13th–14th	CHR53	16	0.7	2	10
14th	SJS30	237	21.9	5	?
late 14th	VR700	14	1.6	1	3
14th–15th	VR792	451	40.0	33	
15th–16th	VR756	1	0.1		1
16th	VR763	4	0.3		4
16th	SJS49	0	0.0		
17th	CHR56	3	0.2		3

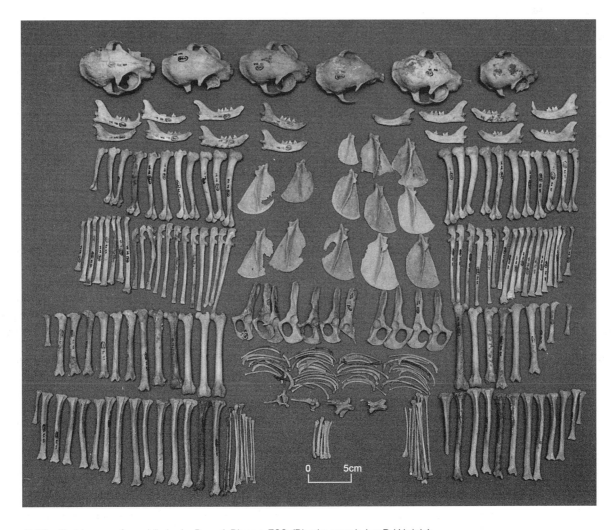

Figure 5.50   Cat bones from Victoria Road, Phase 792 (Photograph by D Webb)

**Table 5.36   Cats: age at death. Saxo-Norman (above);
13th–14th century (below) (approximate fusing age in months (MO) shown)**

	FUSED	UF	FG	F	
	BY (MO)	%	%	%	n
Saxo-Norman					
acetabulum	8.5	17	0	83.3	6
p radius	8.5	18	0	81.8	11
glenoid	8.5	10	0	90.0	10
d humerus	8.5	25	0	75.0	12
d radius	11.5	20	0	80.0	10
d tibia	11.5	73	0	27.3	11
p humerus	11.5	73	0	27.3	11
d ulna	11.5	75	0	25.0	8
p tibia	11.5	73	0	27.3	11
p femur	11.5	80	0	20.0	10
d femur	11.5	80	0	20.0	10
13th–14th century					
acetabulum	8.5	0	0	100.0	40
p radius	8.5	0	0	100.0	50
glenoid	8.5	10	0	89.7	39
d humerus	8.5	11	1.8	87.7	57
d radius	11.5	52	0	48.0	50
d tibia	11.5	53	1.4	45.9	74
p humerus	11.5	56	3.5	40.4	57
d ulna	11.5	57	0	43.1	58
p tibia	11.5	59	2.7	38.4	73
p femur	11.5	61	0	39.4	66
d femur	11.5	61	0	38.8	67

KEY: UF unfused, FG fusing, F fused, MO months, p proximal, d distal

later Middle Ages were dead before the age of eleven–twelve months (Table 5.36). In the tables the proportion of bones unfused, fusing, and fused is shown, in order of fusion (Habermehl 1975). The numbers of bones for the Saxo-Norman period is between six and twelve, and includes the skeletons and the disarticulated bones. Up to 20 per cent are from kittens, and most are from young cats under about eleven months of age. The proportion of skeletally adult cats is only between 30 per cent and 20 per cent.

The samples are larger for the 13th to 15th centuries, with between 39 and 74 examples of each skeletal element. Only 10 per cent were kittens (represented by unfused glenoid and distal humerus). The percentage of unfused late fusing bones ranges from 39 per cent to 48 per cent, suggesting that more than half were under one year at death (Fig 5.51, *see* colour section). The majority of cats from Schleswig Schild were below one year of age, and at least half from Lincoln (O'Connor 1982, 38) were dead by eighteen months.

Cut marks were seen on some of the skulls and mandibles, and also on one or two metapodials and limb bones. Those on the skull are on the parietal or the frontal (see Fig 5.52) or both and those on the mandible are in the region of the mental foramen or below P1 (see Fig 5.53). The cuts are fine and some were only visible under a hand lens. The highest proportion with cuts was in the 16 bones from Chester Road, Phase 53, which includes five with cuts: the skull, two of the three mandibles, a metacarpal, and an ulna. The proportion on which cuts were seen is lower in the large group from Victoria Road: one skull only and three mandibles have cuts.

Discussion

It is pertinent to the question of when cats became common as pets in England to note the rarity of finds from the 9th- to 10th-century deposits discussed in Chapter 4, and their abundance from the Saxo-Norman period onwards. This points to cats being fully estab-

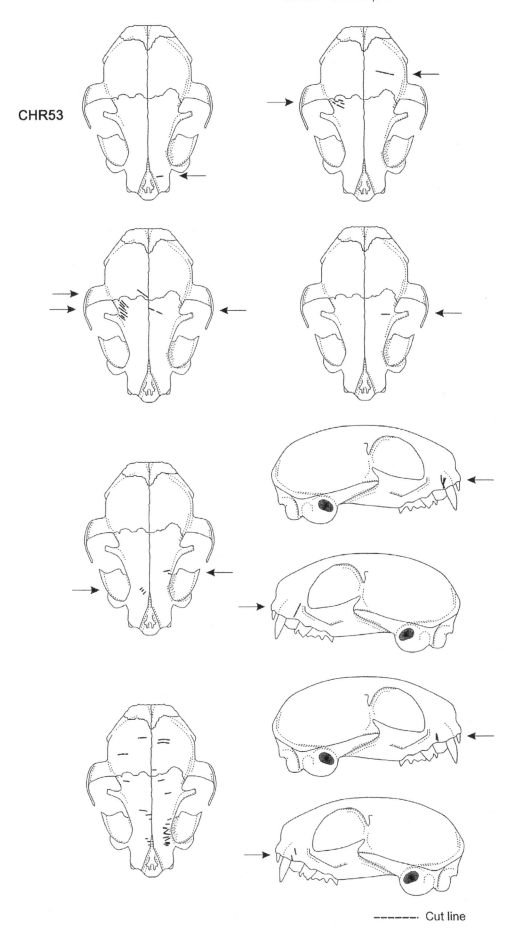

CHR53

-------- Cut line

Figure 5.52   Cat skulls showing location of cut marks, from Chester Road, Phase 53, c.61 (the one labelled) and St John's Street, Phase 30, c.500 (the remainder) (Drawing by P Copeland)

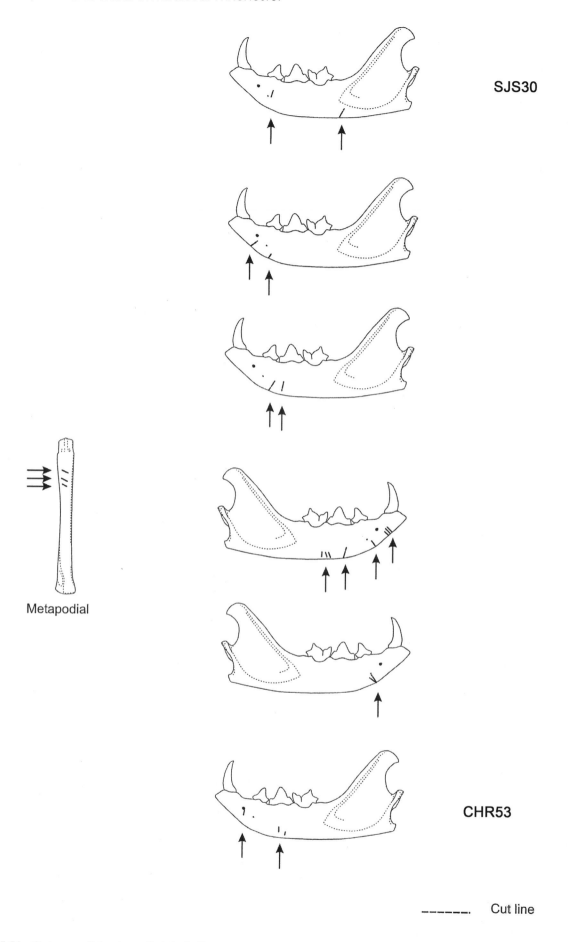

SJS30

Metapodial

CHR53

– – – – – –.   Cut line

Figure 5.53   Cat mandibles from St John's Street, Phase 30 and Chester Road, Phase 53, showing cut marks (Drawing by P Copeland)

Table 5.37 Dogs: skeletons (SKEL) and disarticulated bones (DISART)

Date	Phase	NISP	SKEL	DISART
10th–11th	VR530	40	1	3
10th–11th	HG29	4		4
13th–14th	VR637	1		1
13th–14th	VR783	1		1
13th–14th	VR975	2		2
late 14th	VR700	2		2
15th–16th	VR756	1		1
16th	VR763	6		6
17th	CHR56	22	1	
Total		**79**	**2**	**20**

lished as commensals or pets in towns by the 11th or possibly as early as the 10th century in Winchester. This date is confirmed by the evidence from Lincoln, where they were scarce before the late 11th century, but in subsequent centuries made up 2 per cent of the total. Such written and pictorial evidence as there is also suggests that cats were rarely kept before the Conquest (Thomas 1983). The age at death, especially in the Saxo-Norman period, shows that few of the cats which were buried in the pits lived to a good age. In addition, few bones show any trace of disease.

One obvious interpretation of the high mortality of young cats is that they were not yet accorded the status of pets, as were dogs, and this too fits such evidence as we have for cats in the Middle Ages. Then they were kept, if at all, to keep down the population of rats and mice. As mousers, they were expected to feed themselves on the product of their hunting (Thomas 1983). However, the age distribution of the sample studied may not be fully typical of the cat population as a whole, if the excavated skeletons are mostly of cats captured and killed for their skins. Older cats, both more mangy and more wary, may have escaped capture and be under-represented in the deposits.

The finds of whole skeletons and the rarity of butchery other than skinning cuts contrasts with the main food animals and makes it clear that in the Middle Ages, as now, cats were not eaten, except perhaps unknowingly and rarely. This is explicable not only because they were perceived as individuals with a status closer to humans but also because their diet was carnivorous; even if cats themselves were not unclean, the vermin which they ate certainly were. We have already seen with the birds that carrion eaters were shunned as human food.

Cut marks similar to those described above have now been noted on cat bones from many other medieval towns in Britain and continental Europe. Several examples with cuts were found at Schleswig Schild and Haithabu (Spahn 1986). There is little doubt that they are made when the cat was skinned. The presence of several cats together, with cut marks on some, also strongly suggests that the corpses were collected for skinning, an interpretation originally proposed for the collections of cat skeletons from Southampton (Noddle 1975). It is hard to see another origin for the collection from Victoria Road in the 15th century. The absence of cut marks cannot be taken to mean the cat was not skinned, as careful skinning need leave no evidence. Collecting cats for their skins is also probably the origin of the cat bones in other contexts where more than one skeleton was found, some with cut marks. Even where there is no direct evidence that cats were deliberately captured for skinning, large groups such as that from Victoria Road Phase 792 must have been collected systematically.

Though amongst the cheapest, cat furs were of value for sale and for export. The sumptuary laws governing dress permitted the use of cat fur to the lower orders (Veale 1966). It has been suggested (O'Connor 1989) that there may have been feral populations of cats in medieval towns, encouraged, but heavily cropped, for the fur trade, and the Winchester evidence would not conflict with this.

Dog

In the Middle Ages, dogs were kept as guard dogs and pets, and the upper classes kept hunting dogs. There was also a class of dogs referred to as 'butchers' dogs', which suggests some were also kept or tolerated as scavengers around the periphery of towns (Cummins 1988; Thomas 1983), living on what they could obtain from butchers' shops.

Two skeletons were found, and a skull was recovered from Phase 783 at Victoria Road (see below). A further 21 disarticulated bones were found in the groups studied (Table 5.37). The skeleton from Saxo-Norman Victoria Road (Phase 530) is a puppy with all epiphyses unfused, certainly below three months and perhaps younger. That from the 17th-century soil deposit in the eastern suburb (Chester Road, Phase 56) is adult.

No cut marks were seen on any of the bones, and none was certainly chopped, though one has a clean break midshaft which could have been a deliberate chop.

Figure 5.54   Dog skull from Victoria Road, Phase 783 (Photograph by N Bradford)

Dog skull (KMC)

The dog skull from Victoria Road (Fig 5.54) was recovered from a 13th-century pit (F413) which was incompletely sampled, so there is no means of knowing if this was originally disarticulated or from a skeleton. The teeth are fully in wear, but the cranial sutures are visible, suggesting that the animal was mature but not elderly. The left P1 is missing, with the alveolus filling, so the tooth had been lost before death. The dog had the congenital anomaly of a supernumerary caudal right molar tooth. The length of the skull is comparable to that of a modern greyhound, although the general conformation is less gracile. The relationship of the frontal area to the length of the cranial vault has a greater resemblance to a labrador type. The snout index is 50.4 and the snout width index 40.0, to compare with 52.7 and 34.5 for a modern greyhound and 49.3 and 38.6 for a labrador (Harcourt 1974). What is particularly interesting in this specimen is that it has a very square muzzle compared with a modern greyhound or labrador. Although the skull is not massively built, the conformation of the muzzle would probably have given the dog a plain, heavy-jowled look.

Discussion

Even without the evidence of the bones, the food remains leave no doubt that dogs were ubiquitous. Deposits of food remains invariably have a high proportion of gnawed bones, as discussed above.

The inhibition against eating dogs is confirmed in these samples. Though dog skins have been used until recently for leather work (Serjeantson 1989), unlike with the cats, there is no evidence of this from the bones analysed. The dogs were allowed to live to a greater age than the cats, but not all dogs appear to have been buried carefully, as disarticulated finds are fairly common, as indeed they are in all urban sites of the period.

Horse

From this sample, some of the questions about the role of horses in medieval life can be investigated: we can gain some information on the size of horses, the age to which they lived, how the horse was treated in life and in death, including the extent to which horse flesh was eaten.

The proportion of horse bones varies. They are absent in some groups but make up *c* 50 per cent of the bones from 13th- to 14th-century pit F1022 (Phase 743) at Victoria Road (Table 5.38). There are no groups with several horse skeletons, as have been found in Kingston-upon-Thames (Serjeantson *et al* 1992). One Victoria Road pit of the Saxo-Norman period, F798 (VR 530) contained much of the skeleton of a horse, as did three of the 13th to 14th centuries at the same site (Phases 635, 743, and 783). The last feature also contained a large number of cattle horn cores. The parts of the body recovered (Table 5.39) suggest that carcasses were complete, probably including phalanges, but possibly without the tail, when buried. Isolated horse bones were found in a further fourteen phases.

The skeleton from Victoria Road Phase 530 has no teeth, but the late fusing epiphyses are unfused sug-

Table 5.38 Horse: n and % (skeletons and part skeletons indicated, with age at death)

Date	Phase	n identified	n horse	% horse	
10th–11th	VR529	361	1	0.3	
10th–11th	VR530	828	116	14.0	skeleton < 3 years
10th–11th	VR532	964	1	0.1	
10th–11th	HG29	603	3	0.5	
13th	SJS13	115	0	0.0	
13th	SJS16	186	1	0.5	
13th–14th	CHR53	733	9	1.2	
13th–14th	SJS29	38	1	2.6	
13th–14th	VR616	88	1	1.1	
13th–14th	VR635	458	11	2.4	part skeleton
13th–14th	VR637	261	3	1.1	
13th–14th	VR743	95	47	49.5	part skeleton 7–8 years
13th–14th	VR783	204	34	16.7	part skeleton 13–15 years
13th–14th	VR975	407	1	0.2	
14th	SJS30	623	7	1.1	
late 14th	VR700	412	2	0.5	
14th–15th	VR685	89	0	0.0	
14th–15th	VR792	643	7	1.1	
15th–16th	VR756	384	0	0.0	
16th	VR763	615	1	0.2	
16th	SJS49	1030	2	0.2	
17th	CHR56	798	4	0.5	

gesting an age at death of less than three years. That from Phase 743 is skeletally mature, and the crown heights (Table A5.52) indicate an age of seven to eight years (Levine 1982). The third skeleton is an older animal, with an estimated age of at least twelve years. All the disarticulated long bones with fusion evidence are fused; the only disarticulated material from a younger horse is an immature radius and lower third molar with open roots from Chester Road, Phase 53. The radius and phalanges of the horse from VR Phase 743 show signs of pathology, discussed further below.

The withers height of the Saxo-Norman horse from VR Phase 530, estimated from the long bones (Driesch & Boessneck 1974), was between 1.02m and 1.35m, the estimation varying from the different bones used. The horse from VR Phase 743 was of a similar size, with an estimated height of *c* 1.04m to 1.37m. None of the bones from the third skeleton were complete enough to measure. The complete humerus, radius, and metacarpal from VR Phase 792 suggest heights of 1.06m, 1.58m, and 1.39m respectively.

All the measurable horse bones from the Winchester suburbs are therefore of small animals, ponies in modern terms, with the exception of the radius from VR Phase 792. The generally small sizes confirms the findings from 14th-century Kingston.

The skeletons from VR Phases 530 and 783 have

no traces of butchery. That from VR Phase 743 has a groove on the right femur, probably a knife mark. Some of the disarticulated bones found have been chopped and some have cut marks. A metacarpal from a 13th- to 14th-century context at Chester Road, Phase 53, has been chopped midshaft; the most likely interpretation of this is crude removal of the feet with the hide when the horse was skinned. A calcaneum from Victoria Road (Phase 637) has been hacked through, probably when the leg was disarticulated at the tarsal joint. A distal tibia from Phase 763 has been chopped through the shaft at the distal end. Cuts around the shaft, made in skinning, were noted on a phalanx from the 17th-century finds from Chester Road, Phase 56. All these chops are associated with skinning or dismembering the carcass.

Only three horse bones appear to have been chopped for marrow: it is hard to explain in any other way two mandibles from Phase 30 at St John's Street which have been chopped through the ramus either side of the tooth row and a humerus from the same suburb.

Discussion

The maturity of the horses, the finds of complete skeletons, and the relative scarcity of butchery traces

Table 5.39 Horse: anatomical distribution of skeletons and part skeletons

Phase	VR530	VR743	VR783
skull	1	1	3
upper teeth	11		5
mandible		2	5
lower teeth	20		1
cervical vts	5	6	(8)
thoracic vts	11	6	(7)
lumbar vts	6		(3)
sacrum		2	
caudal vts			
ribs	28	7	(14)
scapula	2	2	
humerus	2	2	
radius+ulna	2	2	2
pelvis	2		4
femur	4	2	7
tibia	2	2	2
patella	2	2	
astragalus	2	2	2
calcaneum	2	2	
tarsals		3	
metacarpal	2		
lat. metap.	1	2	
metatarsal	3	1	1
phalanx 1	3	1	1
phalanx 2	2		1
phalanx 3	3		
Total	**116**	**47**	**34**

Note: ( ) Vertebrae and rib identified as cow- / horse-size

associated with food consumption on the horse bones contrasts with the cattle bones and confirm the assertion of Walter of Henley that horses were not normally eaten (Oschinsky 1971). The factor that contributes to the taboo against eating cats and dogs, that they are carrion eaters, does not apply to the herbivorous horse. Nevertheless, the explicit taboo on eating of horse flesh which was emphasised by the Church in Europe in the late Saxon period was maintained in medieval England, where horses were accorded higher status than the three main food animals (Thomas 1983). The fact that horses were kept to a greater age than cattle, would not have enhanced the popularity of the flesh as a luxury food. Horse bones with butchery evidence suggesting that some were indeed eaten from time to time have been found on other medieval sites and a few examples of bones chopped for marrow in Winchester may support this. If so, it is likely to have been outside the normal institutionalised consumption of meat bought from butchers.

The hide of a horse was of value for the leather and also the hair. Traces of skinning are most likely on the lower limbs, but skinning a horse, like other animals, need leave no traces at all. Some of the disarticulated bones have skinning traces; there is no positive evidence that any of the complete or partially complete horses were skinned, but this cannot be ruled out.

It is unfortunate that the very intriguing question of the increase in the use of horses for transport and for farm work during the Middle Ages (Langdon 1986), cannot be tackled from the Winchester bone finds, or indeed from medieval animal assemblages. Horses were treated differently in death, as in life, and the bones are consequently found in different contexts, and treated differently from those of cattle, as these groups from Winchester have shown. Deposition of rubbish was to a considerable degree ordered, and horse bones are only found sporadically in contexts in which they are mixed with the three main domestic food mammals. Except for the small group from St John's Street, Phase 29, the number of horse bones as a proportion of identified bones is consistently below 1 per cent, and does not increase by the 16th to 17th centuries, a time when other evidence suggests that horse numbers were relatively higher than in earlier centuries.

Butchery

Some features of the butchery of the minor species have been discussed earlier in the chapter. Here, some aspects of the butchery of the main food species, especially cattle and sheep, will be considered. All groups contained examples of butchery carried out as part of the preparation of the carcass for sale and consumption, and one, discussed below, has a group of metapodials with an unusual type of butchery, which may be related to craft activities.

Evidence of skinning and of other butchery on the species not normally eaten, cats, dogs, and horses, has been considered above as part of the discussion of that species. The only mammal species other than the three main food mammals for which the bones show evidence of how they were prepared for consumption are hares and rabbits, also discussed above.

There are contrasts between the treatment of goose and domestic fowl. Bones of the latter are more often complete than those of geese. A higher proportion of the bones of the wing and leg have clearly visible cut marks, including the characteristic nick below the femoral head, already noted on material from Southampton and Winchester (Coy 1989). Most of the geese were adult, in contrast to the domestic fowl, so any cut used remove the muscle was heavy enough to show clearly.

In many of the groups analysed, mandibles of cattle and sheep were less common than post-cranial bones. The interpretation of this was that these parts of the carcass were not bought for food by the town population. Parts of the skull and jaws of pigs, by contrast, are relatively more common. This contrast has also been noted at monastic sites, La-Charité-sur-Loire in

Figure 5.55 Selection of 10th- to 11th-century cattle metapodials from Henly's Garage, Phase 29, F172, chopped on one or other or both sides of the proximal articulation (Photograph by J Crook)

France (Audouin-Rouzeau 1987) and St Albans Abbey (Serjeantson 1991)

In all periods cattle limb bones were routinely chopped through the shaft, as were most of those of pigs and sheep, though metapodials of sheep were sometimes left complete. In the Saxo-Norman period and the later Middle Ages the radius was invariably chopped midshaft, but by the 17th century, some were found complete. As much of the fragmentation of the bones from these deposits at Winchester is from chopping, comparison of NISP and MNE gives some indication of how heavily these bones were chopped. It is by no means clear whether they were usually chopped as part of the preparation of the carcass for sale and for cooking, constrained perhaps by the size of the pot in which meat was boiled, or whether this was done with a view to exposing the fat and marrow. Today the radius is complete in a whole shoulder of lamb, and the many finds of these complete in the post-medieval deposits at Winchester suggest that at that time too shoulders of mutton were sold and cooked whole.

The unbroken bones also suggest that meat provision was sufficient by the post-medieval period for one potential source of food, the marrow, to be ignored. In earlier centuries it was normal for the bone to be split, so that the marrow could be used in making soup.

Cattle metapodial butchery

A collection of cattle metapodials excavated from Saxo-Norman pits close to the city defences (Henly's Garage, Phase 29) has been butchered in an unusual manner. As the pits also contained horn cores of both sheep and goat it is likely that these metapodials, like the horn cores, represent industrial waste. There are over 40 metacarpals and metatarsals, with over

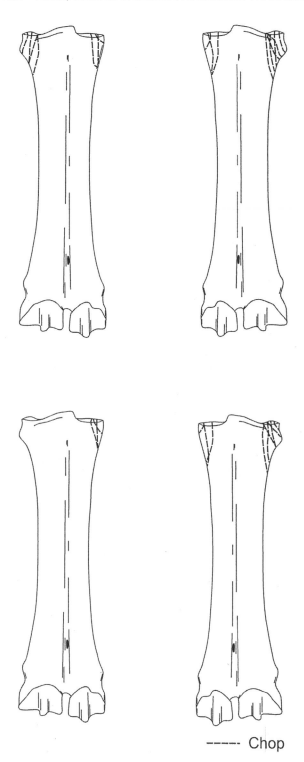

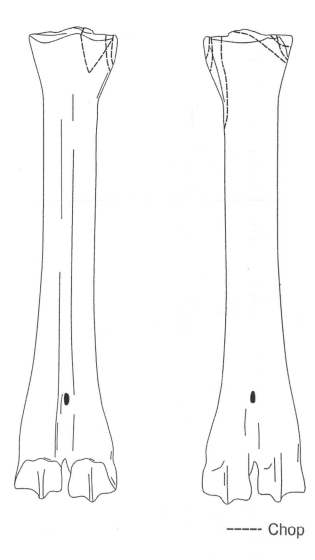

------ Chop

Figure 5.57   Cattle metatarsals from Henly's Garage, Phase 29, F172, showing location of chops at the proximal articular ends (Drawing by P Copeland)

------ Chop

Figure 5.56   Cattle metacarpals from Henly's Garage, Phase 29, F172, showing location of chops at the proximal articular ends (Drawing by P Copeland)

40 specimens of each. Only a few (<5 per cent) have traces of gnawing: the absence of gnawing is often an indication of rapid burial of bones which did not reach the kitchen or table. None is complete: all have been chopped midshaft or through the shaft at the distal end (Fig 5.55) a few were chopped diagonally. This clean chop is not very efficient for marrow removal

(Binford 1978), and is more likely to be a method of separating the upper and lower leg. A single example, a right metatarsus, has been sawn across above the distal epiphysis. None join.

On the distal ends there are fine cuts on the lateral epicondyles and the distal condyles of five out of the 25 distal metapodials, showing that from these at least the phalanges were carefully detached. On a further three, chops had been used, as on the proximal articulations. Further evidence that the phalanges were removed before the distal metapodials were discarded is that only 6 per cent, 3 per cent, and 2 per cent respectively of the phalanges were recovered for the numbers which would be expected for metapodials found. The traces of disarticulation of the metapodials are not obviously part of the skinning process. There was evidence on seven of the sixteen distal metapodials that the skin had been removed by cutting round the distal shaft, using short sharp cuts.

Some of the proximal ends of the metacarpals (Fig 5.56) and the metatarsals (Fig 5.57) have been chopped

Table 5.40 Butchery: incidence and location of butchery chops on cattle metapodials from the Saxo-Norman city defences (Henly's Garage, Phase 29)

Midshaft chop	MC P	MC D	MT P	MT D	n
Below prox epiphysis	3	2		3	8
Midshaft	6	2	5	3	16
Above dist epiphysis	7	2	7	2	18
Chop marks on articulations					
Chopped either side	13		8		33
Chopped dist condyles				3	16
Cuts dist condyles		3		2	25

Key: MC metacarpal; MT metatarsal; P proximal; D distal

down the side of the shaft at the proximal end, on either the medial or lateral side of the articulation, or both sides (Table 5.40). The chop has removed the area of attachment of the ligaments which attach the bone to the carpals and tarsals. The author has not up to now found a description of this method of butchery in any other bone assemblages. These chops at either side of the proximal articulation may be the characteristic of a single individual butcher, disarticulating the metapodial from the upper leg in an unusual and rather heavy-handed fashion.

Overall Conclusion

This chapter has illustrated the great variety of contexts and deposits in the northern and eastern suburbs from which animal remains have been studied. Each has some characteristic assemblages. The finds from the northern suburb in the early period are compatible with the use of the area as an extra-mural farm or settlement. By the time Hyde Abbey was built outside the city to the north, some deposits include food remains which indicate an origin in a more wealthy and varied diet, while others contain rubbish such as the horse skeletons and the cattle horn cores more characteristic of industrial activity. The eastern suburb came into prominence later; the food remains disposed of in that part of the city suburbs do not suggest that the area was one where specialised craft activity took place, but do show some of the changes in the diet and husbandry of the herds brought to the market which are characteristic of the later Middle Ages, discussed here and in the final chapter. The diet, the wealth, and the animals from these areas of the city are discussed further in the context of the material from the suburbs as a whole and in the context of other urban assemblages in the final chapter.

6 Pathologies of the sheep *by K M Clark*

Introduction

The pathology of the bones from the medieval northern and eastern suburbs and city defences was studied under two regimes. Firstly, two conditions which are known to manifest themselves in sheep were investigated and are discussed in this chapter. Secondly, those specimens identified as pathological by the analysts were re-examined and described, and the data stored in the archive.

The first condition is the development of osteophytes in the humero-radial joint, commonly termed 'penning elbow'. This has already been noted as present in all periods at Winchester (Baker, pers comm). The second condition is a depression or depressions which take the form of 'thumb-prints' in the horn cores, which have been seen from time to time in sheep from prehistoric times onwards.

Arthropathies in the forelimb

Sheep appear to be uniquely susceptible to a particular condition of the humero-radial joint wherein an osteophyte of consistent morphology develops on the lateral distal humerus and proximal radius. In its mature form, this exostosis is easily recognisable in archaeological material, even where the osteophyte has become broken or abraded post-mortem. It has been reported in material from Northampton, North Elmham Park, Barnsley Park, and Aikerness (Baker & Brothwell 1980), and commented on as being present in all levels at Winchester (Baker, pers comm). In modern animals it is recorded in the island populations of St Kilda (Clutton-Brock *et al* 1990) and North Ronaldsay (Clark, nd), and has been observed in bones from Welsh mountain sheep (Hamilton-Dyer, pers comm.). Probable examples of the same condition were noted in eight bones from at least six sheep in the late Saxon deposits, as described in Chapter 3.

Traditionally the explanation for the anomaly is that it is a consequence of a trauma sustained when animals are put through races or pens – hence the common term 'penning elbow'. Recent work with North Ronaldsay sheep suggests that it may also be related to the environment and that repeated minor shocks, such as might be experienced through moving repeatedly over rocky ground, may produce the same lesion. The condition has not been recorded in either modern or archaeological goat, and yet it is not uncommon in sheep. The osteological morphology of the elbow joint is distinctive between sheep and goat – in goat the medial epicondylar area of the humerus is more developed, and the trochlea as a whole has a slightly more posterior presentation. In the proximal radius, the lateral tuberosity is more pronounced in sheep. Although these features have not as yet proved susceptible to metrical differentiation, they may possibly have a bearing on why sheep develop an exostosis under stress in the lateral elbow joint and goats do not.

In the humerus, the lesion presents as a broadly based osteophyte on the dorsal part of the periphery of the capitulum, which develops in the ventral direction (Fig 6.1). In the centre of the basic exostosis, a secondary, narrower excrescence erupts. In the radius, the osteophyte appears on the lateral tuberosity and develops dorsally. The morphology of the lesions is consistent in all specimens and at all stages, and is measurable. The points of departure of the exostosis from the normal bone are visible as changes in angle accompanied by a line of vascularisation.

The areas of origin of the osteophytes in both the distal humerus and the proximal radius are the sites of attachment of the lateral collateral ligaments of the elbow joint. Ligaments have very limited elasticity, and osteoblastic activity can be generated by stresses

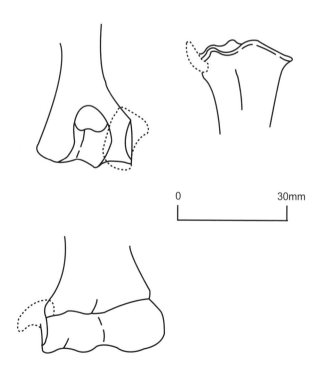

Figure 6.1 Sheep from the medieval northern and eastern suburbs and the defences: lateral exostoses at the humero-radial articulation (Drawing by M Barden)

at their attachments where their structure penetrates the periosteum and enters the underlying bone. This stimulation of the sub-periosteal obsteoblasts causes the development of bony nodules, which will build up as long as the stresses are maintained.

The aetiology of the lesion therefore presents a problem; it may be a single or occasional trauma such as collision which initiates the bony development, or it may be a long period of minor action on that joint for which the animal has not adapted.

However, either of these initiating processes might be of interest in archaeological material if they are occurring in particular circumstances – either husbandry and / or environmental. There is perhaps the argument that they are manifestations of random accidents. The random accident element will only be defined when sufficient data has been assembled to show that the condition occurs under all circumstances in all periods. The current work on comparative material suggests that the incidence is not random, and on this basis the archaeological occurrences are both interesting and relevant.

Ideally, any condition observable in bone should be analysed within the background of the normal elements in the specific assemblage, and should also acknowledge all other recognised osteological anomalies in that species within the periods under review. Indeed, for rural assemblages there is an argument for considering the anomalies of all species together, in that conditions may have common environmental, social, or management origins.

The sample from Winchester

In the case of the sheep from the Winchester suburbs and defences, all examples of selected limb bone articulations – distal humerus, proximal radius, proximal, and distal metapodia – were examined and pathological circumstances were recorded. The sub-samples date from the 10th to 17th centuries, with most examples from the 16th century. The sample included material from HG Phase 20, two flint-lined wells not included as assemblages in Chapter 5. Few sub-groups are of appropriate size for any statistical analysis or percentage expressions and the observations are therefore mainly presented as unprocessed data, ie either as absolute numbers of specimens or derived minimum numbers of individuals.

Table 6.1 shows the minimum number of individuals per phase as estimated from the particular element, and the minimum number of animals which exhibit an arthropathic anomaly other than the humero-radial lateral exostoses. As only complete, fused articular ends were studied, the figure for the minimum number (MNI) is not the same as that from the assemblage as a whole. This can therefore be considered an 'arthropathic background' against which the more particular lesion can be viewed.

In the metapodia, these other lesions are predominantly what appear to be incompetences of the subchondral bone. They appear as splits or fissures in the articular surface, or as more rounded depressions. They are almost certainly due to some stress on,

Table 6.1 Northern and eastern suburbs and city defences: sheep limb bones: MNI examined and n with arthropathies other than humero-radial lateral exostoses

Date	Phase	Humerus		Radius		Metacarpal		Metatarsal	
		n	n Arthro	n	n Arthro	n	n Arthro	n	n Arthro
10th–11th	VR529	5		3		1	1	1	
	VR530	1		2	1			1	1
	VR532			1		3		3	2
	HG29	4	1	10	4	4	1	2	1
13th	SJS16	1				1	1		
13th–14th	VR616	1							
	VR635	1		4		3		2	1
	VR637	1	1			1		1	1
	HG20	2		1					
	CHR53	4	2	4	1	3	2	1	1
14th	SJS30	2		3		1		2	
	VR700	2		1		2	1	2	
14th–15th	VR792	1	1						
	VR685			1					
16th	VR763	12	3	17	4	9	2	10	4
	SJS49	9	1	13	1	6	2	5	1
17th	CHR56	15	1	5	2	6	2	3	2
Total		**61**	**10**	**65**	**13**	**40**	**12**	**33**	**14**

Table 6.2 Sheep: limb bones: MNI examined and n with humero-radial lateral exostoses

Date	Phase	Humerus		Radius	
		n	n extososis	n	n extososis
10th–11th	VR529	5		3	
	VR530	1		2	
	VR532			1	
	HG29	4		10	1
13th	SJS16	1			
13th–14th	VR616	1			
	VR635	1		4	
	VR637	1			
	HG20	2		1	
	CHR53	4	1	4	1
14th	SJS30	2		3	1
	VR700	2		1	1
14th–15th	VR792	1			
	VR685			1	
16th	VR763	12	3	17	2
	SJS49	9	3	13	4
17th	CHR56	15	1	5	
Total		61	8	65	10

or in, the joint (Brothwell, pers comm.) but they rarely occur in association with other manifestations and are probably sub-clinical. The linear lesions are always aligned in the plane of joint movement and occur most commonly at the articular margins, although some do appear close to the sagittal ridge. In the Winchester metacarpals, the medial trochlea is more often affected than the lateral. These lesions have been noted in herbivores from other sites at all periods.

In the humerus, lesions other than lateral exostoses again appear mainly as splits in the subchondral bone, usually on the medial facet. In the radius, however, the splits are absent although depressions in the articular surface do occur. In this element, the most common lesion, apart from the lateral osteophyte, is extension of the proximal articular surface, predominantly at the medial margin of the medial facet.

Table 6.2 presents the occurrence of the lateral humero-radial lesions within the minimum numbers represented by each of these two elements. Two inconsistencies in the data warn against making substantive comments. Firstly, there is a discrepancy between MNIs derived for the same phase from different elements, arising mainly, although not entirely, from the under-representation of the metapodia. Bones of the upper limb are more common in the deposits studied because they constitute food remains. This will affect the arthropathic profile negatively, in that the distal limbs are more susceptible to sub-clinical arthropathies. Secondly, there is an imbalance in the numbers from the different phase groups.

Incidence over time

If the samples are grouped into broader date ranges, however, sample sizes become more compatible (Tables 6.3 and 6.4). At this coarse level it is possible to make some general observations. The relationship of the number of arthropathic individuals to the group totals is reasonably consistent, with the metapodia suggesting a higher incidence, which is as expected. The 16th- and 17th-century humeri and radii are relatively low in arthropathic lesions, but not in lateral exostoses.

With regard to the dimensional analysis of the articulations, again the imbalance in sample size mitigates against statements made on observation of variation. However, the form of the distal humerus, as shown in the bivariate plot in Figure 6.2 (*see* colour section), suggests that perhaps the pre-16th-century group is more homogenous morphologically.

The absolute and cumulative distributions of the distal humeral articular width (BT) (Figs 6.3 and 6.4; *see* colour section), suggest a trend over time towards a more slender elbow, but there is no statistical significance between groups on any absolute measurements or derived ratios for the humerus or radius. This suggests that any trend in the articular width indicates a slight difference in type and not a significant morphological variant.

Parametric statistical analysis was carried out on the distal metapodia. Results were significant at the 5 per cent level. Figures 6.5 and 6.6 illustrate the cumulative distributions of two metrical determinants for which it is possible to present statistical results, albeit

Table 6.3 Sheep: distal humerus & proximal radius: MNI examined, n arthropathic, and n with lateral exostoses

Date	Total	Arthropathic	Lateral exostoses
10th–11th	16	5	1
13th–15th	15	5	4
16th	30	5	7
17th	15	2	1

Table 6.4 Summary of sheep metapodia: MNI examined and n arthropathic

Date	Total	Arthropathic
10th–11th	9	5
13th–15th	11	5
16th	16	6
17th	6	2

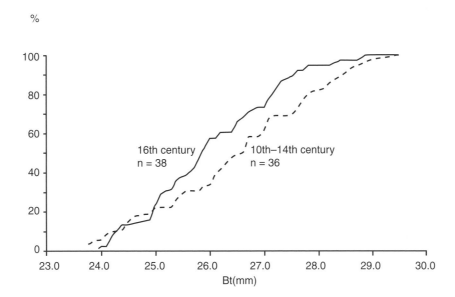

Figure 6.4 Sheep humerus: cumulative distribution of the breadth of the articular surface (Bt) (measurements after Driesch 1976)

at the bottom end of justifiable sample size. For the metacarpus, there is a significant difference between the pre-16th-century group and the later material in the relationship of the medial trochlea to the intertrochlear, or sagittal, notch (Getty 1975, 753). The relative width of the notch is greater in the later group. There is, however, no significance in the absolute width of the notch for the metacarpus. For the metatarsus, on the other hand, it is the absolute width of the notch which is significant – the width is greater in the 16th- and 17th-century material. Again, this suggests that there is a slight shift in type, but that shift would not be apparent as a physiological anomaly, and would not necessarily be visible in terms of gross size.

To summarise, it appears that there is a minor but significant difference in the joint morphologies of the later sheep. However, it is likely that the heterogeneity of the 16th- and 17th-century flock, compared with the earlier animals, is possibly the greater factor, based on the very limited data available here.

The arthropathic evidence does not contravene this view. There is no group of specimens, either by phase or by period, which suggests any extreme of age or husbandry. On the basis of comparative studies the arthropathic load of a normal population of this species

might be expected to be around 30–40 per cent, and this is the kind of proportion displayed by this Winchester assemblage. Certainly there are no manifestations at any period of clinical age-related arthropathy, if the lateral exostoses of the humero-radial articulation are excluded. The exhibited lesions, apart from these particular anomalies, are those of deficiencies in the subchondral bone which were likely to have been apparent as fibrillations in the articular cartilage but which did not produce any incapacity in the animal under the conditions in which it was maintained.

Discussion

As far as these exostoses of the elbow joint are concerned, the observations of Baker and Brothwell are confirmed – that the lesions do occur at all levels at Winchester. Furthermore, on the limited evidence available here, advanced lesions occur in all periods. Table 6.5 presents the measurements of the osteophytes. In this assemblage, where the condition has occurred, it has been able to progress to maturity.

Analyses of the metrical data have produced no justifiable relationships between the dimensions of the

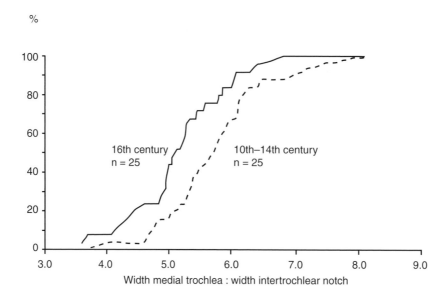

Figure 6.5   Sheep metacarpus: cumulative distribution of the ratio of the width of medial trochlea: width intertrochlear notch (as defined by Getty 1975, 753)

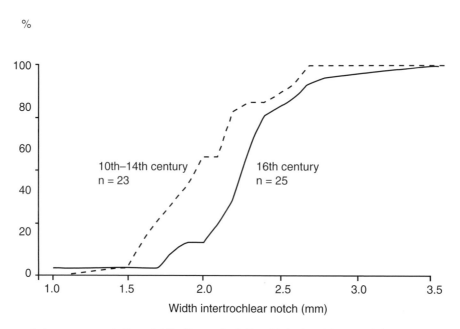

Figure 6.6   Sheep metatarsus: cumulative distributions of width of intertrochlear notch

the distal humerus or proximal radius and the occurrence of lateral exostoses. In this assemblage, there are no grounds for saying that there is a susceptibility to this condition in the conformation of either the distal humerus or the distal radius. There is no observable concurrence between period and incidence, or between period and severity. Although the animals of the 16th century appear to have a minor variation in the limb joint morphology, this is not reflected in the arthropathy. Overall, this assemblage from the Winchester suburbs has not produced evidence to contradict the traditionally held view that the lateral

osteophytes of the elbow joint in sheep are due to an osteological reaction to trauma. Whether such injuries are sustained by collision with pens or races is still an open question as we have, as yet, no independent knowledge of the extent of use of pens at any period. Penning was practised in the Middle Ages, but the extent then and in earlier periods is unknown.

Recent work on a large body of comparative material from Orkney indicates that the incidence of these humero-radial lesions may not be related exclusively to husbandry practice, but also to environment, joint morphology, and possibly age. As far as possible,

Table 6.5 Sheep: dimensions of humeral osteophytes

Date	DW	DWL	HL	WL	WX
13th–14th	28.6	29.1	1.9	7.6	1.4
16th	26.5	27.6	1.9	8.9	2.4
16th	28.1	28.6	2.7	7.7	3.4
16th	27.7	28.8	2.2	8.3	
16th	28.5	29.7	1.7	6.1	3.2
16th	29.1	30.6	3.3	9.8	4.0
16th	29.1	31.6	5.3	7.0	4.1
16th	29.1	31.9	4.6	10.7	7.1
16th	31.5	32.6	3.3	8.6	3.9
16th	30.9	37.8	5.5	12.1	9.5
17th	28.6	29.5	3.9	10.0	2.9
17th	29.9	32.6	5.0	10.2	7.6

Key: DW distal width; DWL distal width including lesion; HL height of lesion; WX width of excrescence

Table 6.6 Sheep horn core measurements

Date	Site and phase	B	D	R	L
10th–11th	HG29	55.7	40.5	1.38	
	HG29	36.7	25.3	1.45	
	HG29	31.0	23.4	1.32	
	HG29	37.7	25.9	1.46	
	VR529	31.4	20.0	1.57	
	VR529	24.6	24.2	1.02	
	VR530	34.7	24.2	1.43	
	VR530	29.3	17.5	1.67	
	VR530	42.5	28.5	1.49	
	VR530	30.4	21.0	1.45	1
	VR530	35.1	22.1	1.59	2
	VR530	38.7	25.8	1.50	3
	VR532	29.6	20.5	1.44	
13th	SJS16	44.3	36.0	1.23	
	SJS16	37.0	22.1	1.67	
	SJS16	33.6	23.0	1.46	2
13th–14th	HG20	26.5	19.7	1.35	
	VR635	20.0	11.9	1.68	
	VR637	29.5	20.4	1.45	
	VR637	49.1	39.4	1.25	
	VR637	26.3	19.3	1.36	
	VR637	31.6	19.9	1.59	1
16th	VR763	27.2	19.3	1.41	1
	VR763	28.8	22.8	1.26	1
	VR763	22.5	16.6	1.36	2
	SJS49	33.3	23.2	1.40	2
	SJS49	33.9	21.3	1.60	2
	SJS49	38.3	23.5	1.60	1
17th	CHR56	35.6	22.6	1.58	1

Key: latero-medial breadth (B); oro-aboral depth (D); breadth/depth ratio (R); and occurrences of lacunae (L)

the latter two parameters have been addressed for Winchester insofar as they can be defined by metrical analysis and the application of fusion sequence data. The question of environment, which in comparative studies has proved to be the primary factor, cannot be addressed for this Winchester assemblage because the size and range of environments in the catchment area in which the sheep were raised is not known with certainty. While the catchment area must include Salisbury Plain, there is no reason to suppose that it was confined to the chalk downland, as Winchester was an important market which attracted sheep from a wide area.

Indentation in the horn cores

All horn cores were examined for the presence of anomalous indentations. Similar anomalies have been noted and discussed in both archaeological and modern material by Hatting (1975), Clutton-Brock *et al* (1990), and Albarella (1995), and in archaeological material only by Polloth (1959) and Clason (1977).

The condition presents as shallow lacunae usually in the basal half of the core and situated on the flatter medial face. The perimeters of the depressions are poorly defined and usually integrate smoothly into the normal plane of the core. They are therefore difficult to measure, but are the area of a small thumb print.

Polloth attributed the condition as seen in the Manching material to castration, but subsequent observations in modern ewes have revised the aetiology to malnutrition. Indeed, amongst Hirta and mainland Soays, the anomaly is only found in ewes (Clutton-Brock *et al* 1990; U Albarella, pers comm.).

Both Hatting and Clutton-Brock have demonstrated that the core walls of females are thinner than those of males, and the cavities are more extensive, which may make them more vulnerable to deformation. This is,

however, also true of wethers, particularly where castration takes place early. Clutton-Brock considers that the horn cores of female sheep can respond to malnutrition or depletion of essential nutrients during breeding or lactation with a regression in growth, or loss of bone from the horn cores, producing the 'thumb print'. The implication may be, therefore, that the underlying factor in the development of the anomaly is hormonal, acting upon a secondary sex characteristic. Alternatively or additionally, a deficiency of Vitamin D – as

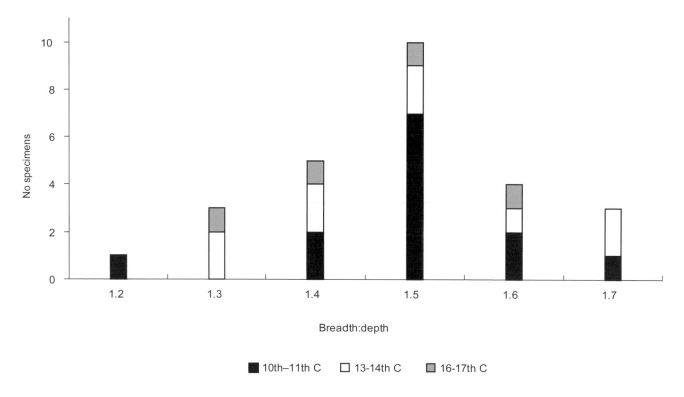

Figure 6.7   Sheep horn core: ratio of greatest diameter (breadth) x least diameter (depth) of the horn core base

might occur where only poor quality winter fodder is available – will inhibit uptake of calcium; this may have an effect on ewes which lamb in years where a late spring follows a cold winter, and the spring flush is delayed.

The Winchester sample

The Winchester suburbs have produced 29 measurable sheep horn cores from 10th-century to 17th-century contexts. The measurements taken are the latero-medial breadth and the oro-aboral depth (Driesch 1976), and these are summarised (Table 6.6), together with the occurrences of lacunae. One specimen, from the 10th–11th centuries, has three depressions, two on the medial face and the third on the lateral. The breadth:width ratio has been calculated to express the range of cross-sectional morphology of the cores between round and D-shaped. Distribution across this range is shown for the groups from the 10th–11th, 13th, 13th–14th, 16th, and 17th centuries (Fig 6.7).

Figure 6.8 shows the incidence of anomalous horn cores within the ranges of the two dimensions. There is clearly no morphological difference between normal and abnormal cores, but the abnormality has not occurred in the few cores which are significantly larger. This would conform to the observations of Albarella and Clutton-Brock in present-day Soay sheep that

thumb prints in horn cores only occur in ewes. Additionally, this adds some weight to the argument that it is associated with breeding animals.

Conclusion

For both classes of pathology described here – the arthropathy in the elbow joints and the horn core depressions – it is clear that the occurrence of the anomalies is open to interpretation only when considered within the whole group. It is the pattern of these developing lesions within the assemblage which constitutes the valid data on which inter-site and inter-period comparisons can be made. It is also the correct level at which to compare archaeological and modern comparative material.

Until pathology is recorded systematically as a matter of course by faunal analysts, the comparisons and interpretations will be very tentative, as they are with this Winchester material. Furthermore, this is a relatively large group, and in smaller and more restricted assemblages it may not be possible yet to express any interpretations until there is a substantial body of relevant pathological reporting. This, however, is a more justifiable position, with far greater potential for future understanding, than the unsubstantiated explanations of husbandry, agro-economics and cultural attitude on the basis of single, discrete, and gross abnormalities.

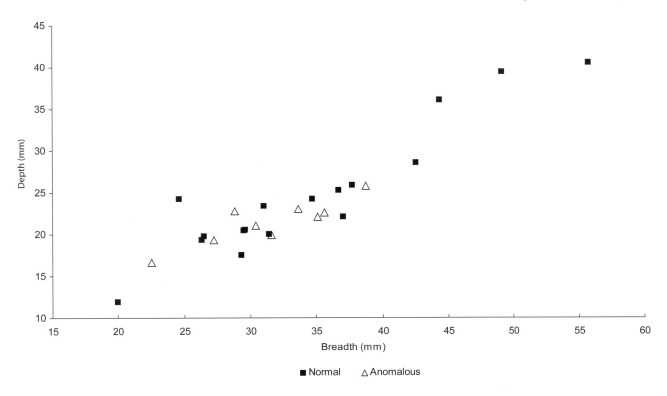

Figure 6.8 Sheep horn core: bivariate plot of breadth and depth (mm), showing anomalous horn cores

7 Food, craft, and status: the Winchester suburbs and defences in a wider context *by D Serjeantson*

Introduction

Animal bones and plant remains from over 50 different groups from medieval and post-medieval Winchester have been described in the preceding chapters. The reports on the faunal material are the most comprehensive from an English town to be published to date. Even here, however, despite the number of bone groups studied, there are omissions from the range of sites. All the material has come from the suburbs and defences around the periphery of the city; the authors have not been able to draw on comparisons with the city centre. It is likely that households within the city were wealthier; furthermore, the areas where the main urban crafts concerned with animal materials were carried out were also within the city proper, close to the streams of the River Itchen. The scope of the data is nevertheless wide enough to permit an attempt to bring together the evidence which the plant and animal remains provide for food, for craft activities, and for the relative status of the different areas of the town, as reflected in the biological remains. This chapter will also attempt to place the Winchester material within the wider context of medieval England.

In the late Saxon period, Winchester was one of the two most important cities in the land. The city declined in relative importance, but was one of the great wool towns of England in the later Middle Ages (Postan 1972, 235). Though it began a relative decline in the later Middle Ages, when international trade became centred on London, and after the city lost the important fair of St Giles which had been held annually on St Giles Hill to the east, it remained a wealthy town. Food consumption and craft activities of the population might be expected to reflect this. Though Winchester was losing its high status relative to London and other cities, it was still a wealthy city in the high Middle Ages. We might therefore expect some evidence of the changes in this wealth in the animal foods and crafts involving animal materials.

For the purposes of this discussion of change over time, the material has been considered within the following broad periods:

Late Saxon (9th–10th centuries)
Saxo-Norman (late 10th–12th centuries)
High medieval (13th–14th centuries)
Late medieval (15th–early 16th centuries)
Post-medieval (16th–17th centuries)

There are more details in Tables 1.1 and 1.3 of the date and location of the groups described.

It is now (at the time of writing, 2001) nearly 30 years since the major programmes of rescue excava-tion in towns began, and more than 60 reports have been completed on English towns since that date. However, they are of varying scale and nature, with many covering small, unrepresentative assemblages. Published reports are also available on an increasingly wide range of types of medieval sites: from castles, manors, villages, and religious houses, as well as towns. A list of the major medieval sites and many of the minor ones can be found in Albarella & Davis (1996, table 31). It is becoming clear that excavations of villages and minor manorial complexes tend to produce poor animal bone assemblages, probably because domestic waste was not discarded into pits and other cut features at these sites, but towns and wealthier sites such as castles – where rubbish disposal was more organised – have produced large and sometimes very well-preserved bone and plant assemblages.

Surprisingly few of the towns have yielded comprehensive reports on material from all periods. As their authors acknowledge, the medieval bone assemblages studied from York, Lincoln (Dobney *et al* 1996), and Norwich (Albarella *et al* 1997) cannot be taken as typical for the city as a whole. The comment made of York by Bond & O'Connor (1999), 'As the city grew, so it diversified, and no one medieval site will represent medieval York' could as well be said of medieval Winchester.

The first major urban study completed was of material from Exeter (Maltby 1979), and it set the agenda for many of the questions which have been asked since. What were the changes in the relative numbers of the different animals and the changes in age at death? How are these reconciled with the local historical knowledge of animal husbandry and diet? Do any of the deposits contain waste from crafts as well as food? Though the Exeter report with hindsight can now be seen to lack detail about context (Maltby, pers comm), it was a model of how such reports might be written. Here, the same questions have been asked, but there has been greater emphasis on distinctions between individual assemblages.

Each of the chapters on animal remains has emphasised the variation between groups. This variation in Winchester calls into question the usefulness of some of the comparisons with material from other towns where there was a less rigorous examination of the origin and status of the deposit. Most of the reports which have been written in the past have discussed the material as though it was a general deposit of food remains, but, as this book has shown, this is not always the case. The variety of origins of the faunal remains from Winchester forced a critical look at how species should be grouped and classified in the tables and discussion (Serjeantson 2000); this problem was explicitly addressed for the assemblages described in Chapter 5.

Food

Selected aspects of the plant and animal food in the diet are summarised and discussed here and compared between the Winchester suburbs and other contemporary sites. Food consumption varied between rich and poor, and it is possible to identify some characteristics of the urban diet. The relative importance of the animals which made the main contribution to the meat diet: sheep, cattle, and pigs, is considered. Some measure is attempted by which changes in fish consumption can be quantified, and the indirect evidence for dairy produce is also briefly considered.

Using the evidence of maintenance agreements for widows, Dyer (1989b, 152) inferred that the diet of the medieval poor was overwhelmingly from cereals, but other sources of evidence make it clear that dairy produce and meat were also eaten. The aristocracy and the members of the richer religious establishments, however, ate large quantities of meat. The Benedictine houses at least enjoyed 'high and rising levels of sustenance' throughout the Middle Ages. According to Dyer (1989b, 197), townspeople ate more meat and less cereal foods than country dwellers. The consumption of meat increased generally over time; it increased among the rural workers between the 12th and the 15th centuries (Dyer 1988) and from the second half of the 14th century onwards, there appears to have been a general increase in quantities of meat eaten, with some decline in consumption of dairy produce and fish.

Plant foods

Though more plant foods were consumed than foods of animal origin, the evidence from the excavations in the suburbs of Winchester is inevitably even more patchy than that for animals. The disparate evidence (Chapter 2) is mostly from a series of samples with a low density of charred plant remains, though a few large samples represent episodes in which a substantial quantity of grain and other plant remains became charred. Most of these are interpreted as from domestic accidents. There are also samples from the base of pits and wells, where plant remains have survived due to mineralisation.

In the charred samples, wheat, mainly bread wheat, is more common than barley. Historical records suggest that more wheat bread was consumed in the towns than in the villages, and the evidence from Winchester could be seen as supporting this, but even in the wide range of contexts sampled, accidents of survival affect the results. Oats were the next most common cereal found; though oatmeal may have been part of the human diet, oats were also important as a fodder crop, especially for the increasing numbers of horses kept, and surviving grains need not have been from crops harvested for human consumption. Rye grains were

also found, again not necessarily waste from human consumption. Peas and beans were recovered, both local crops, and also lentil, found in one sample only, which must have been imported. The imported fruits are grapes, presumably dried as currants or raisins, and figs, also presumably dried. The contribution to the diet of the nutritious hazelnut is emphasised by the presence of charred fragments in each sample examined. The widest range of fruit and berry seeds, with various species of *Prunus* including cherry and bullace, raspberry and blackberry, are from an 18th-century context. There is some patchy evidence for other plants which may be garden crops from the town. Other species identified such as opium poppy and mint may have been garden crops with culinary or medicinal purposes.

Some of the plant food remains identified are best interpreted as residues from beverages rather than foods. Elderberry seeds were found in both late Saxon and later medieval samples, though these need not invariably have been of anthropogenic origin. A possible interpretation of sprouted barley grains from the western suburb is that they were accidentally burned during malting. There were a few finds of hops from the northern suburb.

The deposits from the suburbs did not provide the rich samples which have been found elsewhere in Winchester (Green, in progress) and in other towns, and are a partial reflection only of the diet of the townspeople.

Cattle, sheep, and pigs

The meat eaten in medieval Winchester was mainly from cattle, sheep, and pigs, whether it was eaten as beef or veal, mutton or lamb, pork, ham or bacon. While the wealthy ate roast pork, bacon and ham was the food of the poor. 'Cured pork' was 'the primary meat for city-dwellers and peasants alike in the 12th and 13th centuries' (Montanari 1994). The fact that the secondary products of cattle and sheep had a monetary value equally as great as or greater than the meat, did not mean that they were not eaten; but it did dictate that many were maintained to an age which allowed these to be made use of before eventual slaughter. The nutritional value of meat derived not only from the muscle protein, but also from the fat (as lard, etc.) and the marrow within the bones. The main limb bones of cattle are invariably chopped, as were most of those of sheep and pigs except for those of very young animals, so that the marrow could be used in soups and other dishes. The intensity of exploitation of the bones for this purpose varied between the groups from the northern and eastern suburbs, as discussed by individual authors earlier.

Changes in the percentages of cattle, sheep, and pigs over time reveal trends in meat consumption. At all periods beef provided most of the meat eaten in the city but the percentage of bones varied in a manner which allows us to identify trends. This is shown in Figure 7.1, in which the data from all groups from

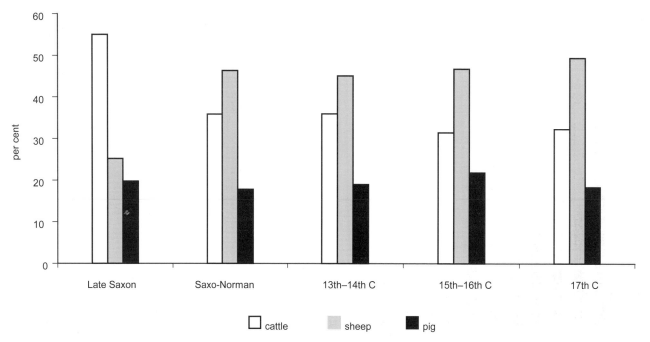

Figure 7.1   Percentage (NISP) of cattle, sheep/goat, and pig, 9th- to 17th-century Winchester, all sites

Winchester have been totalled for each period. The relative proportions of the three main species (NISP) are also compared between the different parts of the city, so as to show the effect of individual variation within the city. Deposits which are mainly of industrial waste and also individual groups with fewer than 100 identified bones of the main food mammals have been omitted. In each of the graphs showing the ratios of individual groups the western suburb are shown on the left, the northern in the middle, and the eastern on the right-hand side of the graph.

The comparisons between Winchester and other medieval sites shows how consumption of the different species varied between town and country, and rich and poor. Fragment numbers (NISP) have been used for the comparison. As discussed in Chapter 5, if the percentages of the MNI are used rather than percentage NISP, pigs and sheep are higher and cattle lower. It should be noted that the method of counting fragments used for Eckweek (Som) (Davis 1991), Launceston (Albarella & Davis 1996), and West Cotton differs from that used on other sites. For these sites a restricted suite of bones was counted, which is effectively a compromise between NISP and MNI. It will therefore overestimate pig and sheep, compared with cattle. Sites from Albarella & Davis' list have been included where the sample of cattle, sheep, and pigs exceeds 500 and where the dating is defined closely enough to fit one of the time periods selected. The number of fragments of sheep and goat, cattle, and pig have been summed and the percentages shown in bar graphs, used in preference to triangular graphs (as in Albarella & Davis), as these allow individual sites to be identified in the comparison. The sites are shown with castles on the left, followed by religious establishments, manors, town and finally rural settlements.

In the late Saxon period cattle bones exceed 50 per cent of the total (Fig 7.1) and the number is greater than 40 per cent in all but two groups (Fig 7.2, *see* colour section). There is greater apparent variation between contexts in the northern suburb and defences than in the western suburb. Cattle bone counts are higher than sheep in all but four of the fifteen groups. Coy in her comparison of types of deposits (Chapter 3) found, rather surprisingly, that the percentage is not necessarily lower in pits than in ditches. This preponderance of beef continues the trend from mid Saxon Hamwic, as Bourdillon points out in Chapter 4. The high proportion of cattle in towns of the period has also been noted in Lincoln: Flaxengate (O'Connor 1982). Sheep bones are more frequent than those of pig in all but a couple of groups where the numbers are closely similar.

It is in the Saxo-Norman period (Fig 7.1) that sheep become more numerous. From this period onwards in Winchester, bone numbers never fall below 40 per cent of the three main species. The increase is mainly at the expense of cattle and is evident at each site other than one in the western suburb (Fig 7.3, *see* colour section). This increase in the consumption of mutton seems to have taken place earlier in Winchester than elsewhere. In other towns at this period (Fig 7.4), the most frequent species continues to be cattle; the only other towns where sheep are as frequent are Beverley and Oxford. At the sites in York, Skeldergate (O'Connor 1984, 16–19) and Fishergate (O'Connor 1991), as well as in Flaxengate (Lincoln) – cattle continue to be most frequent. Rural settlements such as West Cotton (Albarella & Davis 1994) also have over 40 per cent cattle.

In the 13th–14th centuries the overall percentage of sheep is similar to the earlier period, but there is considerable variation between the groups studied from

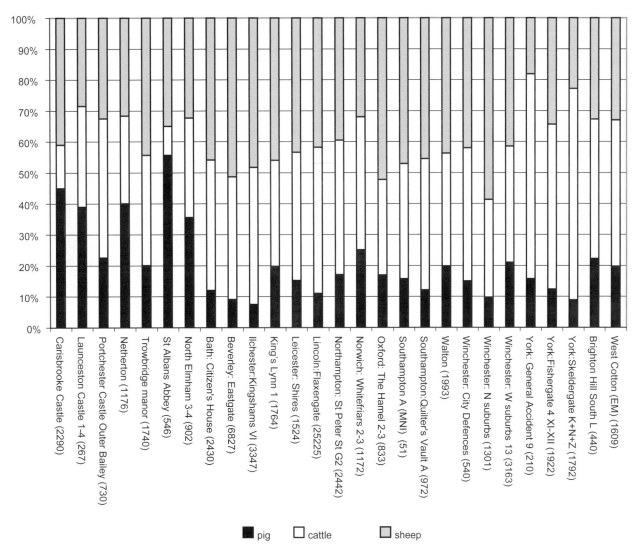

Figure 7.4 Percentage of cattle, sheep/goat, and pig from Saxo-Norman sites in England (arranged by site type)

Winchester (Fig. 7.5, *see* colour section). Sheep bones are exceeded in fragment numbers by cattle in four of the fifteen groups, two in the western, one in the northern, and one in the eastern suburb. The percentage of sheep bones is greater than 40 per cent in many urban assemblages (Fig 7.6). Towns in the north such as York and Newcastle still have higher ratios of cattle to sheep. The proportion of sheep in certain villages is even greater: examples are Eckweek and Wharram Percy. There is little doubt that the increase in sheep from the 11th century onwards is associated with the growing importance of Winchester as a wool town with a market which acted as a focus for the sale of sheep as well as their fleeces. The inhabitants of the city of Winchester may have developed an early preference for mutton, but it will have developed as a consequence of the ready availability of carcasses generated by the wool trade.

In each of the four groups dating from the 15th century and later in Winchester, sheep remains are consistently the most common of the three main food species, with between 40 per cent and 50 per cent of the three main species (see Chapter 5). Elsewhere

(Fig 7.7), the highest proportion of sheep is again in the villages: Brighton Hill South (Hatch Warren) (Coy 1995), West Cotton, and Wharram Percy – but Winchester, together with Northampton and York (Skeldergate), has the highest proportion of sheep of the towns. Again, though this is partly a reflection of the continuing importance of sheep breeding for wool in the hinterland of the city, it also reflects a national trend (Albarella 1997). However, as in the previous two centuries, there is little discernible pattern in the proportions from other towns and more detailed analysis of the types of context sampled would be needed before definite conclusions can be drawn.

In analyses of the proportion of meat from cattle, sheep, and pigs from a series of records dating from the late 15th–early 16th century, the relative role of these in the diet has been calculated by meat weight (Table 7.1): the first is the proportion of meat served to the monks in the misericord at Westminster Abbey over the course of an average year in the early 16th century (Harvey 1993, 53) and the second and third are the same proportions from two aristocratic house-

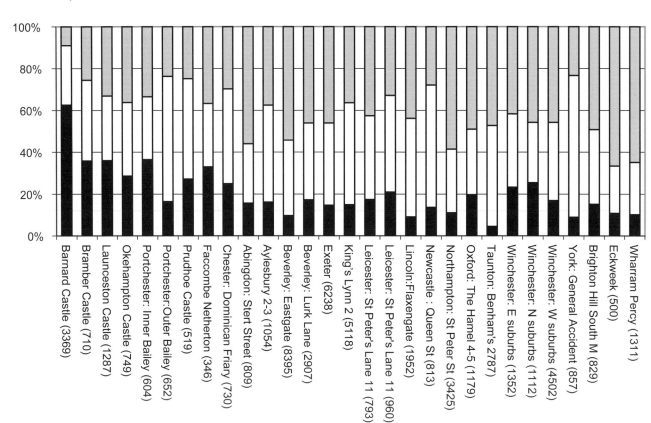

Figure 7.6   *Percentage of cattle, sheep/goat, and pig from 13th- to 14th-century sites in England (arranged by site type)*

Table 7.1   **Quantities of different types of meat provided for the monks at Westminster Abbey in the early 16th century (Harvey 1993, 53) and for two aristocratic households in the early 15th century (Dyer 1986b, 59)**

	Westminster Abbey	Alice de Bryene	Earl of Oxford
Beef and veal	35.5	48	56
Mutton and lamb	47	14	14
Pork	14	28	17
Other	3.5	10	13

holds of the early 15th century, that of Dame Alice de Bryene and that of the earl of Oxford (Dyer 1989b, 59).

Though for many purposes the monks ate a diet that was close to that of the aristocracy, as emphasised by Table 7.1, the latter show a preference for beef, while the monks ate more mutton. Of all three, only Alice of Bryene ate nearly one third of the meat as pork. Certainly, using the criterion of a preference for beef over mutton, it is notable that four of the six sites where sheep are below 35 per cent of the three main species are Launceston Castle, Prudhoe Castle, Sandal Castle, and Faccombe Netherton (Sadler 1990), all of which can be assumed to have been used by the aristocracy.

There is little evidence for consumption of veal in Winchester. Bones of calves below one year were only seen in any quantity in one deposit in Winchester, a 16th-century group from the northern suburb (VR763). As discussed in Chapter 5, there is little evidence for the consumption of veal until the 13th–14th centuries. The evidence increases, but the increase is not as strongly marked as at Norwich (Albarella 1997). Albarella argues that the taste for the consumption of veal is part of the increase in meat eating of the later Middle Ages, and that it drove the production of veal calves. However, there is an alternative interpretation for the increase. Veal was produced as a by-product of the increased demand for milk, butter, and cheese from cows in the later Middle Ages, and especially from cows kept on the periphery to supply milk for the inhabitants of the town (Serjeantson *et al* 1986).

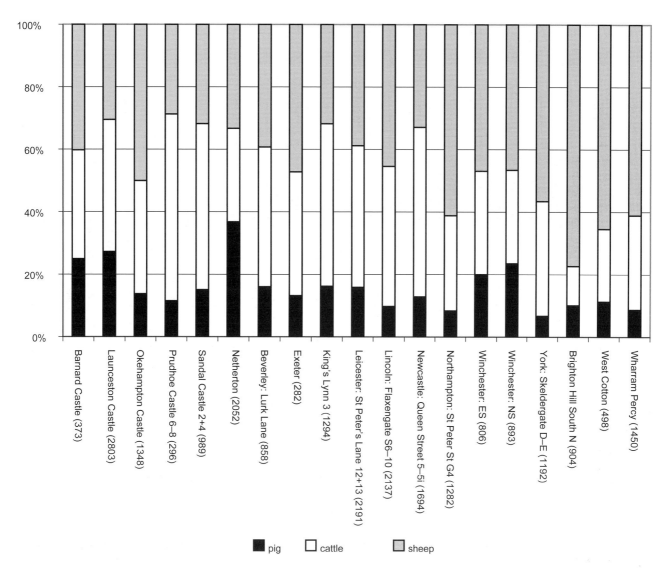

Figure 7.7   Percentage of cattle, sheep/goat and pig from 15th- to 16th-century sites in England (arranged by site type)

Fish

In the Middle Ages, fish – especially preserved fish – was eaten and traded in quantity. The studies of fish consumption in medieval society (Dyer 1989b; Woolgar 1995; Barrett 1999; Woolgar 2000; Serjeantson & Woolgar 2006) make it clear that among the gentry, patterns of fresh fish consumption varied more between individual households than did patterns of meat consumption. However, the quantities of fish consumed in the towns, and also in the villages, are uncertain. According to Rossiaud (1990, 166), in Europe, fish was unknown in the villages. Records suggest that fish consumption increased from the early middle ages, reaching a peak in the fourteenth century and to have declined thereafter. Certainly in Winchester itself, there were more fishmongers than butchers in the 13th century, though butchers were more common in later centuries (Keene 1985).

The fish remains from Winchester provide some insights into fish consumption in towns, particularly for the centuries before there is documentary evidence

for fish consumption. Below, I shall summarise some of the changes over time in the species consumed, and will also attempt some limited comparisons between Winchester and other sites in the south of England, to investigate whether there were distinctions between different types of sites and an increase or decrease in fish consumption over time. Most of the discussion here is based on fish retrieved in samples sieved to 1mm, but the comparison of the larger fish also takes into account fish bones retrieved by hand.

Species change

Eels and herring are the most common species in the late Saxon and Saxo-Norman period in the western suburb, but from the 13th century onwards herring becomes the more common of the two. This holds true for both the western and northern suburbs (Tables 3.16–3.19, 5.32). These species are found only where both preservation and recovery is good: neither is recorded in town deposits with poor preservation

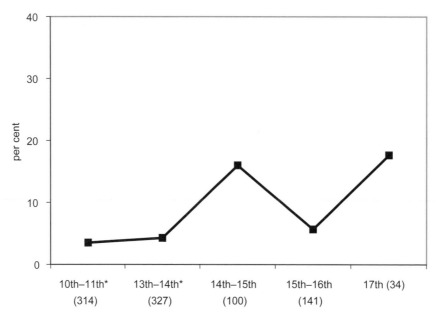

Figure 7.8   Percentage of fish from hand retrieved bird and fish on Winchester sites

and/or where sieving was not carried out, such as at Exeter (Wilkinson 1979): where 'almost all [the fish were] recovered by hand-sorting', and few were recovered in the Saxon northern and eastern suburbs. The high proportion of eels from Winchester in the earlier centuries accords with the many references to eel fisheries in Domesday (Darby 1976, 57). The herring remains are more likely to be from preserved fish, and their presence in Winchester is early evidence for this trade in England.

Flatfish, including plaice, flounder and turbot, were also eaten in some quantity from the Saxon period onwards. A wide range of other marine fish was eaten, but in smaller numbers.

Preserved cod was traded widely from the 11th century onwards (Barrett 1999), but there is surprisingly little evidence for the consumption of cod in Winchester before the 13th century. Some hake and ling were also found from the 13th century or later. Conger eel is the most frequent large fish found in Winchester, which fits a regional pattern for consumption of large preserved fish (Serjeantson, & Woolgar 2006). In medieval Southampton for instance (Bourdillon 1978), as in Winchester, conger was the most common large fish. The larger cod species, which were mainly a North Sea and North Atlantic catch, were more common further east. In the south-west, including Exeter, Launceston Castle, and some other towns (Smith 1995), hake was the most common of the large marine fish

Relative quantities

It is not at all straightforward to derive the quantities of fish eaten relative to other types of animal foods. Differential deposition and survival and recovery is too great between the larger mammals and fish bones

for comparisons of fragment numbers to have validity. However, it is possible to compare the relative consumption of birds and the larger preserved fish. Both sieved samples and material recovered by hand can be included since it can be argued that conditions for preservation and recovery are likely to be similar between domestic fowl and geese on the one hand and the larger fish, conger eel, cod family, and hake on the other. The main bones of all these are large enough to be noticed in recovery in the trench and are equally robust.

This comparison has been made for the groups of food remains from the eastern and northern suburbs. (The western suburb is omitted because the hand-retrieved and sieved material was not distinguished.) By this measure (Fig 7.8), the proportion of large marine fish to birds is quite low until the 14th century, at which time it rises to nearly 20 per cent. There is a decline in the late and post-medieval period, which accords well with the historical evidence for Winchester. The 17th century sees a rise in the proportion of fish: this is a single context with a small sample and we may be seeing no more than the individual taste of a household or street.

The Winchester material has also been compared with some sites in southern Britain. The comparisons are again based on hand retrieved bird and fish bones, where the total sample of the birds and fish is greater than 50. The sites for which the comparison can be made are surprisingly few, often because the fish have been reported on separately from the other vertebrate species. The graphs show fish bones as a percentage of all birds and fish and sites are again arranged by type.

In the Saxo-Norman period (Fig 7.9) two sites only have more than 20 per cent of fish: St Albans Abbey, a wealthy religious house where the abbot installed after the Conquest was known to have encouraged

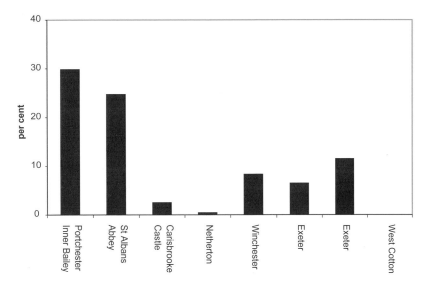

Figure 7.9 Percentage of fish compared to birds from Saxo-Norman sites in southern England (arranged by site type: West Cotton had none)

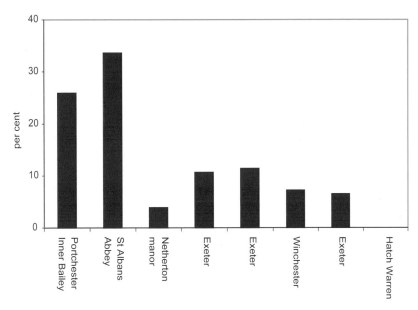

Figure 7.10 Percentage of fish from 13th- to 14th-century sites in southern England (arranged by site type)

the eating of fish (Serjeantson 1991), and Portchester Castle (Coy 1985b). At the second castle, Carisbrooke, and the urban and rural sites, it appears that very little fish was eaten at this time (Smith 1994). While this may have been dictated by choice at the wealthier sites, the villagers were probably unable to purchase fish during this period. By the 13th–14th centuries (Fig 7.10) the percentage of fish in the urban sites has increased slightly compared to birds, with figures closer to 10 per cent, and remains high at Portchester and St Albans Abbey. Again, there were no marine fish from the rural settlement. Among the small number of assemblages of the 15th to 16th centuries (Fig 7.11), the assemblage from Hextalls, Bletchingly, stands out as having a high percentage of fish compared to birds. This was a Tudor manor with royal connections. The deposits are from a single pit which appeared to contain

the debris from a single visit or feast (Bourdillon 1998). Hundreds of small wild fowl were consumed, as well as the domestic birds and the fish. The towns of Winchester and Exeter are intermediate in the proportion of fish and it is again absent in the rural settlement of Hatch Warren.

Fish consumption varies hugely at the wealthier sites at all periods, with the proportion higher in religious establishments and certain wealthy sites. The surprising dearth at sites such as Carisbrooke Castle and Netherton and the exceptional quantity at Hextalls must reflect the taste of the owners and visitors and perhaps occupation during days of fasting. Town dwellers at all periods ate more fowl than fish, but the quantity of fish eaten seems regularly to have been intermediate between that at the wealthy sites and the villages. This evidence

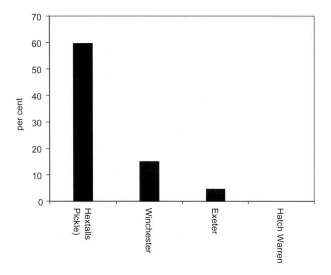

Figure 7.11   Percentage of fish from 15th- to 16th-century sites in southern England (arranged by site type)

for provision of preserved marine fish to the towns and to large households confirms what is known of the fish trade. These comparisons do of course presuppose that the consumption of fowl did not also increase over time. As Albarella (1997) has argued, it may have done so in the later Middle Ages, but if so the consumption of larger fish also rose. The sites with fewest fish bones are rural settlements, such as Brighton Hill South (Hatch Warren) (Coy 1995) and West Cotton. The few fish bones found at these sites include none from the cod family, conger eel, or hake. The small quantities of fish from the villages do confirm Rossiaud's assertion that the large fish at least were not eaten by rural communities.

Discussion

Techniques have not been developed which allow the distinction to be made between fresh and preserved fish from archaeological deposits. At Westminster Abbey in the early 16th century, approximately half the fish consumed was fresh and half was preserved. While the occupants of a wealthy abbey might be expected to have eaten more fresh fish than town dwellers in keeping with their stricter adherence to fast days, those of a city within a day's journey of the coast would also have been able to eat much fresh fish. The records for the fish trade suggest that herring, common eel, and the larger cod fish were preserved, but species such as the flatfish and mackerel may well have reached Winchester fresh. Most of the fish eaten is likely to have come via the port of Southampton. Conger eel, for instance, was imported through Southampton not only from the south-west but also from the east coast (Darby 1976). Though the inhabitants of the Winchester suburbs do not appear to have eaten fish in great quantities, it appears that they consumed both fresh and preserved varieties.

Domestic birds

The bones of domestic chicken were found in each area and period, and in nearly every deposit. Domestic geese, also present in each period, were surprisingly uncommon in the late Saxon suburbs. Overall, the bones were more numerous than fowl in a few special contexts only, as discussed in Chapter 5. Positive evidence for domestic duck is lacking, though records suggest that these were kept. Surprisingly, since some Winchester gardens had dovecotes from the 14th century, very few pigeon bones were found. The quantity of meat provided by domestic fowl was clearly considerable; the sex ratio and age at death show that hens, capons, and pullets were eaten (Tables 4.23 and 5.29). The percentage of immature birds – and therefore percentage of pullets and capons – which might have been roasted rather than boiled – is low until the 13th century, when it rises to 40 per cent of all domestic fowl (Fig 7.12). The evidence from the Winchester suburbs does not support the increase over time in the consumption of young birds observed elsewhere (Albarella 1997). The percentages of fowl are affected in all periods by finds of part skeletons and by variations in conditions for survival. These variations preclude comparisons of the quantity of meat from birds and domestic mammals. For instance, a crude comparison of fragment numbers would suggest that the late medieval deposits in the eastern suburb have a smaller proportion of fowl to the larger mammals, but detailed consideration of the context (Chapter 5) suggests that this reflects depositional practice rather than a change in diet.

There is no means by which any estimate can be made from archaeological finds of the quantity of eggs eaten by the city dwellers of Winchester. There has been no examination of samples to recover eggshell, so any archaeological evidence for egg consumption can only be circumstantial. One of the miracles performed by St Swithun, Winchester's local saint who was canonised in the 10th century, was to restore the broken eggs of a poor woman who fell as she was crossing the bridge at East Gate on her way to market. The scene is depicted in a surviving wall painting in the church at nearby Corhampton (James 1997, 47). Later the importance of eggs in the diet can be seen in accounts such as those of the kitchener at Westminster Abbey. These show that there 5 per cent of the expenditure on foodstuffs was on eggs (Harvey 1993, 37), which were part of the 'repertoire of monastic refectories' (*ibid*, 11), except in Lent. Avoidance of meat at certain times and in certain parts of the abbey meant that eggs (together with fish and dairy produce) may have been consumed in greater quantities within religious houses than in other households. The likelihood is that eggs also featured prominently in the diet of the townsfolk. The percentage of hens, especially in the earlier period, confirms the importance of the production and consumption of hens' eggs in the diet of the townspeople.

Before the 14th century, goose and duck husbandry shows a different pattern. It is argued in Chapter 5 that the absence of casualties among the deposits earlier

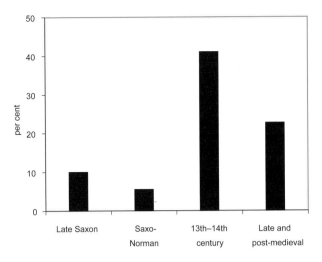

Figure 7.12   Percentage of immature fowl on Winchester sites

than the 14th century suggests that geese were not raised in the city, and the overall paucity of evidence makes this unlikely also for ducks. From the 14th century it is on record that ducks and geese wandered in the streets (Keene 1985, 153), but the first deposit from the suburbs to confirm that geese were kept is one from the 16th century. Neither geese nor ducks lay as prolifically as domestic fowl, so the presumption must be that eggs were of very much lesser importance.

Dairy products

The evidence of market regulations, estate and household accounts and recipes (Best 1986) make it clear that dairy products were consumed, even if expenditure on dairy products was relatively low (Dyer 1989b, 56; Harvey 1993, 37; Woolgar 1995). Indeed, dairy produce was exported from England in the 14th century (Darby 1976, 176). Consumption of milk and cheese in houses which produced much of their own food may not have reached the account books, as the produce of the animal kept for milking might not have been recorded. Cheese is believed to have been more important for the peasants than for the rich, who could afford to buy meat. In the late Saxon and Saxo-Norman period sheep were probably more important dairy animals than cattle. The Peterborough Abbey records (Biddick 1989) suggest that sheep milking was abandoned from the 12th century onwards, as sheep were increasingly valued for wool and cattle appear to have become the more important dairy animal.

While there is no means of establishing consumption of butter, cheese, and other milk products from the archaeological evidence, some circumstantial evidence can be considered. In the discussions in Chapter 5 of cattle, sheep, and goat husbandry, the age at death of each species was considered in the light of the slaughter pattern characteristic of dairying. The cull pattern of the sheep from the late Saxon and Saxo-Norman deposits in the settlements beyond the northern and eastern walls may reflect dairying, with the western suburb showing a different pattern. As discussed, at this period the northern suburb may in fact have been a farmstead outside the town. O'Connor suggests that the age at death of sheep from Flaxengate could suggest that the sheep there were kept for milk, documented for the region in Domesday. The age to which the sheep were kept before slaughter rises throughout the Middle Ages in Winchester, as it does elsewhere in Britain.

Goats were primarily a dairy animal. If the horn cores are discounted (see below), remains from Winchester are very few. However, they include some in the Saxo-Norman period which are from kids slaughtered at an age compatible with a dairy herd. After the 14th century no remains of goats were identified, which could reflect a decline in goat keeping in the rural hinterland of the city.

The rise in the age at death of sheep in the later Middle Ages would support the hypothesis that sheep (and goat) milking declined, to be replaced by cattle dairying. Positive evidence for cattle dairying in the remains from the town is, however, lacking. As discussed in Chapter 5, there is very little evidence for the calves which were surplus to requirements in a dairy herd being consumed in the city before the 16th century. After this time, there is an increase in the proportion of juveniles. From this date, dairies which could provide milk as well as the more durable dairy products for sale began to be set up on the periphery of towns. It has been argued that the use of butter in recipes and sauces increased at the expense of oil between the 15th and the late 16th century (Flandrin 1990), and this too would fit with more intensive cattle dairying at this time, referred to above.

Discussion of food

There is much continuity in food consumption over time. The evidence has revealed a trend towards increased consumption of mutton, though this is seen clearly rather later than the period when wool was the main source of the wealth of Winchester (like much of England). The towns do not apparently show any decrease in consumption of fish, or at least the larger marine fish. The Winchester remains are unhelpful over the quantities of domestic fowl and geese consumed in the later Middle Ages, as the picture is distorted by differences in the types of deposits analysed. An increase or decrease in the consumption of dairy products cannot be demonstrated. Horse meat seems to have been consumed in the late Saxon period, but in very small quantities judging from the number of bones and the percentage of these which have been butchered. Slight evidence for hippophagy continues at a low level until the late Middle Ages. Some individual deposits demonstrate that the variety of species eaten is greater towards the end of our period; to some extent this is associated with the status of the households in the suburbs and is discussed in detail below.

Crafts

The medieval town has been defined as a settlement 'in which a large concentration of people pursued a variety of occupations' (Dyer 1989b), and indeed a major *raison d'être* for the re-establishment of towns in the 1st millennium AD was to bring together in one place craft activities which were better carried out on a larger scale than the household or the village. Many of these trades and crafts made use of organic materials, and a significant number used animal products. The organisation and practice of those associated both with food production and with other trades, can often be identified from the debris which was generated (Serjeantson 1989b). The crafts listed for Winchester in the Winton Domesday include horner, tanner, furrier, and plumer (Keene 1985). A comprehensive study of evidence for crafts in medieval Winchester has been published (Biddle 1990) with which the finds from the suburbs can be compared. Butchery became an increasingly professional activity during the period, as discussed in Chapter 3. This has been seen in York and elsewhere, and was identified in the western suburb from the Saxo-Norman period onwards. This development was no doubt a response to the needs of an increasing population which was purchasing its meat already prepared for the pot and the table.

Some crops destined for use in the textile manufacture, flax and hemp, were recovered, but the plant analysis (Chapter 2) did not offer any evidence that major industrial activites using plant products were taking place in the suburbs.

No workshops using animal products were identified in the suburbs, but the finds of partly worked bone, some of which are described with the small finds (Rees *et al* 2008) and some with the animal bone, show that there is a little evidence for bone working. Some of the waste associated with horn working, the collection of hides, skins, furs, and feathers was also found. The earliest deposits which show a clear separation between food remains and waste that is mainly or exclusively from crafts and disposal of material other than food remains are seen in the 13th–14th centuries, but city centre deposits suggest an earlier date.

Bone working

The worked bone objects and some of the waste bone from the suburban deposits are described in another volume in this series (Rees *et al* 2008). One deposit from the city centre has been published (Biddle 1990); waste from preparation of cattle metapodials for manufacture into objects of bone was found within the city walls at Lower Brook Street (Biddle 1990). Crummy's study (in Rees *et al* 2008) shows that bone mounts and hairpins were being manufactured on a small scale in the western suburb and also that button or bead manufacture was taking place at Victoria Road in the later medieval period.

Bones were sawn only when they were to be used for the manufacture of objects. The only example of a bone that had been sawn, a cattle metatarsus, was found in 10th- to 11th-century deposits close to the southern gateway (HG 29). Other cattle metapodials in the same group were chopped. Sawing is so rare other than on horn cores that Coy believed that a sawn pig humerus in a 10th- to 11th-century context might represent contamination with later material.

A few fragments of antler of red, roe, and fallow deer have been found, many of which have been chopped. The scant records parallel the few bones of these species, and do no more than provide a reminder that some antler working continued to take place throughout the Middle Ages, but it was on a small scale.

Though, as Biddle argues, bone working must have taken place in the city from its earliest foundation, no large concentrations of refuse from bone or antler working was encountered in the suburbs and city defences (cf also Rees *et al* 2008, 360–3, 401).

Bones associated with horn working

Horn was a valuable raw material until recent times, valued for its capacity to be bent and moulded, and for its translucent quality. It was made into vessels, spoons, combs, lantern ('lanthorn') panes as well as hunting and drinking horns (Armitage 1982; MacGregor 1985). Horn itself, which decays quickly under normal conditions and survives only in an anaerobic waterlogged environment, was not found here, and none of the suburban deposits discussed here had surviving horn objects or offcuts. The bony horn core, however, survives as well as other bones. As horn was such a useful commodity, polled or naturally hornless animals appear to have been uncommon. In the suburbs one example only of a polled sheep skull was found and none of cattle.

There are records from Winchester of the purchase of horns in quantity. The horns, still on the horn cores, were often left attached to the hides and skins which were collected for use by professional tanners and tawyers. The assumption must be that use was made of the horn itself, but it is not always clear whether it was removed for this purpose by the tanner or the horn worker. Collections of horn cores have been found associated with tanning waste, as well as with horn workers' waste. The horn can be removed from the bony core after a short period of rotting without the use of cleavers or knives, so removal need not leave a mark on the horn core, but many examples of sheep, goat, and cattle horn cores from the suburbs have been chopped at the base or through the skull, or have cut marks at the base of the horn core where the horn was detached from the core.

Goat and sheep horn

Horn from goats has an advantage over that from sheep, as the horns are straighter, and often more massive; both were used in Winchester. There was a concentration of goat horn cores, with fewer of cattle and sheep, at Lower Brook Street in deposits from the 9th to the 13th centuries (Biddle 1990), with most from the 12th century. Four-fifths of those which could be distinguished between sheep and goats are from goats. No deposit from the suburbs contained goat horn cores in comparable numbers; but they were present is smaller quantities in deposits of the same period in the western and northern suburbs. Saxo-Norman collections of goat horns were found near the southern gate (HG29), and in each of the suburban areas (Table 4.11, Table 5.25). Finds continue until the 13th century, but none was found in layers dating from later than the 14th century.

Most of the goat horn cores analysed have some evidence for removal of the horn core from the skull or for removal of the horn from the horn core. In the city centre and in the western suburb in the late Saxon period, some horn cores were sawn from the skull, as were some from Lower Brook Street, but most of the sheep and goat horn cores from the 13th to 14th century have been chopped through the base of the horn.

As in the city centre, the proportion of horn cores is higher than would be suggested by the post-cranial bones. This confirms the observation already made for Saxon Southampton and the city centre that horns were brought into the town from elsewhere for processing, as was argued for the 11th-century goat horn cores from York: Skeldergate and those from Perth (Hodgson, n.d.). The archaeological evidence suggests that this practice died out after the 14th century.

Cattle horn

Whereas a few fragments of sheep and goat horn cores were found in most of the deposits from the suburbs, those from cattle were rare (see tables in Chapter 5). One large collection was however found, in a pit of 13th- to 14th-century date in the northern suburb (VR783). These are from full grown mature cattle: the sample does not include the horn cores of the younger cattle for which there is evidence among the bones (Chapter 5). As with the goats, it cannot be taken for granted that all the horns originated within the town. As well as obtaining them from cattle slaughtered within the town, the Winchester horners probably purchased horn from further afield, as did the London horners (Robertson 1989).

The pit was clearly used for the disposal of cattle horn cores in quantity, but it was not necessarily associated with a horner's workshop on site (cf Rees *et al* 2008, 363). It also contained other rubbish, and all of which may have been carted to the outskirts of the town for disposal. Similar deposits of cattle horn cores have been found in many towns in Europe where widespread excavation has been carried out: the first reported example from an English site was York (Wenham 1964), and they have also been found in London, Kingston-upon-Thames (Armitage 1980; Penn, Field, & Serjeantson 1984), and elsewhere.

Hides, skins, and pelts

Tanning and the production of leather was one of the major crafts in medieval Winchester; the part of the city where tanning was carried out seems to have been the Lower Brook Street area, the former *Tannerestret*: there tanning pits, waste, and artefacts associated with tanning were found (Biddle 1990). No tannery was identified in the suburbs.

Certain animal remains indicate either the presence of a tannery or the collection of hides and skins (Serjeantson 1989b). As hides and skins were commonly bought and delivered to the tanner with the head and feet still attached, if the bones from these parts of the skeleton are found in disproportionately high numbers, they are likely to be waste associated with hides and skins. Both skulls and foot bones were found in the pits and contemporary layers at Lower Brook Street.

Hides

Bones which are likely to be from the collection of hides – the skins of larger animals such as cattle and horses – are present in at least two groups. The 10th- to 11th-century assemblage from the city defences (HG 29) included cattle metapodials in numbers out of proportion to the rest of the skeleton (Fig 5.8) butchered in a uniform fashion (Figs 5.55–5.57). One of the pits in the eastern suburb (SJS 49) which dates from the 16th century contained a proportion of cattle phalanges (Fig 5.29, Table A5.19) which is higher than that usually found. Why the distributions of these foot bones should be complementary is unclear. Cattle phalanges in quantity have also been found in King's Lynn (Noddle 1977) and post-Dissolution levels at St Albans Abbey.

Some of the horse remains show evidence for skinning: this includes those buried complete or partly articulated and some of the disarticulated horse bones found. Skinning cuts were noted on foot bones from the late Saxon western suburb and on isolated phalanges from later centuries in the eastern suburb, but the horse skeletons described from the northern suburb have no cut marks associated with skinning. This need not however mean that the horse was not skinned, as the process need leave no trace on the bones (Serjeantson, Waldron, & Bracegirdle 1992).

Skins

The organisation and processes of tawying, the treatment of the skins of smaller mammals such as sheep, goats, calves, fallow deer, and dogs, differed from that employed for the larger animals. The evidence from the excavations at Lower Brook Street was chiefly for the preparation of leather from sheep and goat skins.

Several of the groups from the suburbs include horn cores of sheep and goats and metapodials of sheep in numbers which suggest that the deposit includes the waste from the collection of skins as well as from food. This is argued for the northern suburb in the 10th–11th centuries and also for some 13th- and 14th-century deposits in the eastern suburb. Among the few finds of fallow deer were foot bones unassociated with remains of the rest of the carcass, which suggested that these too may be from skins rather than from animals which had been consumed locally. Some of the disarticulated remains of dogs found in the western suburb also have cut marks from skinning.

Pelts and furs

The pelts of the small fur-bearing animals were much in demand for clothing. Furs from different species were appropriate to different classes of society (Veale 1966), with cat furs and budge (from lambs) of low value and appropriate for the poorer classes. These furs were also recommended to monks, who were exhorted to avoid rich furs. Cat furs feature as items processed and sold; indeed they were exported from England. There were no assemblages with bones of wild animals which suggested collection for pelts and furs among those from the Winchester suburbs, but some of the cat bones strongly suggest that furs were collected.

Remains of at least 50 cat skeletons were found. There is a large collection of bones from a pit (VR 792) of the 14th–15th century (Chapter 5). It originally contained the skeletons of a minimum of 33 cats. A few have cut marks on the skull and mandible (Figs 5.52 and 5.53), made in skinning. Other pits had fewer skeletons, but also included some with skinning cuts. About 50 per cent of the cats died before the age of about eleven months (Fig 5.51). It has been elegantly argued (Spahn 1986) that the concentration on cats of this age suggested that kittens were mostly born in a single season, the spring, and were then killed at the beginning of their first winter when the fur was in prime condition. This implies that cities had feral cat populations encouraged not only because they controlled the vermin but also as a supply for furs, since pampered domestic cats would not necessarily show the seasonal pattern of birth visible in the Winchester finds, and also might well be less vulnerable to capture. Similar collections of cat bones have now been found in many medieval towns throughout Europe. In addition to those from Schleswig Schild discussed by Spahn, they have been found at Southampton (Noddle 1975), Haithabu (Johansson & Hüster 1987), Dublin (MacCormick 1988), Leicester (Gidney 1991), and Beverley. The general immaturity of cat bones from medieval towns has often been observed.

The sheep remains from phase VR 792 also includes a high proportion of skulls and metapodials of lambs, and the association with the cat remains strongly suggests that these are from lambskins also collected to make garments.

Feathers

The argument that feathers were one of the main products from domestic geese is discussed in Chapter 5. There is evidence for collection of feathers for quills in the debris from a group of 13th- to 14th-century pits in the northern suburb. These pits contained a high proportion of the carpometacarpus and digits, bones from the distal wing, the area to which the quill feathers are attached, which have appropriate cut marks (Fig 5.46). A pen made from a goose radius was identified by Crummy (in Rees *et al* 2008). Even larger collections of the bones from the distal wing have been found in other towns: 75 were found in contemporary deposits in Leicester, also with few bones from other parts of the skeleton.

Discussion of crafts

Some indirect evidence for craft is present in the suburbs, to complement the evidence from the city proper. In the absence of clear evidence that crafts such as leather working were carried out at the sites excavated, the material interpreted as industrial waste has to be seen as waste from products collected for further processing elsewhere; while some of the later finds may be material which was generated within the city but was disposed of outside the walls.

While, in general, evidence for crafts becomes more common as towns become larger and more specialised from the 13th century onwards, in Winchester craft activities have a longer history. Biddle's study of crafts in the city has shown that many originate considerably earlier than the 10th–11th century, from when the first documented records survive. In the suburbs, the only finds which appear to be associated with crafts which are from deposits earlier than the 13th century are the goat horn cores. Most of bones associated with crafts are from the 13th- to 14th-century deposits. This fits with the likelihood that some craft activities spread beyond the confines of the city, particularly with the foundation of Hyde Abbey beyond the north gate.

Wealth and status

Food is central to any study of status and social relations in complex societies. The production and consumption of food is one 'strongly conditioned by the relationships of power and social inequality' (Montanari 1994). Here I consider selected foods and discuss whether they can reveal differences in status and wealth between different areas of the city, between Winchester and other medieval sites, and differences over time. While food is the most important source of evidence, other animal remains found can also contribute to the debate. The foods considered in this exploration of wealth and status are game, including wild fowl, freshwater fish, and pork.

Within towns, too, 'wealth …. was distributed with

extreme inequality', with wealthy merchants at the one extreme and day labourers and servants at the other (Dyer 1989b, 195). Rossiaud cited the ratio of households of different status in St Omer as typical for medieval Europe: 5–10 knights, 300 'wealthy men', 3000 property owners, and 10,000 households of which 2–3000 were poor. There are as yet no reports on the bone remains from the establishments of the very wealthy in Winchester, the Royal Palace, the Castle, the Bishop's Palace or the religious houses within and outside the city of Winchester; a few of the assemblages may belong to households of 'wealthy men' or property owners, as discussed in earlier chapters, but most of what is considered here will be from the lower end of the scale of wealth. The presence of remains from craft processes is a reminder that the areas investigated were occupied by the city's craftsmen.

Game

Hunting was reserved for the aristocracy; the capture and consumption of game was visible evidence of ownership of land, and the consequent wealth and status this implied. The meat obtained by hunting was often, perhaps usually, consumed on special occasions such as the banquets and the feasts that formed a regular part of the annual calendar. There are finds of red, roe, and fallow deer, possibly wild boar, hare, and rabbit from the deposits analysed, but the preceding chapters have shown that they are relatively few in any period. There are also a few records only for wild fowl. In Chapter 3 it was observed that the presence of wild animals among the food remains suggested the survival of wild countryside around the city; however, it is argued here that the presence – which is not great – instead has a relationship to the wealth and standing of the households of suburban Winchester.

Deer

Overall, few deer bones were found. In the late Saxon period, fewer than a dozen roe deer bones were identified from all excavated areas together. There are scarcely more red deer bones, and half of these are antler, some of which are certainly worked. Fallow deer is found from the 13th century onwards: it was present in three groups from the western suburb and eight from the northern and eastern suburbs. Deer are never more than 1–2 per cent of the animal bone from any deposit. Deer were present in most of the late and post medieval groups, but still not more than 2 per cent of the identified bones. The first appearance of fallow deer in the deposits fits what is known of the introduction of that species (Sykes 2004). It is on the sites with a royal or noble association such as the castles at Trowbridge (Bourdillon 1993), Launceston, and Carisbrooke, or the manor at Netherton that deer bones are most common.

Wild boar

References to hunting wild boar (Phoebus 1984) and its consumption at feasts (Markham 1986) continue into the later medieval literature, but positive evidence for wild boar in excavated bone samples is very rare from sites in southern England. A maximum of half a dozen pig bones from the western suburb, and two from the northern suburb were comparable in size with male wild boar; they were clearly from large boars, but not necessarily wild. Since the original reports were written, very few additional medieval finds of wild boar have been recorded from southern England.

Hare

Over half of the groups from the northern and eastern suburbs have no evidence for hare in any period; the balance have a single bone or a few bones. Two bones from the western suburb were positively identified as brown hare (*Lepus europaeus*), the most likely species; others were not distinguished between the brown and mountain hare. The single largest collection is from a 13th- to 14th-century pit from the northern suburb which had more than 100 bones, including vertebrae and numerous phalanges. These were not associated with a notably high proportion of deer or other wild species and their origin remains enigmatic.

Rabbit

As discussed in Chapter 5, rabbits, introduced after the Conquest both for fur and meat, have an ambiguous status. When first introduced they were confined to warrens, which were an expensive investment restricted to the gentry and aristocracy, so are included here with game animals. Later, they were managed for commercial purposes. Rabbit bones are not found in Winchester before the 13th century, and then only in small numbers. From the 15th century, however, they were found in deposits from each of the suburbs, and in one fifteenth-sixteenth century pit group from the eastern suburb they make up nearly 7 per cent of identified bones, the fourth most common species after cattle, sheep, and pig. By the end of the Middle Ages, rabbits were sold in the city, and appear to have become rather more easily obtained by the general population. Elsewhere, finds of rabbit bones in quantity are also very late or post-medieval in date: they were, for instance, found in quantity in 16th-century deposits at Hextalls and Whitefriars, Coventry (Holmes 1981).

Wild fowl

Accounts of banquets and of household feasts list wild fowl among the delicacies eaten (Woolgar 1995, 1999). These were obtained by hawking, and later with guns, but for capture on any scale nets and decoys were used. By the later Middle Ages wild fowl were captured for sale as well as for provision at feasts and banquets. Wild fowl, like other game animals, are very rare in Winchester in all periods. One bone from a white stork was found in the western suburb in the Saxo-Norman period, and there are a few ducks in each period. In the high Middle Ages one or two bones only were recovered of other large wild fowl such as swan, crane, and grey heron. Wild fowl appear to be even rarer in the Winchester suburbs than in other town assemblages that have been analysed: the absolute numbers and range of species is for instance greater in some of the deposits at York, Lincoln, and Northampton: St Peter's Street: House 1 (Cowles 1979) which had a particularly wide range of wild birds. Again it is characteristically sites associated with the wealthy – both laymen and the religious – where there is most evidence for consumption of wild fowl. Locally, for instance, the largest assemblage of bones of wild birds was found at the Bishop of Winchester's manor at Netherton.

Discussion

Before the 13th century, the proportion of game animals and wild fowl is low in all suburbs. No single suburb was wealthier overall than any other on the criterion of the presence of game animals. However, some individual households in the 13th–14th century have higher proportions of game animals than others. These are the properties in Sussex Street in the western suburb, and one group (VR 975) in the northern suburb. The Chester Road (CHR 53) group from the eastern suburb has the widest range of food species of any group analysed, with at least sixteen different species, including four of fish.

Deer, hare, and rabbit feature in all the late and post-medieval groups. By this period, these suggest that there is greater variety in the foods consumed by the middle classes, rather than enhanced social status in the suburbs. This no doubt reflected the transformation of the role of the game species, from objects of status to objects of commerce more freely available for purchase in the cities and towns from the 15th century onwards.

High status fish

The wealthy preferred meat to fish, but, as meat was avoided on at least two days a week, consumption of good fresh fish on meatless days was also a sign of wealth and status. The ability to build and maintain ponds for the cultivation of fresh fish was a prerogative of the wealthy (Dyer 1989a), so consumption of these species is also a sign of high status. The freshwater fish for which the ponds were maintained were mainly pike and bream; carp (*Cyprinus carpio*), was added to these following its introduction to England in the 15th century. Pike was particularly highly prized; it was associated with the powerful, by analogy with its behaviour as a 'water wolf' the most powerful

predator of the lakes and rivers (Hoffman 1987). The sturgeon, which enters rivers to spawn, is the largest of the fish formerly found in England and has noble associations – all sturgeon found in English rivers are due to the monarch.

Finds of freshwater and anadromous fish from the suburbs, whether from sieved samples or from hand recovery, are confined to a single bone of a small salmon or trout from a late Saxon context in the western suburb, and sturgeon scutes from a 13th- to 14th-century house in the western suburb. Remains of other anadromous and freshwater fish other than salmonids would have survived at least as well as most other fish species of similar size. The absence of evidence for freshwater fish does suggest strongly that they were not available to the inhabitants of the suburbs.

The larger marine fish such as turbot and halibut were expensive to buy and, like game, were often purchased for feasts. 'The larger species of flatfish were highly esteemed; the duchess of Brittany was able to consume nine turbot between 20 September 1378 and 23 October 1378' (Woolgar 1995). Finds of these species are also rare: they are confined to some bones from large turbots in the Saxo-Norman period in the western and northern suburbs.

Sturgeon is rare on medieval sites in the British Isles, despite the fact that the hard parts survive well and are large enough to be visible in excavation. The find from Winchester stands out as evidence for local wealth, and it may be significant that it was found in the same context as bones of the gyrfalcon, a hawk with royal associations (see below). Sturgeon remains were also found at St Mary's Abbey within the city (James 1997, 81). Before the 16th century, sturgeon remains in the south of England have been mainly at wealthy religious houses; they have been found, for instance, at the abbeys of Westminster (Jones 1976), St Albans, and Eynsham (Ayers *et al* 2003). It is typically in the wealthier religious houses where freshwater and marine fish of high value are most often encountered. Freshwater fish remains other than eel are rarely found in towns: in the large assemblage of fish from Flaxengate, only two bones were identified, and none was recovered from Exeter. If meat was avoided on days of abstinence by the burgers and the urban poor, it was replaced by preserved fish, as discussed above, but not, in southern England, by freshwater fish.

Pork

Roast pork was 'the most consistent source of more delicate meat' (Dyer 1989b, 60); of beef, mutton and pork, pork was the meat eaten on special occasions (Woolgar 1995). While the most notable foods provided for Henry III's famous Christmas Feast of 1251 at York were the immense numbers of game animals, 400 domestic pigs were also provided. Unfortunately, while written records distinguish pork from bacon and ham, archaeological finds cannot yet satisfactorily do so, as discussed in Chapter 5. The presence of a relatively high proportion of pig bones might be taken as a reflection of wealth; conversely, it might be taken as evidence that the main meat consumed was bacon and ham. The percentage of pig bones at Winchester is compared with sites of different types to identify whether a high percentage is indeed associated with wealth.

In late Saxon Winchester, pig bones were on average 20 per cent of the sample. This is a slightly higher proportion than at contemporary Portchester, using the same calculation, but considerably below that at contemporary Netherton where the proportion was 36 per cent.

In the Saxo-Norman period the proportion of pig was over 30 per cent in five of the 27 sites shown (Fig 7.4). Of these, two – Carisbrooke and Launceston – were castles; two – St Albans and North Elmham (Noddle 1980) – were religious houses, and Netherton was a wealthy manor. Since castles, the wealthier rural manors, and the wealthier religious houses were occupied or visited and used by the nobility, there seems to be a direct correlation between wealth and eating pigs. At St Albans the pigs were very young, probably younger than bacon animals, and the head as well as the rest of the carcass was present, which tends to confirm that they were eaten as roast pork rather than bacon. As discussed, St Albans, Netherton and, to a lesser extent, Carisbrooke also have the other elements in the diet, especially deer, which also reflect wealth and status, and this serves to confirm the association. The correlation between deer and pigs in the food remains from a range of castles and other sites was found by Albarella & Davis (1996). The other sites with over 20 per cent pig are Norwich (Whitefriars), Portchester Castle (Grant 1976), Brighton Hill South (Hatch Warren), which at this period was a comparatively wealthy manor (Fasham & Keevill 1995). Other than the western suburb of Winchester, most other urban deposits have between 10 per cent and 20 per cent pig, with the percentage from the northern suburb of Winchester notably low. Though the western suburb do not have game animals at this time, the high percentage of pigs, confirms that the people of the western suburb were wealthier than the inhabitants of other suburban areas at this time.

Several assemblages from the high medieval period with samples of over 500 identified bones of cattle, sheep, and pig have been published (Fig 7.6). The nature of the sites where the proportion of pig remains is high is similar to the previous period: of the seven with the highest percentage, six are castles and the seventh is again the manor at Netherton. Brighton Hill South has declined in status, and the relative proportion of pig is lower than in the previous two centuries. By comparison, Barnard Castle (Co Durham), with pigs comprising over 60 per cent of the domestic species, is a wholly exceptional assemblage, also with a very high proportion of deer; nothing similar has been found in the south of England. Towns show a consistent proportion of 20–10 per cent pig, with some assemblages below that figure. In two groups from Winchester at this time, the percentage of pig is well above that level; both are in the northern suburb (Fig 7.5), while in the

western suburb at this time proportion of pig is consistently lower than cattle and sheep. By this criterion, during this period, households in the northern suburb of Winchester had become wealthier than elsewhere in the suburbs and than other towns.

Pigs are relatively less frequent on late medieval sites in general; few assemblages have more than 20 per cent of pig bones (Fig 7.7). Netherton again has the highest percentage, and otherwise only two castles have more than 20 per cent. The northern suburb of Winchester has a similar proportion, more than other towns and more than the villages. Evidence from villages further afield – West Cotton, Brighton Hill South (Hatch Warren), and Wharram Percy shows notably small quantities of pig.

The percentage of pig from Winchester in the 15th and early 16th centuries (Fig 7.8) is again higher than from other towns and cities of the period, despite the overall importance of sheep. The paucity of evidence for pigs in the rural settlements is unexpected. The settlements at Eckweek, Wharram Percy, West Cotton, and the Benham's Garage site on the rural outskirts of Taunton, have very low proportions of pig, and a similarly low proportion has earlier been identified from other rural assemblages (Dyer 1989b, 155–6). If the meat consumed by the poor was mostly bacon and ham, it might be expected that the proportion of pig among the remains at such sites would be high.

Are the records suggesting that the poor ate bacon misleading? Or do the archaeological remains not reflect the real situation? Dyer suggested that the bone evidence did not reflect reality: bacon bones would mostly have come from young animals, and these suffer greater destruction than those of older animals. This is a possible explanation for the discrepancy, though the age at death of the pigs is not notably different between the rural sites and the remainder. An alternative explanation is that bones from preserved meat survive less well than those from freshly cooked meat. This has never been established, and would merit investigation. Dyer's calculations of peasant income (Dyer 1989b,116, 135) assume that even where peasants kept one or two cows and a few sheep, they ate only bacon and dairy produce from their own animals. The possibility should perhaps be considered that some cattle and particularly sheep consumed in the villages went unrecorded. The stock which died before it could be fattened for the market, particularly aged dairy cows and ewes, may have been consumed without record, and it is the bones from these which might have survived.

Animals associated with hunting

Some animals other than those which were eaten were closely associated with the human population of the city and had a specific association with individuals of high rank. The animals used for hunting signified the aristocracy who indulged in that pastime: fine horses, hunting dogs, and hawks.

Despite the series of laws stating that only stallions

over a certain size should be used for breeding, there is little evidence in Winchester or elsewhere (Serjeantson, Waldron, & Bracegirdle 1992) for the large horses which were needed to carry a knight in armour. The deposits analysed only contained bones of the smaller animals used by the middle classes and the richer peasantry. Two only, one from the late Saxon period and one from the high medieval period, are from horses over 1.4m (14 hands). No evidence of bit wear was seen, though this does not necessarily mean the horses had not been bitted. Most of the bone remains are from ponies in everyday use as wagon and pack horses.

The right to own a hawk and go hawking was controlled by law and custom (Cummins 1988). Only one species has been identified among the finds from the suburbs: most unexpectedly, some bones of the gyrfalcon were found in the western suburb. The seven bones must be from at least two birds. The gyrfalcon is the largest falcon in north-west Europe and was already extinct in the British Isles, so any bird must have been imported from Scandinavia or Iceland. According to *The Book of St Albans*, this gyrfalcon was reserved for use only by the king and the remains were indeed found in three associated contexts in the western suburb close to the location of the King's Mews. Remains of other hawks are found from time to time: goshawks at Portchester (Eastham 1985) and Ilchester (Levitan 1982, 281) and peregrine falcons at Ilchester and St Albans.

The dog remains found include some which were interpreted as hunting hounds (Chapter 3). Several skeletons were found buried in the same place in 13th- to 14th-century contexts in the Oram's Arbour ditch (which by this time had been recut to form a property boundary) – one of the contexts close to the King's Mews in which some bones of the gyrfalcon were found. All were mature, robust, and of similar size. Thus the western suburb has some burials of animals associated with hunting, but in the other suburbs there is a distinct lack of such species.

Discussion

Some changes over time can be seen in the wealth of the suburbs as revealed by the food remains and other animals. In the late Saxon and Saxo-Norman period most of the evidence is for a plain diet. From the criteria for high status defined above, some bone assemblages from the northern suburb in the 13th–14th centuries suggest a degree of wealth compared to others. Some wild species, swan, duck, hare and rabbit, were present in assemblages from Victoria Road, though in low proportions, and three groups had a relatively high proportion of pig. If game animals are diagnostic of wealth and aristocratic status it is not surprising that assemblages from the suburbs are poor in such species, since the houses and palaces of the knights and wealthier burgers were in the city proper, not in the suburbs. However, the proportion of pig, also a criterion which appears to denote wealth, is higher

in Winchester than other towns from which animal remains have been analysed. The fish show the same contrast. Freshwater fish, which were used for gifts, are absent, but there is some evidence for the larger marine fish that could be purchased.

It is argued that it was only following the transformation to an economy based on money for all classes that the products of the chase became available for purchase. In the later groups, deer, hare, and rabbit, as well as wild fowl are ubiquitous. This should probably be interpreted as reflecting the appearance of such species in the market and a general trend towards consumption of meat in greater quantities by all sections of the population from the 15th century onwards, rather than as evidence for relatively greater wealth and status in the suburbs in the later Middle Ages.

Conclusion

This volume has brought together work done over more than twenty years on the animal and plant remains from Winchester. During that time, techniques have developed for assessing excavated material from towns which has merited further analysis, so each author has used different criteria for selection. The aims pursued in the animal bone studies have however been basically similar and the data has been presented in a way which makes comparisons between periods and between the different suburbs mostly compatible.

Taken together, the chapters in this book have confirmed the point raised earlier, that there is so much variation between context groups that it calls into question generalisations about towns based on a single group or a few groups of bones. This is especially the case from the 11th century onwards. Nevertheless, despite the disparate quality of the evidence, some conclusions have been drawn. This chapter has focussed on consumption of food, but production in the suburbs and in the hinterland of the city has also been addressed in earlier chapters. Greater quantities of mutton were eaten at an earlier date in Winchester than in other towns, a consequence, it is argued, of the importance of wool to the city, but consumption of other meat and fish follows trends seen elsewhere, with some individual variation.

The evidence for crafts involving animal products has been found among deposits of materials which are not otherwise clearly associated with urban industrial production, highlighting how often such deposits are likely to become mixed in settlements of a complex character such as medieval Winchester. They include waste materials such as goat and cattle horn collected for horn working, and cattle hides, lambskins, and cat pelts. There is also waste from making quill pens from the wing feathers of geese.

The title of this volume refers to status as well as to food and crafts. The suburbs did not, in general, exhibit evidence for the consumption of foods which suggest high status, but there were individual exceptions in the 13th to 14th centuries. Close to the site of the Royal Mews in the western suburb the animal and food remains suggested hunting; while in the northern suburb at the same time the food remains indicate wealthy households. However, there certainly was wealth in the city, at least until the middle of the 14th century, but evidence for it in the diet is likely to be found in the city proper in the residences of the clergy and laymen of high rank. Nonetheless, even the suburbs confirm that Winchester was one of the wealthier cites. Like other towns, Winchester, shows greater variety and wealth in the diet than the villages. During the period from the 9th to the 17th centuries, the city declined from that of a national capital to that of a major market town second only to London, and then to a minor city no wealthier or poorer than a dozen others. At the same time, many changes took place nationally in food production, exchange, and consumption and it is these latter changes that are more evident in the food remains from the suburbs than simply a decline in wealth.

Appendix 1   The circumstances in which the sites were excavated

Northern suburb

Hyde Abbey (HA 72, HA 74)

Altogether, sixteen trenches were opened up for excavation, an area of around 995sq m. Due to problems with funding and the contractors' timetable only Trenches I, II, and IV (1972) were fully excavated by hand (138sq m). In addition, Trench XI (1974) was excavated nearly to natural at its western end. Natural was also reached in Trench XII (1974), whilst Trench XIII (1974) was partially excavated, but natural was not seen. Trench X (1974), the site of the almoner's hall still partly standing in the present day, could only be cleaned in the time available. The stratigraphy in the other trenches was observed, either as part of trial trenching or during construction work.

Further investigations at Hyde (HA 95–99) have gone some way to elucidate the internal plan of the abbey, especially the site of the church. The results of these excavations have been included in this series of publications, but it was too late for the finds to be assessed and written up, and they are omitted here.

Lido (LIDO 85/86)

An area of around 400sq m was observed in 1985. Within this area 63sq m were cleaned and planned (Trenches I–IV), and parts of Trenches I and IV were fully excavated (23sq m). Trench V (1986) represented an area of 59sq m to the south, which was fully excavated apart from very deep pits.

Victoria Road (VR 72–80)

This code was given to two large areas of excavation and a linking trench, which were seen as parts of a single response to the proposed construction of a major new road. The area to the west (Trenches I–VI) was adjacent to Victoria Road and to the north of Swan Lane, and that to the east (Trenches X–XV), closer to Hyde Street. The linking trench (VII/XVI) sampled an area across the Roman road to Mildenhall and Cirencester; thus, the excavation revealed the character of Roman occupation on both sides of the road, as well as that of medieval properties fronting both Hyde Street (X–XV) and Swan Lane (I–VI). In all, around 2500sq m were excavated by hand.

Eastern suburb

Chester Road (CHR 76)

Four trenches were opened, but only two (Trenches I and III) excavated. In Trench I (about 250sq m) excavation reached late Roman deposits and exposed a few later Roman graves, whilst Trench III (about 270sq m) was plumbed mostly to early Roman levels and all of the graves in this area investigated under controlled conditions.

St John's Street (SJS 76–80; SJS 82)

Proposals for quite large-scale housing development in St John's Street led to archaeological intervention beginning in 1976. Eight trenches (I–VIII) were opened, and watching briefs maintained over the whole development throughout the period 1976–82. Controlled excavation on any scale was possible only in Trenches I (SJS 76) and IV (SJS 82). Very small areas were excavated as Trench VIII and in part of Trench VI.

Trench I was around 325sq m, and was excavated to the top of Roman deposits in its eastern part. In the western part, excavation ceased at levels of the 13th to 14th centuries. An area of around 28sq m was excavated as Trench IV. Medieval and later deposits were fully excavated, but earlier remains could only be sampled.

Western suburb

Crowder Terrace (CT 74–77)

An area of just over 500sq m was opened for investigation as Trenches I–VIII. Most of this area was excavated by hand, although in some places rather rapidly.

New Road (NR 74–77)

Trial excavation (Trench I) of 6sq m was followed by controlled investigation of 735sq m (Trenches II and III), but safety considerations meant that part of the Oram's Arbour Iron Age ditch remained unexcavated in this area. A watching brief was maintained in two further trenches (IV and V), parts of which were salvage excavated.

Sussex Street (SXS 76–79)

Trial trenching (I–VI) on the west side of Sussex Street in 1974, in advance of road widening, showed that archaeological deposits had mostly been destroyed on the street frontage, but survival in former garden areas was good. Accordingly, Trenches VII and VIII were opened, but no archaeological features were seen in Trench VII. Hand excavation took place in Trench VIII in 1976 (184sq m) but natural was only reached in part of it (90sq m).

During road construction in 1977, a watching brief was maintained and some rapid excavation carried out over the whole of the development area (Trenches XIII–XVI and XVIII). A delay in the construction programme also allowed the Oram's Arbour ditch to be identified in Trench XIV and a 2m wide section excavated under controlled conditions.

Trial trenching (IX–XII) of 1976 had also tested the survival of deposits to the south of Trenches VII and VIII. Modifications to the scheme meant that this area was no longer under threat when the road was constructed in 1977, but proposals for new housing caused part of the area to be excavated in 1979 as Trench XVII. The unexpected complexity of the stratigraphy, and the withdrawal of funding restricted the area which could be investigated under controlled conditions. The full area of 250sq m was excavated to the level of the chalk and clay deposit interpreted as the upcast from digging the late 9th-century city defences (see Part 1). Within this, 38sq m were excavated to natural.

City defences

Henly's Garage (HG 84–85)

Three trial trenches (I–III) were opened in 1984, and controlled excavation of an area around 215sq m subsequently agreed. Trench IV, an enlargement of Trench II, was designed to investigate the sequence on the Roman defences. Extension of Trench III was intended to elucidate the deposits relating to the Roman building and subsequent industrial activity observed in the trial trench. Trench IV was fully excavated with the exception of deep features, but lack of adequate finance meant that the Roman building could be examined only briefly, and the industrial deposits sampled.

27 Jewry Street (27 JS 84)

A total of just over 110sq m was investigated. This consisted of 21sq m of mechanical trial trenching (Trenches I and II), about 22sq m of rapid manual excavation (Trench III) and 70sq m of controlled excavation in those areas of Trenches I and II which had not been destroyed by 19th-century cellaring. Deep pits remained unexcavated in all areas, and no watching brief was carried out during building construction. Investigation was constrained to the areas away from the standing buildings.

Intra-mural site

Trafalgar House (TH 74)

A controlled archaeological excavation of 8sq m to the base of the Iron Age Oram's Arbour ditch was carried out This followed mechanical lowering of the ground surface to a depth of 1m over an area of 33sq m where late Saxon and early medieval deposits had been encountered.

Appendix tables

Table A3.1   Western suburb: key to abbreviations used in Tables A3.2–A3.46

SXS	Sussex Street	roe	roe deer *Capreolus capreolus*
OA	Oram's Arbour (New Road)	fal	fallow deer *Dama dama*
NR	New Road	har	brown hare *Lepus europaeus*
CT	Crowder Terrace		
		fow	domestic fowl *Gallus* sp.
C-size	Cattle-size	goo	domestic goose *Anser anser*
S-size	Sheep-size	mal	mallard *Anas platyrhynchos*
l.b.	limb bone	ana	duck wigeon-size *Anas* sp.
DOG	Domestic dog	col	rock / stock dove *Columba* sp.
CAT	Domestic cat	sco	wader
RED	Red deer *Cervus elaphus*	cor	corvid crow-size

Table A3.2 Late Saxon (Phase 10): Sussex Street pits: anatomical distribution of horse, cattle, sheep, goat, and pig

	Horse	Cattle	Sheep	Goat	Pig	C-size	S-size	Total
horn core		9	8	1				**18**
cranium		47	21		16	54	35	**173**
hyoid		2						**2**
maxilla		9	5		13		1	**28**
mandible		38	32		28	9		**107**
vertebra		86	21	1	35	37	35	**215**
rib	2	94			15	197	179	**487**
sternum		1	1			1		**3**
scapula	1	22	6		21	47	13	**110**
humerus		11	9		14	8	2	**44**
radius		22	12		7	3	1	**45**
ulna		16	5		6	1		**28**
pelvis	2	23	8		10	8	3	**54**
femur		18	1		10	9	1	**39**
patella			1		1			**2**
tibia		18	19		11	6	2	**56**
fibula					6			**6**
carpal/tarsal		43	7		6	1		**57**
metapodial	2	35	66		11	1	9	**124**
phalanx	1	42	7		7			**57**
loose teeth	3	23	20		18		3	**67**
l.b. fragments						128	69	**197**
fragments					2	85	327	**414**
Total	**11**	**559**	**249**	**2**	**237**	**595**	**680**	**2333**

Table A3.3 Late Saxon (Phase 10): Sussex Street various layers:
anatomical distribution of horse, cattle, sheep, and pig

	Horse	Cattle	Sheep	Pig	C-size	S-size	Total
horn core		2	3				5
cranium		7	6	2	3	6	24
hyoid		1					1
maxilla				3	1		4
mandible		10	6	4			20
vertebra		7	8	3	13	10	41
rib		16	2	2	46	64	130
sternum				1			1
scapula		5	6	2	3	1	17
humerus		9	6	6	3	1	25
radius		9	9	2		3	23
ulna		3	4	7			14
pelvis		11	5	4	5		25
femur		6	4	2	4	1	17
tibia		6	10	4	6	2	28
carpal/tarsal		14	6	3			23
metapodial		11	18	10	2	1	42
phalanx		12	4	5			21
loose teeth	1	6	9	7			23
l.b. fragments		1			28	33	62
fragments					19	35	54
Total	**1**	**136**	**106**	**67**	**133**	**157**	**600**

Table A3.4 Late Saxon (Phase 10): Oram's Arbour enclosure ditch, New Road:
anatomical distribution of horse, cattle, sheep, and pig

	Horse	Cattle	Sheep	Pig	C-size	S-size	Total
horn core		1	2				3
cranium	1		6			8	15
maxilla			1				1
mandible		6	3	5			14
vertebra	1	5	4	1	8	4	23
rib		3		1	3	5	12
scapula	3	1			1		5
humerus		2	1	1	4	1	9
radius	1	3	4		2	1	11
ulna	2						2
pelvis	2	2	2		2		8
femur	1	2				1	4
tibia	1	1	3	1	3		9
carpal/tarsal		1	1		3		5
metapodial		8	3				11
phalanx		1					1
loose teeth	1	11	23	7			42
l.b. fragments					31	20	51
fragments					13	20	33
Total	**13**	**47**	**53**	**16**	**70**	**60**	**259**

Table A3.5 Late Saxon (Phase 11): pits: anatomical distribution of horse, cattle, sheep, goat, and pig

	Horse	Cattle	Sheep	Goat	Pig	C-size	S-size	Total
horn core		11	13	2				26
cranium		103	59		191	76	81	510
hyoid		4	3				1	8
maxilla		16	20		50			86
mandible		85	62		73	7		227
vertebra	1	186	174		150	200	125	836
rib	1	298	34		82	434	703	1552
sternum		3	5			4	1	13
scapula	1	79	63		42	81	10	276
humerus		38	24		29	10	4	105
radius		37	36	1	14	12	2	102
ulna		32	15		26	1	1	75
pelvis	2	70	48		26	27	5	178
femur	3	29	23		24	16	6	101
patella		3						3
tibia	1	38	49	1	27	37	15	168
fibula		2			18			20
carpal/tarsal	1	41	25	2	23		6	98
metapodial	1	75	92	1	55	1	2	227
phalanx	1	64	13		15			93
loose teeth		52	39		32		2	125
l.b. fragments						269	312	581
fragments					3	317	391	711
Total	**12**	**1266**	**797**	**7**	**880**	**1492**	**1667**	**6121**

Table A3.6 Late Saxon (Phase 11): various layers: anatomical distribution of horse, cattle, sheep, and pig

	Horse	Cattle	Sheep	Pig	C-size	S-size	Total
cranium		6		2	5	1	14
mandible		4	3	4	4	1	16
vertebra		9	4	5	12		30
rib		18		2	18	28	66
sternum					1		1
scapula		6	5	2	9		22
humerus		2	6	4	2	1	15
radius		2	6	2	2	1	13
ulna		2	3	4			9
pelvis		2	4	2			8
femur					2	3	5
tibia		3	7		3		13
fibula				1			1
carpal/tarsal	2	3	1	1			7
metapodial		9	19	12			40
phalanx		12		4			16
loose teeth		12	9	5			26
l.b. fragments					59	35	94
fragments					44	24	68
Total	**2**	**90**	**67**	**50**	**161**	**94**	**464**

Table A3.7 Late Saxon (Phase 11):
Oram's Arbour enclosure ditch, New Road: anatomical distribution of horse, cattle, sheep, and pig

	Horse	Cattle	Sheep	Pig	C-size	S-size	Total
horn core		2					2
cranium		4		10	7	1	22
maxilla		1		2			3
mandible		2	1	2			5
vertebra		2	1		1		4
rib		1		1	21	6	29
scapula		4				1	5
humerus		2	2	3	3		10
radius		1	2			1	4
ulna		1		2	1		4
pelvis			1		1		2
tibia		3	2		1		6
carpal/tarsal	1	5					6
metapodial	1	5	5				11
phalanx		1					1
loose teeth	1	1	5	14	1		22
l.b. fragments					14	15	29
fragments					6	8	14
Total	3	35	19	34	56	32	179

Table A3.8 Late Saxon (Phase 12): pits: anatomical distribution of horse, cattle, sheep, goat, and pig

	Horse	Cattle	Sheep	Goat	Pig	C-size	S-size	Total
horn core		67	11	5				83
cranium		18	22	1	10	32	33	116
hyoid			1					1
maxilla			5		7			12
mandible		11	28		14		3	56
vertebra		22	35		5	44	15	121
rib	1	25	5		3	40	165	239
scapula	2	10	24		8	3	6	53
humerus		13	9		4	1	1	28
radius	1	3	20		2	2		28
ulna		3	2		4			9
pelvis		8	11		1		3	23
femur		5	7		5	3	2	22
patella	1							1
tibia	1	7	32		6	4	4	54
fibula					2			2
carpal/tarsal	1	12	6		1			20
metapodial		10	37	1	11			59
phalanx		6	7		10		1	24
loose teeth	1	10	10		15			36
l.b. fragments						40	68	108
fragments						48	78	126
Total	8	230	272	7	108	217	379	1221

Table A3.9 Late Saxon (Phase 12): Crowder Terrace boundary ditch (F74): anatomical distribution of cattle, sheep, and pig

	Cattle	Sheep	Pig	C-size	S-size	Total
horn core		2				**2**
cranium	1	2		4	17	**24**
maxilla	1	2				**3**
mandible	2	6	3			**11**
vertebra	4	5		1		**10**
rib				3	14	**17**
scapula	1	2			1	**4**
humerus	1	3		1	1	**6**
radius		4			1	**5**
ulna		2				**2**
pelvis	1			1		**2**
femur	1	1	1		1	**4**
tibia	1	1		1		**3**
fibula			2			**2**
carpal/tarsal	1	1				**2**
metapodial		6		1		**7**
phalanx	3	1				**4**
loose teeth	7	2	6			**15**
l.b. fragments				9	20	**29**
fragments				24	32	**56**
Total	**24**	**40**	**12**	**45**	**87**	**208**

Table A3.10 Saxo-Norman (Phase 13): pits: anatomical distribution of horse, cattle, sheep, goat, and pig

	Horse	Cattle	Sheep	Goat	Pig	C-size	S-size	Total
horn core		15	41	8				**64**
cranium		85	40		44	55	24	**248**
hyoid		3	3		1		1	**8**
maxilla	1	9	6		15		1	**32**
mandible	1	131	36		38	4	2	**212**
vertebra	2	127	80		79	60	42	**390**
rib	3	128	30		52	110	214	**537**
sternum		1	1			1	1	**4**
scapula		47	33		23	10	6	**119**
humerus	1	16	43	1	30	2	1	**94**
radius	2	20	52		18	2	1	**95**
ulna		12	12		23			**47**
pelvis		27	37		30	6	3	**103**
femur		21	32		32	2	4	**91**
patella		1			1			**2**
tibia		24	97		34	12		**167**
fibula					9			**9**
carpal/tarsal	2	22	10		10		31	**75**
metapodial	5	50	112		29	1	4	**201**
phalanx	2	71	20		12		1	**106**
loose teeth	1	48	27		30	1	2	**109**
l.b. fragments			17			130	113	**260**
fragments						158	239	**397**
Total	**20**	**858**	**729**	**9**	**510**	**554**	**690**	**3370**

Table A3.11 Saxo-Norman (Phase 13): other layers: anatomical distribution of horse, cattle, sheep, goat, and pig

	Horse	Cattle	Sheep	Goat	Pig	C-size	S-size	Total
horn core		13	19	2				**34**
cranium		24	44	1	14	18	17	**118**
hyoid		1	2					**3**
maxilla		2	6		3			**11**
mandible		18	59		16	1		**94**
vertebra	1	35	38		8	27	17	**126**
rib	1	46	28		6	53	152	**286**
scapula		12	10		11	1	2	**36**
humerus		3	10		4			**17**
radius		14	25		6	2		**47**
ulna		1	8					**9**
pelvis	1	10	16		2	2	1	**32**
femur	1	6	17		3	1		**28**
patella			1					**1**
tibia		6	23		7	1	2	**39**
fibula		1			7			**8**
carpal/tarsal	1	15	13		8			**37**
metapodial	1	11	61	2	6			**81**
phalanx	1	31	16		9			**57**
loose teeth	2	33	96		27			**158**
l.b. fragments			14			198	316	**528**
fragments						165	365	**530**
Total	**9**	**282**	**506**	**5**	**137**	**469**	**872**	**2280**

Table A3.12 Saxo-Norman (Phase 13):
Oram's Arbour enclosure ditch, New Road: anatomical distribution of horse, cattle, sheep, and pig

	Horse	Cattle	Sheep	Pig	C-size	S-size	Total
horn core		1	1				**2**
cranium		2		1		6	**9**
maxilla				1			**1**
mandible		3	6	1			**10**
vertebra		1	7	1	1		**10**
rib		11				10	**21**
scapula		3	2	2			**7**
humerus		1	3	1			**5**
radius		3	6	1			**10**
ulna			1				**1**
pelvis		1	2	2			**5**
femur			1	1			**2**
tibia		4	6				**10**
fibula				1			**1**
carpal/tarsal		1	2				**3**
metapodial		4	14	2			**20**
phalanx		4	2	2			**8**
loose teeth	1	7	10	2			**20**
l.b. fragments					57	34	**91**
fragments					19	22	**41**
Total	**1**	**46**	**63**	**18**	**77**	**72**	**277**

Table A3.13 Late 12th–14th century (Phase 14): pits: anatomical distribution of horse, cattle, sheep, and pig

	Horse	Cattle	Sheep	Pig	C-size	S-size	Total
horn core		1	1				**2**
cranium		12	2	3	4	5	**26**
hyoid			4				**4**
maxilla				1			**1**
mandible		3	4	1			**8**
vertebra		3	12	2			**17**
rib		2	7	1	6	29	**45**
scapula					2		**2**
humerus			1				**1**
radius		1	1	2			**4**
ulna	1	1	1	1			**4**
pelvis		1	1	2			**4**
femur			3				**3**
tibia		1	3	1			**5**
fibula				1			**1**
carpal/tarsal		2					**2**
metapodial	1		7	1			**9**
phalanx		3	2				**5**
loose teeth		1	2				**3**
l.b. fragments					9	15	**24**
fragments					4	7	**11**
Total	**2**	**31**	**51**	**16**	**25**	**56**	**181**

Table A3.14 Late 12th–14th century (Phase 14): various layers: anatomical distribution of horse, cattle, sheep, and pig

	Horse	Cattle	Sheep	Pig	C-size	S-size	Total
horn core		1	1				**2**
cranium		2	6		3		**11**
mandible		4	8	1			**13**
vertebra		4	6		3	5	**18**
rib		4	6		5	6	**21**
scapula		1	3	4	1		**9**
humerus		2	3				**5**
radius		1	4				**5**
pelvis		2	3				**5**
femur			3	1	1		**5**
tibia		1	2	2			**5**
carpal/tarsal	1	4	1				**6**
metapodial	1	4	11				**16**
phalanx		3					**3**
loose teeth			3	1			**4**
l.b. fragments					12	10	**22**
fragments					3	46	**49**
Total	**2**	**33**	**60**	**9**	**28**	**67**	**199**

Table A3.15 Late 12th–14th century (Phase 14):
Sussex Street ditch (F401): anatomical distribution of cattle, sheep, and pig

	Cattle	Sheep	Pig	C-size	S-size	Total
maxilla		1				1
mandible	1					1
vertebra		1		1		2
rib	1			2	3	6
scapula	1	1	1			3
humerus		1				1
radius		1				1
tibia		1	1			2
carpal/tarsal	2					2
metapodial		2				2
loose teeth	1	12	1			14
l.b. fragments				9	5	14
fragments					2	2
Total	**6**	**20**	**3**	**12**	**10**	**51**

Table A3.16 Late 12th–14th century (Phase 15):
Crowder Terrace pit (F60): anatomical distribution of horse, cattle, sheep, and pig

	Horse	Cattle	Sheep	Pig	C-size	S-size	Total
horn core			5				5
cranium		20	33	4		18	75
maxilla		4	6				10
mandible		10	12	2			24
vertebra		14	11		1	14	40
rib		1			19	110	130
sternum			4				4
scapula	1	2	4	2			9
humerus		4	4				8
radius		6	15	3			24
ulna		1	3	1			5
pelvis		3	4	1			8
femur		2	8	2			12
patella			1				1
tibia	1	4	11				16
fibula				1			1
carpal/tarsal		11	22	2			35
metapodial		8	21	1			30
phalanx		9	26	10			45
loose teeth	3	13	40	8			64
l.b. fragments					94	121	215
fragments					47	69	116
Total	**5**	**112**	**230**	**37**	**161**	**332**	**877**

Table A3.17   Late 12th–14th century (Phase 15):
Crowder Terrace pit (F65): anatomical distribution of horse, cattle, sheep, and pig

	Horse	Cattle	Sheep	Pig	C-size	S-size	Total
horn core			1				**1**
cranium		19	21	9		8	**57**
maxilla		2	8	7			**17**
mandible		7	15	3			**25**
vertebra		15	13	7	3	27	**65**
rib		7		2	45	148	**202**
sternum		1	5				**6**
scapula		3		1			**4**
humerus		2	6	3			**11**
radius			6	1			**7**
ulna			6	1			**7**
pelvis		1	2	5	1		**9**
femur		3	13				**16**
patella			2				**2**
tibia		3	12	2			**17**
fibula				4			**4**
carpal/tarsal		6	20	4			**30**
metapodial		7	21	15			**43**
phalanx		10	19	16			**45**
loose teeth	1	23	47	6			**77**
l.b. fragments					101	121	**222**
fragments					144	487	**631**
Total	**1**	**109**	**217**	**86**	**294**	**791**	**1498**

Table A3.18   Late 12th–14th century (Phase 15): Crowder Terrace pit (F71):
anatomical distribution of horse, cattle, sheep, goat, and pig

	Horse	Cattle	Sheep	Goat	Pig	C-size	S-size	Total
horn core		4	3	2				**9**
cranium		5	9		11	6	5	**36**
maxilla		3	1		4			**8**
mandible	1	14	11					**26**
vertebra	1	11	36		1	10	2	**61**
rib	1	23			3	57	107	**191**
scapula		12	11		7			**30**
humerus	1	2	10		2			**15**
radius		3	11		2			**16**
ulna		2	9		6			**17**
pelvis		12	20		5	2		**39**
femur	1	3	10				1	**15**
tibia	1	9	16		3			**29**
fibula			1		1			**2**
carpal/tarsal	1	15	19		3			**38**
metapodial		21	24	1	10			**56**
phalanx	1	37	16		10			**64**
loose teeth	4	37	72		14			**127**
l.b. fragments						32	175	**207**
fragments						324	118	**442**
Total	**12**	**213**	**279**	**3**	**82**	**431**	**408**	**1428**

Table A3.19 Late 12th–14th century (Phase 15):
Crowder Terrace well (F70): anatomical distribution of horse, cattle, sheet, goat, and pig

	Horse	Cattle	Sheep	Goat	Pig	C-size	S-size	Total
horn core			1					**1**
cranium		27	19		10	5	6	**67**
maxilla		6	1		4			**11**
mandible		10	22		7			**39**
vertebra		40	25		5	10	29	**109**
rib		41			3	57	214	**315**
sternum							1	**1**
scapula		6	9		2	1	2	**20**
humerus		5	17	1	5			**28**
radius		4	24		3			**31**
ulna		4	10		5			**19**
pelvis		3	29			3		**35**
femur		6	8		2			**16**
patella			2					**2**
tibia		9	36		4	2		**51**
fibula					4			**4**
carpal/tarsal	1	13	14		3			**31**
metapodial	1	23	54		16			**94**
phalanx	3	36	20		15			**74**
loose teeth	6	78	84		35			**203**
l.b. fragments		4				221	451	**676**
fragments						205	233	**438**
Total	**11**	**315**	**375**	**1**	**123**	**504**	**936**	**2265**

Table A3.20 Late 12th–14th century (Phase 15):
Sussex Street ?earlier pits: anatomical distribution of horse, cattle, sheep, and pig

	Horse	Cattle	Sheep	Pig	C-size	S-size	Total
horn core		1	7				**8**
cranium		12	30	10		2	**54**
maxilla		3	6	5			**14**
mandible	1	16	16	14			**47**
vertebra	3	48	34	6	12	14	**117**
rib	2	51		5	30	84	**172**
scapula		11	12	6	1		**30**
humerus		7	15	7			**29**
radius		6	16	6			**28**
ulna		3	2	6			**11**
pelvis	1	10	10	4			**25**
femur	1	4	9	3			**17**
patella		1					**1**
tibia	1	12	25	9		1	**48**
fibula				2			**2**
carpal/tarsal		17	3	7			**27**
metapodial		12	45	13			**70**
phalanx	2	21	18	2			**43**
loose teeth	1	14	19	15			**49**
l.b. fragments					120	123	**243**
fragments					72	51	**123**
Total	**12**	**249**	**267**	**120**	**235**	**275**	**1158**

Table A3.21   Late 12th–14th century (Phase 15): Sussex Street ?later pits: anatomical distribution of horse, cattle, sheep, and pig

	Horse	Cattle	Sheep	Pig	C-size	S-size	Total
horn core		1					1
cranium		5	2				7
maxilla		1					1
mandible	1			1			2
vertebra		5		1			6
rib		3		2	6	6	17
scapula				1			1
humerus		2	12				14
radius		3	2				5
pelvis		3	1				4
femur		2	1	1			4
tibia		2	2				4
carpal/tarsal		1		1			2
metapodial	2	2	2				6
phalanx	1	2			1		4
loose teeth		1	1	1			3
l.b. fragments					9	7	16
Total	**4**	**33**	**23**	**8**	**16**	**13**	**97**

Table A3.22   Late 12th–14th century (Phase 15): Crowder Terrace various features: anatomical distribution of cattle, sheep, and pig

	Cattle	Sheep	Pig	C-size	S-size	Total
mandible	1	1				2
vertebra	2	1			1	4
rib		1			4	5
sternum		1				1
femur	3					3
tibia	1					1
carpal/tarsal	2	1				3
metapodial	1	1				2
phalanx	1	1				2
loose teeth	1	2	2			5
l.b. fragments				14	8	22
fragments				7	4	11
Total	**12**	**9**	**2**	**21**	**17**	**61**

Table A3.23 Late 12th–14th century (Phase 15): Sussex Street building 714.2:
anatomical distribution of horse, cattle, sheep, and pig

	Horse	Cattle	Sheep	Pig	C-size	S-size	Total
horn core		2					**2**
cranium	2	5	7	6	3		**23**
maxilla		1					**1**
mandible		10	8	4			**22**
vertebra	31	18	12	6	10	25	**102**
rib	12	13	2		36	55	**118**
sternum			1				**1**
scapula	3	8	7	3		1	**22**
humerus	4	4	9				**17**
radius	1	5	9	1			**16**
ulna	2						**2**
pelvis	1	4	5	3			**13**
femur	2	5	2	5			**14**
tibia		6	10	6			**22**
fibula				1			**1**
carpal/tarsal	5	3	2	3			**13**
metapodial	4	5	12	5			**26**
phalanx	3	10	2	1			**16**
loose teeth		10	5	2			**17**
l.b. fragments					49	42	**91**
fragments					12	5	**17**
Total	**70**	**109**	**93**	**46**	**110**	**128**	**556**

Table A3.24 Late 12th–14th century (Phase 15):
Crowder Terrace various boundary ditches: anatomical distribution of horse, cattle, sheep, goat, and pig

	Horse	Cattle	Sheep	Goat	Pig	C-size	S-size	Total
horn core			1	1				**2**
cranium			1					**1**
maxilla		2	1		2			**5**
mandible		2	2		1			**5**
vertebra	1	6	5			2		**14**
rib		3			2	3	7	**15**
scapula		5	2					**7**
humerus	1	4	2		2			**9**
radius	2	6	4		2			**14**
ulna		1	1		3			**5**
pelvis	2	1	1			1		**5**
femur			2			1		**3**
tibia			3			1		**4**
carpal/tarsal		5	2		2			**9**
metapodial		3	5					**8**
phalanx		5	3		1			**9**
loose teeth	1	5	11		1			**18**
l.b. fragments						79	66	**145**
fragments						5	6	**11**
Total	**7**	**48**	**46**	**1**	**16**	**92**	**79**	**289**

Table A3.25 Late 12th–14th century (Phase 15):
Sussex Street ditch (F126): anatomical distribution of horse, cattle, sheep, goat, and pig

	Horse	Cattle	Sheep	Goat	Pig	C-size	S-size	Total
horn core		5	3	1				9
cranium		6	14		2	3		25
hyoid		1	1					2
maxilla		1			2			3
mandible		12	12		7			31
vertebra	1	15	7		7			30
rib	2	22	3		3	9	43	82
scapula		7	1		1	1		10
humerus		11	7		8		1	27
radius	1	12	13		3	1		30
ulna		4	1		2			7
pelvis		10	8		2			20
femur	1	6	3		3	1		14
tibia	2	8	20		6	1		37
carpal/tarsal	3	8	3		3			17
metapodial		21	32		4			57
phalanx		21	6		3			30
loose teeth	1	31	35		5			72
l.b. fragments		1				127	97	225
fragments						29	49	78
Total	**11**	**202**	**169**	**1**	**61**	**172**	**190**	**806**

Table A3.26 Late 12th–14th century (Phase 15):
Sussex Street ditch (F401): anatomical distribution of horse, cattle, sheep, and pig

	Horse	Cattle	Sheep	Pig	C-size	S-size	Total
horn core			1				1
cranium		1		1			2
mandible		1		1			2
vertebra		3			1	1	5
rib		1			11	10	22
scapula		2		2	1		5
humerus		1					1
radius		3		2			5
ulna		2					2
pelvis		1	1	1			3
femur		3	1	1			5
patella		1					1
tibia			5				5
carpal/tarsal			1				1
metapodial			2	1			3
phalanx			1				1
loose teeth	1	2	2	1			6
l.b. fragments					21	15	36
fragments						3	3
Total	**1**	**21**	**14**	**10**	**34**	**29**	**109**

Table A3.27 Late 12th–14th century (Phase 15): Boundary ditch cutting Oram's Arbour enclosure ditch, New Road (F391): anatomical distribution of horse, cattle, sheep, and pig

	Horse	Cattle	Sheep	Pig	C-size	S-size	Total
horn core			1				**1**
cranium	1	3	6	10	2	1	**23**
hyoid			1				**1**
maxilla		1	1	4			**6**
mandible	1	12	7				**20**
vertebra		5	15	4	15	35	**74**
rib		12	15		29	107	**163**
scapula		8	17	6	2		**33**
humerus	1	5	9	8			**23**
radius		5	21	3			**29**
ulna		4	7	5			**16**
pelvis		6	11	6	3		**26**
femur	1	2	14	4	2		**23**
tibia	1	5	24	11			**41**
fibula		1					**1**
carpal/tarsal	2	18	15	9			**44**
metapodial	9	22	17	20			**68**
phalanx	7	26	10	16			**59**
loose teeth	4	45	43	28			**120**
l.b. fragments					179	315	**494**
fragments					85	186	**271**
Total	**27**	**180**	**234**	**134**	**317**	**644**	**1536**

Table A3.28 Late 12th–14th century (Phase 15): New Road gullies: anatomical distribution of horse, cattle, sheep, goat, and pig

	Horse	Cattle	Sheep	Goat	Pig	C-size	S-size	Total
horn core		3	1	1	3	3		**11**
cranium		4	2		3	3		**12**
maxilla					2			**2**
mandible		9	5		4			**18**
vertebra	1		9			8	1	**19**
rib		9	2		1	2	17	**31**
sternum		1						**1**
scapula		4	3				3	**10**
humerus		1	6		1			**8**
radius		4	9		2			**15**
ulna		2	2		2			**6**
pelvis		1	3		1			**5**
femur		2	2					**4**
tibia		2	10		1	1		**14**
fibula					1			**1**
carpal/tarsal	2	6	4		2	1		**15**
metapodial		6	13		4			**23**
phalanx	1	7	3		5			**16**
loose teeth	1	17	22		5			**45**
l.b. fragments						94	45	**139**
fragments						17	26	**43**
Total	**5**	**78**	**96**	**1**	**37**	**129**	**92**	**438**

Table A3.29 Late Saxon (Phase 10): New Road and Sussex Street pits: anatomical distribution of other species

	dog	cat	red	roe	fow	goo	mal	cor	Total
antler			1	1					2
skull	1	1			3	2			7
mandible	2								2
vertebra	36	15			6				57
rib	55	10			3				68
sternum					7				7
scapula	3	2							5
coracoid					4	1		1	6
humerus	4	2			6		1		13
radius	4	2			5				11
ulna	2	2			11				15
pelvis	4	2			2				8
femur	4	2			8				14
tibia	3	2			7	1			13
fibula	2								2
carpal/tarsal	3								3
metapodial	15	3		1	22				41
phalanx	4				6				10
Total	**142**	**43**	**1**	**2**	**90**	**4**	**1**	**1**	**284**

Table A3.30   Late Saxon (Phase 10): Sussex Street various layers: anatomical distribution of other species

	cat	red	fow	goo	col	magpie-sized corvid	Total
antler		1					1
skull			1				1
coracoid			1				1
humerus					1		1
radius	1		1				2
ulna			1				1
pelvis	1		1				2
femur			1	1			2
patella			3				3
tibia						1	1
Total	**2**	**1**	**9**	**1**	**1**	**1**	**15**

Table A3.31   Late Saxon (Phase 10): New Road ditch (F371): anatomical distribution of other species

	dog	cat	red	roe	fow	blackbird *Turdus merula*	Total
antler			1				1
skull	1						1
vertebra	6						6
scapula				1			1
humerus	2						2
radius	1						1
ulna						1	1
femur					1		1
tibia		1					1
Total	**10**	**1**	**1**	**1**	**1**	**1**	**15**

Table A3.32 Late Saxon (Phase 11): Sussex Street, New Road, and Crowder Terrace pits: anatomical distribution of other species

	dog	cat	roe	badger Meles meles	hare Lepus sp	fow	goo	mal	teal Anas crecca	water rail Rallus aquaticus	woodcock Scolopax rusticola	unident goose/duck	Total
skull						1							1
maxilla						1							1
mandible	1					2							3
vertebra	1					9	2						12
sternum						10							10
furcula						3							3
scapula					1	11							12
coracoid						32							32
humerus	4	1	1			22			1		1		30
radius			1		1	17	1	2					22
ulna	2				1	25	2	1					31
pelvis				1		9	1						11
femur			1			27						1	29
tibia	2					30	1			1			34
metapodial					1	16	1	1			1		20
phalanx						5							5
Total	10	1	3	1	4	220	8	4	1	1	2	1	256

Table A3.33 Late Saxon (Phase 11):
New Road and Sussex Street various layers: anatomical distribution of other species

	dog	red	fow	mal	col	woodcock *Scolopax rusticola*	Total
antler		1					1
sternum				1			1
coracoid						1	1
humerus			2				2
ulna	1		2				3
femur			2				2
tibia			2				2
carpal/tarsal	1						1
tarso-metatarsus					1		1
loose teeth	1						1
Total	**3**	**1**	**8**	**1**	**1**	**1**	**15**

Table A3.34   Late Saxon (Phase 12): Sussex Street pits: anatomical distribution of other species

	dog	cat	red	har	fow	goo	mal	ana	Total
antler			1						1
skull		2							2
maxilla				1					1
mandible	2								2
sternum								1	1
furcula					2				2
scapula					2		2		4
coracoid					4				4
humerus					2	2			4
radius					1				1
pelvis					2				2
femur		1			4	1			6
tibia					4				4
metapodial		1			3	1	1		6
Total	**2**	**4**	**1**	**1**	**24**	**4**	**3**	**1**	**40**

Table A3.35   Late Saxon (Phase 12):
Crowder Terrace ditch (F74): anatomical distribution of other species

	dog	cat	fow	goo	Total
mandible	1				1
vertebra	1				1
humerus		1			1
ulna			1		1
femur			1		1
metapodial				1	1
Total	**2**	**1**	**2**	**1**	**6**

Table A3.36 Saxo-Norman (Phase 13): Sussex Street and New Road pits: anatomical distribution of other species

	dog	cat	red	fow	goo	mal	Grey heron *Ardea cinerea*	White stork *Ciconia ciconia*	Woodcock *Scolopax rusticola*	Common snipe *Gallinago gallinago*	Wood pigeon *Columba palumbus*	Unident goose/ duck	Total
antler			1										1
skull	1			9	1								11
mandible	3	2		6									11
vertebra	4	1		25	1		1						32
rib	13	2		35									50
sternum				20		1							21
furcula				7									7
scapula	1			9									10
coracoid				8									8
humerus	2	1		10		1	1		1		1		17
radius	3			3						1			7
ulna	3			8									11
pelvis	3	2		6									11
femur	3	2		19									24
tibia	2	3		28	2								35
fibula				3									3
carpal/tarsal		2											2
metapodial	4	5		15	5		2	1				1	33
phalanx				4	2								6
loose teeth	1												1
Total	**43**	**20**	**1**	**215**	**11**	**2**	**4**	**1**	**1**	**1**	**1**	**1**	**301**

**Table A3.37 Saxo-Norman (Phase 13):
Sussex Street, New Road, and Crowder Terrace various layers: anatomical distribution of other species**

	dog	cat	fow	goo	ana	Teal *Anas crecca*	Woodcock *Scolopax rusticola*	col	Total
skull		3							3
maxilla		2							2
vertebra	2								2
scapula			1						1
humerus	1	1	3			1			6
radius		2	1						3
ulna		3	4	1	1			1	10
pelvis	2		1						3
femur		1					1		2
tibia			4						4
metapodial	1	1		1					3
phalanx				1					1
loose teeth	1	1							2
Total	**7**	**14**	**14**	**3**	**1**	**1**	**1**	**1**	**42**

Table A3.38 Late 12th–14th century (Phase 14): Sussex Street all layers: anatomical distribution of other species

	dog	cat	har	fow	goo	col	Total
mandible	1						1
vertebra	1			1			2
scapula	1						1
coracoid				2	1		3
humerus		2		2			4
radius			1				1
ulna				3		1	4
femur		2		1			3
tibia		1		1			2
metapodial				2			2
Total	**3**	**5**	**1**	**12**	**1**	**1**	**23**

Table A3.39 Late 12th–14th century (Phase 15): Crowder Terrace pit (F60): anatomical distribution of other species

	cat	Mole *Talpa europaea*	har	fow	goo	Woodcock *Scolopax rusticola*	Total
skull		1					1
mandible	1				1		2
vertebra				1			1
sternum				2			2
furcula					1		1
scapula			1				1
humerus				1			1
radius	1						1
pelvis		1					1
femur				1	1		2
tibia	1						1
metapodial			1	2	2	1	6
Total	**3**	**2**	**2**	**7**	**5**	**1**	**20**

Table A3.40   Late 12th–14th century (Phase 15): Crowder Terrace pit (F65): anatomical distribution of other species

	dog	cat	fal	roe	har	fow	goo	?starling *Sturnus vulgaris*	Total
skull		2				1			3
maxilla					2				2
mandible							1	1	2
vertebra		2			2	2			6
rib						5			5
sternum						2			2
furcula						4	1		5
coracoid						2			2
humerus		1			1	4	1		7
radius						2			2
ulna						7			7
pelvis					1	1			2
femur		1	1		1	8			11
tibia		1			1	2	1		5
fibula						1			1
carpal/tarsal					2				2
metapodial	1	5		6	7	2	2		23
phalanx				7	2				9
Total	**1**	**12**	**1**	**13**	**19**	**43**	**6**	**1**	**96**

Table A3.41   Late 12th–14th century (Phase 15): Crowder Terrace pit (F71): anatomical distribution of other species

	dog	cat	red	fal	har	fow	goo	Total
antler			2					**2**
skull		1	5			4		**10**
mandible		2	2			4		**8**
vertebra	5					16	2	**23**
rib		4				20		**24**
coracoid						7		**7**
sternum						3		**3**
furcula						2	2	**4**
scapula		2				4		**6**
humerus		3				6	3	**12**
radius	1	2				3	3	**9**
ulna	1	2				6		**9**
pelvis	1					2		**3**
femur		3				6		**9**
tibia		4			2	8	6	**20**
fibula						2		**2**
carpal/tarsal				1				**1**
metapodial	2			1	1	6	2	**12**
phalanx			1			1	3	**5**
Total	**10**	**23**	**10**	**2**	**3**	**100**	**21**	**169**

Table A3.42   Late 12th–14th century (Phase 15): Crowder Terrace well (F70): anatomical distribution of other species

	dog	cat	red	?fal	roe	har	fow	goo	ana	Partridge *Perdix perdix*	Total
skull		1									**1**
mandible								1			**1**
vertebra		1					1	2			**4**
sternum							1	1			**2**
furcula							1	2			**3**
scapula		1					2				**3**
coracoid							4	2			**6**
humerus		2	1				2			1	**6**
radius	1						1				**2**
ulna		1					6		1		**8**
pelvis		2				1			1		**4**
femur		2	1				4	1			**8**
patella				1							**1**
tibia		1				2	4	1			**8**
fibula		1									**1**
carpal/tarsal		1									**1**
metapodial	1			1	1	1	2	1			**7**
phalanx		1	1				4	2			**8**
loose teeth	1										**1**
Total	**3**	**14**	**3**	**2**	**1**	**4**	**32**	**13**	**2**	**1**	**74**

Table A3.43 Late 12th–14th century (Phase 15): Sussex Street pits: anatomical distribution of other species

	cat	red	fow	goo	?mal	ana	Lapwing *Vanellus vanellus*	Gyrfalcon *Falco rusticolus*	Total
antler		1							1
mandible	3								3
vertebra			1						1
sternum				1					1
furcula						1			1
scapula			1	1					2
humerus			7					1	8
radius			2						2
ulna			4	1	1			1	7
femur			3				1	1	5
tibia			2	1					3
metapodial			7					1	8
loose teeth		1							1
Total	**3**	**2**	**27**	**4**	**1**	**1**	**1**	**4**	**43**

Table A3.44 Late 12th–14th century (Phase 15): Sussex Street building 714.2: anatomical distribution of other species

	dog	cat	red	roe	har	fow	goo	Grey heron *cinerea Ardea*	Crane *Grus* sp.	Buzzard *Buteo buteo*	Gyrfalcon *Falco rusticolus*	col	Total
antler			1										1
vertebra		6			1								7
furcula							1						1
scapula				1		1							2
humerus						2							2
radius	1			1				1					3
ulna	1	1			1	3	2	1					9
pelvis	4	2											6
femur	1	4	1			2	1			1			10
tibia	1	3			1	1							6
carpal/tarsal		1											1
metapodial	2					1			1		2	1	7
phalanx									2				2
Total	**10**	**17**	**2**	**2**	**3**	**10**	**4**	**2**	**3**	**1**	**2**	**1**	**57**

Table A3.45   Late 12th–14th century (Phase 15):
Sussex Street recut ditch (F126): anatomical distribution of other species

	dog	cat	red	roe	har	fow	goo	Grey heron *Ardea cinerea*	Red kite *Milvus milvus*	Total
mandible	4									**4**
vertebra	1	4				1				**6**
coracoid						1				**1**
scapula		1								**1**
humerus	1	4				2			1	**8**
radius	1	1	1		1			1		**5**
ulna		1		1	1	1		1		**5**
pelvis	3	3								**6**
femur		2				1				**3**
tibia		3				2	3			**8**
carpal/tarsal	2	1								**3**
metapodial	5		1			1		1		**8**
phalanx	2						1	1		**4**
loose teeth	1									**1**
Total	**20**	**20**	**2**	**1**	**2**	**9**	**4**	**4**	**1**	**63**

Table A3.46 Late 12th–14th century (Phase 15): Boundary cutting New Road (Oram's Arbour) ditch (F391): anatomical distribution of other species

	dog	cat	red	fal	har	fow	goo	Gyrfalcon *Falco rusticolus*	Buzzard *Buteo buteo*	Wader *?Tringa sp.*	Wood pigeon *Columba palumbus*	col	Jackdaw *Corvus monedula*	Starling *Sturnus vulgaris*	House sparrow *Passer domesticus*	Total
antler			1													1
skull	9															9
maxilla	3															3
mandible	6															6
vertebra	25															25
rib	8															8
coracoid						1	1									2
sternum																0
furcula																0
scapula	2				1											3
humerus	18	10		1	2	6			1	1				1	1	41
radius	6												1			7
ulna	5	1			1	3	3	1				1				14
pelvis	7	1														8
femur	15	8			1	8					1					33
tibia	2	3		1	1	6	2									15
fibula	1															1
carpal/tarsal	3	1														4
metapodial	17					10	1									28
phalanx	11			1			4									16
loose teeth	12															12
Total	**149**	**24**	**1**	**3**	**6**	**34**	**11**	**1**	**1**	**1**	**1**	**1**	**1**	**1**	**1**	**236**

Table A3.47   Cattle horn cores – measurement ranges

	n	range	X	s	CV
Greatest diameter base					
Late Saxon (Phases 10 + 11)	36	32.2–61.8	48.6	8.1	16.7
Saxo-Norman (Phase 13)	9	38.3–72.5	48.8		
12th–13th century (Phase 15)	1	44.7			
Least diameter base					
Late Saxon (Phases 10 + 11)	33	26.9–52.9	38.3	7.0	18.4
Saxo-Norman (Phase 13)	9	27.8–53.8			
12th–13th century (Phase 15)	1	31			
Length outer curvature					
Late Saxon (Phases 10 + 11)	17	93–174	130	26.7	20.6
Saxo-Norman (Phase 13)	2	120, 130			
12th–13th century (Phase 15)	1	104			

Key: X mean; s standard deviation; CV co-efficient of variation

Table A4.1 Late Saxon northern and eastern suburbs and city defences:
whole fused mammal bones (in mm) with estimated withers heights (in m)

Bone	Site / phase	GL	Bp	SC	Bd	GLl	Withers height
Horse							
radius	27JS11	304	–	–	–	282	1.22
radius	CHR45	327.5	78.2	–	73.5	316	1.37
radius	VR507	307	75.6	33.5	–	285	1.23
metacarpal	CHR45	223	48.3	33.5	49.9	216	1.39
tibia	VR508	357	97.8	42.9	70.8	328	1.43
metatarsal	CHR45	259	48.4	30.1	46.9	252	1.34
phalanx 1	CHR45	83.2	52.8	35.6	47.3	–	–
phalanx 1	VR507	81.7	–	32.6	44.1	–	–
Cattle							
radius	CHR45	291.5	82	43.9	–	–	1.25
metacarpal	27JS11	184	52.3	29.7	52.4	–	1.13
metacarpal	27JS11	187	46.6	29.7	52.4	–	1.15
metacarpal	CHR45	200.3	61	33.2	66.2	–	1.23
metacarpal	VR494	174	49.8	29.1	53.1	–	1.07
Sheep							
radius	27JS11	152.2	31.9	–	29.2	–	0.61
metacarpal	HG18B	127.7	24.2	14.8	–.	–	0.62
metacarpal	CHR45	155.4	22.2	14.2	24.7	–	0.56
metacarpal	CHR47	120.9	22.2	–	–.	–	0.59
metacarpal	VR493	120.7	21.5	14.7	24.8	–	0.59
metacarpal	VR493	125.7	23	–	24.9	–	0.62
metacarpal	VR503	113.7	20.9	13.4	23.1	–	0.56
metacarpal	VR508	117.3	22.3	14.2	25	–	0.57
metatarsal	HG18B	117	19.2	11	21.7	–	0.53
metatarsal	HG18B	123.1	18.4	9.8	21.3	–	0.56
metatarsal	HG18B	126.7	19.4	11.5	23.2	–	0.58
metatarsal	CHR45	126	20	11.9	22.4	–	0.57
metatarsal	VR494	132.6	19.8	11.7	23.3	–	0.60
metatarsal	VR507	115.6	16.4	10.5	21.3	–	0.53
metatarsal	VR508	113.2	16.8	11.4	20.6	–	0.51
metatarsal	VR508	132	21.2	12.4	24.1	–	0.60
metatarsal	VR636	132.9	20.6	12.2	24.9	–	0.60
Dog							
tibia	VR508	105.2	27.3	12.4	19.8	–	0.31

Note: Withers heights factors from Driesch and Boessneck 1974
The radius of horse in VR Phase 507 is an estimated original measurement of cut bone

Table A4.2 Late Saxon: selected measurements in horse (mm) (after Driesch 1976)

		Measurements
scapula	GLP	88.8; 93.8
humerus	GLC	304; 307
	Bd	75.7; 77.6; 78.8
calcaneum	GL	106.2; 107; 109.4
astragalus	GH	56.8; 57.5; 58.9; 59.1

Table A4.3 Late Saxon: selected measurements in cattle (mm) (after Driesch 1976)

		n	x	Range	S	SE	CV
humerus	Bd	11	76.4	63.6 - 92.3	8.5	2.7	11.1
humerus	BT	11	67.7	59.5 - 75.7	5.6	1.8	8.3
radius	Bp	9	73.1	66.7 - 82	5.4	1.9	7.4
metacarpal	Bp	10	52.3	46.6 - 61	4.4	1.5	8.3
metacarpal	Bd	8	54.9	48.2 - 66.2	6.4	2.4	11.7
os coxae	LA	8	59.5	56.9 - 64.7	2.7	1	4.5
tibia	Bd	6	53.7	52.4 - 58	2.2	1	4.1
astragalus	GL	9	61	55.5 - 68.6	5.2	1.8	8.6
metatarsal	Bp	13	43.2	37.7 - 48.3	2.7	0.8	6.3
metatarsal	Bd	8	50.2	45.7 - 53.1	2.6	1	5.2

Key: x mean; S standard deviation; SE standard error; CV co-efficient of variation

Table A4.4 Late Saxon: selected measurements in sheep and sheep/goat (mm) (after Driesch 1976; key as Table A4.3)

		n	x	Range	S	SE	CV
Sheep							
humerus	Bd	10	28.1	25.6 - 30.5	1.5	0.5	5.3
humerus	BT	12	25.9	24.6 - 28	1.1	0.3	4.4
radius	Bp	18	30.2	25.4 - 32.5	1.7	0.4	5.7
radius	BFp	17	27.5	23.6 - 29.2	1.4	0.3	5.1
metacarpal	Bp	9	22.2	20.8 - 24.2	1.1	0.4	4.8
metacarpal	Bd	11	25.4	23.1 - 28.4	1.3	0.4	5.3
metatarsal	Bp	22	19.5	16.4 - 21.2	1.2	0.3	5.9
metatarsal	Bd	13	22.7	20.5 - 25.2	1.5	0.4	6.8
Sheep/goat							
tibia	Bd	20	25.1	21.7 - 27.1	1.4	0.3	5.5

Key as Table A4.3

Table A4.5 Late Saxon: selected measurements in pig and dog (mm) (after Driesch 1976; key as Table A4.3)

		n	x	Measurements or range	S	SE	CV
Pig							
l. molar 3	GL	4	–	26.1 - 30.2	–	–	–
scapula	LG	9	27.8	25.5 - 30.8	1.8	0.6	6.3
radius	Bp	15	23.2	26.6 - 30.1	1.9	0.5	7.2
tibia	Bd	5	29.5	26.1 - 33.6	2.8	1.4	9.4
Dog							
os coxae	LA	–	–	16.6; 18.5; 27.9	–	–	–

Table A4.6 Late Saxon: selected measurements in domestic fowl (mm) (after Driesch 1976; key as Table A4.3)

		n	x	Range	S	SE	CV
coracoid	GL	6	48.4	43.9 - 52.7	3.2	1.4	6.5
scapula	Dic	7	11.3	9.8 - 12.8	1.2	0.5	10.4
humerus	Bd	8	14.4	12.9 - 16.9	1.4	0.5	9.8
radius	GL	6	55.3	51.4 - 61.9	3.7	1.7	6.7
ulna	GL	6	59	47 - 68	6.8	3	11.9
femur	GL	6	70.2	55 - 80.6	7.1	2.4	10.1
femur	Bp	12	14.4	13 - 16.2	6.8	3	11.9
tibiotarsus	GL	6	88.8	69.5 - 97.2	10.6	4.8	12

Table A4.7 Late Saxon: bone articular breadths compared with data from middle Saxon Hamwic (Melbourne Street sites)

cattle	98.6% (n=63)
sheep and sheep/goat	96.4% (n=89)
pig	97.7% (n=36)
domestic fowl	97.4% (n=50)
domestic fowl (length)	94.2% (n=31)

Table A5.1   Saxo-Norman: northern suburb:
Victoria Road, Phases 529, 530, and 532: anatomical distribution of sheep/goat and cattle

	sheep + goat				cattle			
	NISP	MNE L	MNE R	%	NISP	MNE L	MNE R	%
mandible	80	33	23	84.8	22	5	6	45.8
lower tooth	32				28			
maxilla	41				15			
upper tooth	52				46			
id skull	88				80			
horn core	25	10	10	30.3	15	4	7	45.8
hyoid	4				1			
atlas	12			36.4	6			18.2
axis	6			18.2	1			3.0
scapula	25	12	10	33.3	13	2	4	25.0
humerus	35	14	12	39.4	9	2	2	16.7
radius	46	17	18	53.0	22	5	3	33.3
ulna	20	10	8	27.3	8	3	4	29.2
carpals	6				3			
pelvis	39	9	10	28.8	14	4	4	33.3
femur	28	6	7	19.7	22	3	5	33.3
tibia	62	19	22	62.1	29	5	12	70.8
patella					9			
astragalus	3	0	3	4.5	4	1	3	16.7
calcaneum	6	1	4	7.6	7	5	2	29.2
tarsals	5	2	3	7.6	8			0.0
metacarpal	70	12	24	54.5	20	7	6	54.2
metatarsal	67	23	23	69.7	17	4	6	41.7
metapodial frg	8				2			
phalanx 1	27			10.2	17			17.7
phalanx 2	7			2.7	13			13.5
phalanx 3	7			2.7	14			14.6
Total	**801**	**(33)**			**445**			

Key: NISP number of identified specimens; MNE minimum number of element; id skull identified skull; lat metap lateral metapodial; MNI in brackets ( ); metap frag metapodial fragment

Table A5.2 Saxo-Norman: northern suburb:
Victoria Road, Phases 529, 530, and 532: anatomical distribution of domestic fowl

phase	VR529	VR530		VR532		HG29	
age	AD	AD	IMM	AD	IMM	AD	IMM
skull		3		6			
coracoid		6		8	1	2	
furcula		6		4	1		
scapula		6		6		1	
sternum	1	3		4		1	
humerus	2	6	1	7	3		
radius		6		8	1	1	
ulna		7		9		1	
carpomc		6		2	1		
synsacrum	1	3		6		2	
femur	2	8		8	1	5	1
tibiotarsus	3	8		8	3	5	
tarsometarsus	1	5		6	2	1	
other		83		10	1		
Total	10	156	1	92	14	19	1
TMTs with spur	0	0		3		0	
% with spur	0.0	0.0		50.0		0.0	
n skeletons		3?		5?			

Key: AD adult; IMM immature; TMT tarsometatarsus

Table A5.3 Saxo-Norman: city defences: Henly's Garage, Phase 29:
anatomical distribution of sheep/goat, cattle, and pig

	sheep/goat				cattle				pig			
	NISP	MNE L	MNE R	%	NISP	MNE L	MNE R	%	NISP	MNE L	MNE R	%
mandible	26	7	12	73.1	12	3	2	17.9	8	3	2	41.7
lower tooth					6				4			
maxilla	2				2				5			
upper tooth	8				9				1			
id skull	8				17				10			
horn core	24	12	6	69.2	8	3	3	21.4	–			–
atlas	1			7.7	3			21.4				0.0
axis	4			30.8	2			14.3				0.0
scapula	5	2	3	19.2	10	3	3	21.4	7	1	5	50.0
humerus	14	5	4	34.6	6	3	1	14.3	6	2	2	33.3
radius	22	12	7	73.1	21	6	3	32.1	6	5	1	50.0
ulna	7	0	5	19.2	9	4	4	28.6	7	2	4	50.0
pelvis	11	4	3	26.9	13	3	6	32.1	4	1	3	33.3
femur	7	3	1	15.4	9	2	2	14.3	6	1	3	33.3
tibia	30	13	13	100.0	7	4	2	21.4	8	6	2	66.7
fibula									1			
astragalus				0.0				0.0				0.0
calcaneum	1		1	3.8	1	1	0	3.6	2	1	1	16.7
metacarpal	22	9	11	76.9	43	13	12	89.3	4		1	8.3
metatarsal	24	11	9	76.9	41	14	10	85.7				0.0
metap frag					1				1			
phalanx 1	2			1.9	7			6.3				0.0
phalanx 2				0.0	3			2.7				0.0
phalanx 3				0.0	2			1.8				0.0
Total	218	(13)	(13)		232	(14)			80	(6)		

Key as Table A5.1

**Table A5.4   13th-14th century: eastern suburb:
St John's Street, Phase 13: anatomical distribution of sheep/goat, cattle, and pig**

	sheep/goat NISP	cattle NISP	pig NISP		sheep/goat NISP	cattle NISP	pig NISP
mandible	3			patella	2		
lower tooth	1		1	tibia	5	1	
maxilla	1			fibula			1
id skull		2	2	astragalus	1		
horn core*	5		–	calcaneum		2	1
atlas		1		tarsals			1
scapula	2			metacarpal	7	2	
humerus	1		1	metatarsal	2		
radius	2	2		phalanx 1	5	1	
ulna	2			phalanx 2		1	
carpals		1		phalanx 3	2	1	
pelvis	3	2	1	**Total**	**49**	**16**	**8**
femur	5						

* 4 from goat. Key as Table A5.1

**Table A5.5   13th-14th century: eastern suburb: St John's Street, Phase 16:
anatomical distribution of sheep/goat, cattle, and pig**

	sheep (n)	MNE R	MNE L	%	cattle (n)	pig (n)
mandible	8	2	2	28.6	2	2
lower tooth	4				5	2
maxilla	1					
upper tooth	12					
id skull	4				2	3
horn core*	15	3	6	64.3		
atlas	2			28.6		1
axis	2			28.6		
scapula	3	2		14.3		1
humerus	4	1	3	28.6		
radius	6	3	2	35.7	2	
ulna	1	1		7.1	2	
carpals	1				3	
pelvis	6	2	2	28.6	3	
femur	3	2	1	21.4	1	2
tibia	6	3	1	28.6	1	3
astragalus	1		1	7.1		
calcaneum	3	2	1	21.4		1
tarsals					1	
metacarpal	8	2	4	42.9	2	
metatarsal	16	3	7	71.4	1	1
lat metap						2
phalanx 1	7			6.3	1	3
phalanx 2					1	
phalanx 3	1			0.9	1	
Total	**114**				**28**	**21**

* 7 from goat. Key as Table A5.1

Table A5.6   13th–14th century: eastern suburb:
St John's Street, Phase 30: anatomical distribution
of sheep/goat, cattle, and pig

	sheep NISP	cattle NISP	pig NISP
mandible	7	7	14
lower tooth	5	3	9
maxilla	1	2	3
upper tooth	6	3	
id skull	3	4	5
horn core*	9		
axis	3	1	
scapula	1	1	5
humerus	5	4	4
radius	12	8	4
ulna	2	6	4
carpals		3	
pelvis	8	4	2
femur	3	6	5
patella	1	3	
tibia	12	4	4
fibula			3
astragalus	2		1
calcaneum	2	4	1
tarsals	1	2	
metacarpal	10	6	3
metatarsal	11	6	2
phalanx 1	3	11	
phalanx 2		4	1
phalanx 3		3	1
Total	**107**	**95**	**71**

* 4 from goat. Key as Table A5.1

**Table A5.7　13th–14th century: eastern suburb: Chester Road, Phase 53:
anatomical distribution of sheep/goat, cattle, and pig**

	sheep/goat				cattle				pig			
	NISP	MNE L	MNE R	%	NISP	MNE L	MNE R	%	NISP	MNE L	MNE R	%
mandible	14	4	4	30.8	27	3	4	31.8	10	1	2	18.8
lower tooth	23				20				35			
maxilla	3				2				3			
upper tooth	32				26				11			
id skull	6				15				19			
horn core	9	4	3	26.9	7	3	3	27.3	-			
hyoid	1				2							
atlas	4			30.8	3			27.3	1			12.5
axis	3			23.1	3			27.3				0.0
scapula	11	4	2	23.1	15	2	5	31.8	6	4	1	31.3
humerus	21	8	7	57.7	17	2	5	31.8	18	8	6	87.5
radius	16	7	2	34.6	21	5	5	45.5	15	8	5	81.3
ulna	10	3	4	26.9	9	2	4	27.3	14	6	3	56.3
carpals	3				10				3			
pelvis	7	2	2	15.4	10	3	3	27.3	3	1	1	12.5
femur	12	3	3	23.1	11	3	3	27.3	9	7	1	50.0
tibia	45	11	13	92.3	17	2	5	31.8	17	8	7	93.8
fibula									3			
patella					1							
astragalus	10	5	4	34.6	8	2	4	27.3	4	2	2	25.0
calcaneum	3	1	2	11.5	16	4	11	68.2	4	2	2	25.0
tarsals	1				4	2	2	18.2	1			
metacarpal	13	6	3	34.6	22	6	6	54.5	9			28.1
metatarsal	18	5	7	46.2	19	3	3	27.3	3			9.4
lat metap	-				-				10			
metap frag	1				4				2			
phalanx 1	18			17.3	31			35.2	6			9.4
phalanx 2	5			4.8	7			8.0	4			6.3
phalanx 3	1			1.0	7			8.0	2			3.1
lat phals	-				-				2			
sesamoid					1							
Total	**290**		**(13)**		**335**		**(11)**		**214**	**(8)**		

Key as Table A5.1

Table A5.8　13th–14th century: northern suburb: Victoria Road, Phase 616:
anatomical distribution of sheep, cattle, pig, and goose

	sheep	cattle	pig	goose		sheep	cattle	pig	goose
mandible	3				femur	1	1	1	
lower tooth	2	1			tibia	9	1	1	
upper tooth		1	1		fibula			1	
id skull			1		astragalus		1		
hyoid		1			calcaneum		1	1	
atlas	2				tarsals		1		
sacrum		1			metacarpal		2		13
scapula		2	1	1	metatarsal	1	2		1
humerus	4	3	1		lat metap			1	
radius	8	1	2		phalanx 1				11
ulna	1	3							
pelvis		1			Total	31	23	11	26

Table A5.9　13th–14th century: northern suburb: Victoria Road, Phase 635:
anatomical distribution of sheep/goat, cattle, and pig

	sheep/goat				cattle	pig
	NISP	MNE L	MNE R	%	NISP	NISP
mandible	6	3	3	37.5	1	1
lower tooth	1					2
maxilla						2
upper tooth	3					4
id skull	1				1	4
horn core	2	1		6.3		-
scapula	6	2	3	31.3		
humerus	7	3	1	25.0	3	2
radius	15	4	8	75.0	3	2
ulna	5	1	4	31.3	2	2
carpals	4				4	
pelvis	5	2	3	31.3	4	
femur	10	1	5	37.5		2
tibia	19	6	7	81.3		2
patella					1	
astragalus	5	1	4	31.3	1	
calcaneum	3	1	2	18.8		1
tarsals	3					
metacarpal	8	6	1	43.8	3	1
metatarsal	7	4		25.0		6
lat metap		1				3
metap frag	2				1	1
phalanx 1	6			9.4	3	1
phalanx 2					1	1
phalanx 3	1			1.6	1	
Total	119		(8)		29	37

Table A5.10   13th–14th century: northern suburb: Victoria Road, Phase 637: anatomical distribution of sheep/goat, cattle, and pig

	sheep/goat				cattle	pig
	NISP	MNE L	MNE R	%	NISP	NISP
mandible	4	1	1	14.3	3	6
lower tooth	8				1	2
maxilla	1					
upper tooth	4				3	
id skull	1					
horn core	6	2	3	35.7		
hyoid					1	
atlas	2			28.6		
axis	1			14.3		
sacrum	1				1	
scapula	3	2	1	21.4	3	3
humerus	6	5	1	42.9	4	1
radius	10	2	7	64.3	5	2
ulna	4	1	3	28.6	4	1
pelvis	3	2		14.3	1	1
femur	5	1	3	28.6	2	4
tibia	7	2	3	35.7	11	3
astragalus					2	1
calcaneum					2	
tarsals	2					
metacarpal	11	5	4	64.3	4	1
metatarsal	12	7	5	85.7	5	2
lat metap						2
phalanx 1	6			10.7	2	1
phalanx 2	8			14.3	1	1
phalanx 3	3			5.4	1	
Total	**108**	**(7)**	**(7)**		**56**	**31**

Key as Table A5.1

Table A5.11 13th–14th century: northern suburb: Victoria Road, Phase 743: anatomical distribution of horse, sheep/goat, cattle, and pig

	horse NISP	sheep/goat NISP	cattle NISP	pig NISP
mandible	2	2		
lower tooth	–	2	1	
maxilla	(2)	1		1
upper tooth	–	2		
id skull	1	5		1
horn core	–	1		
hyoid		4		
atlas	1			
axis	1			
scapula	2	1		
humerus	2	1		
radius	1	1		1
ulna	1		1	
pelvis		1		
femur	2		1	
tibia	2	1		
patella	2			
astragalus	2			
calcaneum	2		1	
tarsals	3			
metacarpal		7		
metatarsal	1	4		1
lat metap	2			
metap frag	–		1	
phalanx 1	1			
phalanx 2		1		
phalanx 3		2	1	
Total	**28**	**36**	**6**	**4**
cervical	4			
thoracic	6			
lumbar	0			
sacrum	2			
ribs	7			
Total	**47**			

Table A5.12   13th–14th century: anatomical distribution of domestic fowl

phase	SJS13	SJS16	VR616	VR635		VR637		VR783	VR975		SJS29	HG20	CHR53		SJS30	
age	AD	AD	AD	AD	IMM	AD	IMM	AD	AD	IMM	AD	AD	AD	IMM	AD	IMM
skull	0								1						1	
coracoid	2	1			5	2	3		4	1			4		4	3
furcula	1						1						1		1	1
scapula	3				4		2						3		4	
sternum	0				3		2		3				1		2	
humerus	3	1		1	10		3		10	1			10	3	3	4
radius		1			5		1		4				2		2	
ulna	2			1	6	1	5	1	1	1		1	12	2	5	4
carpomc					1		1		2				1		2	
synsacrum	1	1		4	4				1				2		3	
femur	2	1	1	1	8		3	1	3				9	1	2	2
tibiotarsus	3	1	1	1	6	1	2	1	2			1	11	6	6	4
tarsometa-tarsus		1	1	1	11		2	3	3	1	1		3	2	4	4
other	1	1		1	2				1							
Total	**18**	**8**	**3**	**10**	**65**	**4**	**25**	**6**	**35**	**4**	**1**	**2**	**59**	**14**	**39**	**22**
TMTs with spur		0	0	1				1	0		0		2		2	
% with spur		0.0	0.0	100.0				33.3	0.0		0.0		66.7		50.0	
n skeletons															2	

Key as Table A5.2

Table A5.13 13th–14th century: northern suburb: Victoria Road, Phase 975: anatomical distribution of sheep/goat, cattle, and pig

	sheep + goat				cattle				pig			
	NISP	MNE L	MNE R	%	NISP	MNE L	MNE R	%	NISP	MNE L	MNE R	%
mandible	16	5	2	43.8	2	1	1	25.0	10	3	5	50.0
lower tooth	9				10				14			
maxilla					1				6			
upper tooth	3				5				12			
id skull	1				2				5			
horn core	2	1	1	12.5	0			0.0	-			
atlas					1			25				0.0
axis	2			25.0				0.0				0.0
scapula	6	2	4	37.5	7	3	2	62.5	10	8	2	62.5
humerus	11	6	5	68.8	8	2	1	37.5	3	1	1	12.5
radius	9	3	1	25.0	6	2	1	37.5	6	2	4	37.5
ulna	2	2	0	12.5	7	2	4	75.0	5	0	4	25.0
carpals					1							
pelvis	6	2	1	18.8	4	2	1	37.5	2	1	1	12.5
femur	4	1	1	12.5	12	4	2	75.0	4	1	1	12.5
tibia	13	8	2	62.5	8	2	2	50.0	4	1	2	18.8
fibula									3			
patella									1			
astragalus	3	0	3	18.8	3	1	2	37.5	2	1	1	12.5
calcaneum	1	1	0	6.3	3	2	1	37.5	3	1	2	18.8
tarsals	1				1							
metacarpal	6	3	1	25.0	11	4	2	75.0				
metatarsal	6	3	1	25.0	7	3	1	50.0				
lat metap									5			
metap frag					1				4			
phalanx 1	3			4.7	8			12.5	2			3.1
phalanx 2					6			9.4				0.0
phalanx 3					1			1.6	1			1.6
sesamoid					1							
Total	104	(8)			116	(4)	(4)		102	(8)		

Key as Table A5.1

Table A5.14   14th century: northern suburb: Victoria Road, Phase 700: anatomical distribution of sheep/goat and pig

	sheep/goat				pig			
	NISP	MNE L	MNE R	%	NISP	MNE L	MNE R	%
mandible	4	2	2	25.0	8	3	5	57.1
lower tooth	9				3			
maxilla					2			
upper tooth	6				5			
id skull	4				6			
atlas	1			12.5				
scapula	4	3	1	25.0	8	4	4	57.1
humerus	5	2	2	25.0	12	4	7	78.6
radius	11	5	2	43.8	11	4	5	64.3
ulna	1	1		6.3	5	3	2	35.7
pelvis	3	1	2	18.8	5	2	1	21.4
femur	6		4	25.0	8	1	5	42.9
tibia	10	3	4	43.8	6	3	2	35.7
astragalus	1		1	6.3	2	0	2	14.3
calcaneum					3	1	2	21.4
metacarpal	12	7	3	62.5	8	3	3	42.9
metatarsal	13	8	5	81.3	1	1		7.1
metapodial	1				1			
lat metap					1			
phalanx 1	10			15.6				
phalanx 2	1			1.6				
phalanx 3					2			3.6
Total	102	(8)			97		(7)	

Key as Table A5.1

Table A5.15   Late 14th–17th century: anatomical distribution of domestic fowl

phase	VR700		VR685	VR792		VR756		SJS49		CHR56	
age	AD	IMM	AD	AD	IMM	AD	IMM	AD	IMM	AD	IMM
skull	2							2			
coracoid	1	3		1		4		4		1	
furcula								2		1	
scapula	2	2				3	2	5		1	
sternum	2	2				1		10			
humerus	4	5		1	1	4	1	8			
radius		1				4	1	2			
ulna	3	4				7	1	6		1	
carpomc		1								1	
synsacrum		4				4		6	1	1	
femur	4			1	1	5	2	6		3	3
tibiotarsus	6	6		3		2	3	13	2	3	
tarsometarsus	4	1	3	2	1	2		7		3	
other								2			
Total	**28**	**29**	**3**	**8**	**3**	**36**	**10**	**73**	**3**	**15**	**3**
TMTs with spur	1		1	1		1		3		0	
% with spur	25.0		33.3	50.0		50.0		42.9		0.0	
n skeletons	1?										

Key as Table A5.2

Table A5.16 14th–15th century: northern suburb: Victoria Road, Phase 792:
anatomical distribution of sheep/goat, cattle, and pig

	sheep/goat				cattle	pig
	NISP	MNE L	MNE R	%	NISP	NISP
mandible	10	5	5	38.5	2	7
lower tooth	1					
maxilla	4					7
upper tooth	1				3	2
id skull	7					3
horn core	1		1	3.8		
scapula	3	3		11.5	2	3
humerus	4	1	3	15.4		2
radius	5	2	3	19.2	1	
ulna	4	3	1	15.4	1	
pelvis	4	2	2	15.4		3
femur	4	1	2	11.5		1
tibia	2	1	1	7.7	2	7
astragalus					1	3
calcaneum					1	
metacarpal	16	7	9	61.5	3	1
metatarsal	15	2	13	57.7	2	2
metapodial	1					1
phalanx 1	13			12.5	1	2
phalanx 2	3			2.9		2
phalanx 3	1			1.0	3	
Total	**99**		**(13)**		**22**	**46**

Key as Table A5.1

Table A5.17   Later 15th–16th century: northern suburb: Victoria Road, Phase 756: anatomical distribution of sheep/goat, cattle, and pig

	sheep/goat				cattle	pig			
	NISP	MNE L	MNE R	%	NISP	NISP	MNE L	MNE R	%
mandible	15	6	5	91.7	14	17	2	6	66.7
lower tooth	14				13	18			
maxilla	6				2	7			
upper tooth	13				7	12			
id skull	11				1	4			
horn core	3	2	1	25.0		-			
scapula	9	3	3	50.0	7	2		2	16.7
humerus	6	1	5	50.0	3	6	1	5	50.0
radius	13	5	4	75.0	3	3	3		25.0
ulna	4	2	1	25.0	1	6	4	2	50.0
carpals					2				
pelvis	5	2	2	33.3	6	4		3	25.0
femur	6	3	1	33.3	3	2		1	8.3
tibia	8	4	2	50.0	3	5	2	3	41.7
calcaneum					1	4	1	3	33.3
metacarpal	5	2	1	25.0		4		1	8.3
metatarsal	5	2	2	33.3	3	4		1	8.3
lat metap						1			
metap frag	1								
phalanx 1	1			2.1	4	1			0.5
phalanx 2					2				
Total	**125**	**(6)**			**75**	**100**		**(6)**	

Key as Table A5.1

Table A5.18 Later 15th–16th century: northern suburb: Victoria Road, Phase 763:
anatomical distribution of sheep/goat, cattle, and pig

	sheep/goat				cattle				pig			
	NISP	MNE L	MNE R	%	NISP	MNE L	MNE R	%	NISP	MNE L	MNE R	%
mandible	22	9	5	87.5	6	3	1	22.2	7	4	3	50.0
lower tooth	17				4				13			
maxilla	1				1				1			
upper tooth	16				11				7			
id skull	5				3				5			
horn core	7	3	3	16.7					–			
axis	2			11.1								
sacrum					1							
scapula	22	11	11	61.1	7	3	1	22.2	5	3	2	35.7
humerus	28	13	8	58.3	15	3	4	38.9	12	7	5	85.7
radius	34	18	13	86.1	20	5	8	72.2	15	7	6	92.9
ulna	6	3	3	16.7	9	3	2	27.8	7	4	1	35.7
carpals					1							
pelvis	15	5	5	27.8	10	5	2	38.9	2		2	14.3
femur	22	10	3	36.1	11	4	2	33.3	11	5	5	71.4
tibia	34	9	13	61.1	17	5	4	50.0	7	4	3	50.0
patella					3							
astragalus	0				4	2	2	22.2	1		1	7.1
calcaneum	3	1	2	8.3	11	5	6	61.1	1		1	7.1
tarsals	2				3							
metacarpal	18	4	7	30.6	6	2	2	22.2	1			
metatarsal	27	10	11	58.3	14	4	9	72.2	6			
lat metap									4			
metap frag					1				2			
phalanx 1	6			4.2	12			16.7	2			3.6
phalanx 2	2			1.4	12			16.7	1			1.8
phalanx 3	1			0.7	10			13.9				
Total	**290**	**(18)**			**192**		**(9)**		**110**	**(7)**		

Key as Table A5.1

Table A5.19   Later 15th–16th century: eastern suburb: St John's Street, Phase 49:
anatomical distribution of sheep/goat, cattle, and pig

	sheep/goat				cattle				pig			
	NISP	MNE L	MNE R	%	NISP	MNE L	MNE R	%	NISP	MNE L	MNE R	%
mandible	33	13	9	55.0	10	3	3	42.9	17	8	6	87.5
lower tooth	16				6				10			
maxilla	10				2				11			
upper tooth	11				2				5			
id skull	17				9				20			
horn core	4	1	1	3.0					–			
hyoid	3				2							
atlas	7			35.0	2			28.6				
axis	5			25.0	1			14.3	2			25.0
scapula	27	11	15	65.0	8	3	2	35.7	7	4	3	43.8
humerus	26	10	9	47.5	11	3	4	50.0	15	4	4	50.0
radius	35	13	20	82.5	18	5	2	50.0	15	6	8	87.5
ulna	11	6	4	25.0	7	3	1	28.6	2	1	1	12.5
carpals	1				8				1			
pelvis	40	12	12	60.0	15	4	6	71.4	9	1	5	37.5
femur	35	14	4	45.0	20	5	3	57.1	4	1	2	18.8
patella	1				3							
tibia	46	12	13	62.5	13	4	3	50.0	8	2	3	31.3
fibula									6			
astragalus	6	4	2	15.0	6	1	4	35.7	2		2	12.5
calcaneum	6	2	4	15.0	5	1	4	35.7	2	1	1	12.5
tarsals	3				3							
metacarpal	18	8	4	30.0	13	4	4	57.1	–			
metatarsal	13	4	7	27.5	15	3	7	71.4	–			
metapodial					6				14			
lat metap					1				3			
phalanx 1	3			4.8	32			17.9	4			2.6
phalanx 2	1			1.6	22			12.3	4			2.6
phalanx 3					25			14.0				
sesamoid					2							
Total	**378**		**(20)**		**267**		**(7)**		**161**	**(8)**	**(8)**	

Key as Table A5.1

Table A5.20   17th century: eastern suburb: Chester Road, Phase 56:
anatomical distribution of sheep/goat, cattle, and pig

	sheep/goat				cattle				pig			
	NISP	MNE L	MNE R	%	NISP	MNE L	MNE R	%	NISP	MNE L	MNE R	%
mandible	12	6	6	40.0	10	2	4	60.0	8	3	3	42.9
lower tooth	23				26				14			
maxilla	2								3			
upper tooth	20				6				6			
hyoid					1							
id skull	2				5				2			
horn core	2	1	1	6.7	3	1	1	20.0	-			
atlas	5		3	20.0	2			40.0				0
axis	2		2	13.3	4			80.0				0
scapula	9	1	5	20.0	7	2	2	40.0	5	1	3	28.6
humerus	23	13	8	70.0	17	4	5	90.0	18	7	7	100.0
radius	34	10	9	63.3	10	2	1	30.0	8	1	5	42.9
ulna	10	4	4	26.7	7	2	2	40.0	3	2	1	21.4
carpals					7				3			
pelvis	24	7	6	43.3	15	3	2	50.0	10	3	3	42.9
femur	12	8	2	33.3	13	2	2	40.0	5	2	3	35.7
tibia	44	12	11	76.7	12	4	4	80.0	11	3	5	57.1
fib/lat mall					2				1			
patella					1							
astragalus	3	2	1	10.0	2	1	1	20.0	1	1	0	7.1
calcaneum	6	2	4	20.0	9	5	2	70.0	6	3	3	42.9
tarsals	1								1			
metacarpal	35	12	8	66.7	14	3	4	70.0	9			32
metatarsal	38	13	15	93.3	8	1	2	30.0				
lat metap									2			
metap frag	3				5							
phalanx 1	13			5.4	21			52.5	4			7.1
phalanx 2	9			3.8	7			17.5	2			3.6
phalanx 3	2			0.8	4			10.0				0.0
sacrum									2			
Total	**334**		**(15)**		**218**	**(5)**	**(5)**		**124**	**(7)**	**(7)**	

Key as Table A5.1

Table A5.21   All sites: sheep: eruption and wear of teeth (after Grant 1982: age classes follow Payne 1973)

Site and Phase	anatomy	side	DP4	P4	M1	M2	M3	Stage
Saxo-Norman								
VR529	jaw	R	a					A
VR530	jaw	R	a		C			A
HG29	jaw	L	a		E			A
VR530	jaw	L	d					B
VR530	jaw		b					B
VR532	jaw	L	c					B
VR532	jaw	L	c		V			B
VR532	jaw	R	c		V			B
VR532	jaw	R	c		V			B
VR530	jaw	R	h		c			C
VR532	jaw	L	n		g	d	V	D
VR532	jaw	L			g	d	V	D
VR532	jaw	R		b	g	e	V	D
VR532	jaw	L	k		g	e	V	D
VR530	tooth	R					a	D
VR532	jaw	R	k		g		a	D
VR530	jaw	L		c	g	f	a	D
VR532	jaw	L		f	g			D/E
VR532	jaw	R		f	g	g		D/E
VR532	jaw	R		f	g	g		D/E
VR530	jaw	R		d	g	g	b	E
VR532	jaw	L		f	g	g	b	E
VR532	jaw	L		d	g	e	c	E
VR532	jaw	L				g	c	E
VR532	jaw	R		g	g	g	c	E
VR532	jaw	L		f	g	g	c	E
HG29	jaw	R		f	g	g	c	E
VR530	tooth	L					e	F
VR530	tooth	L					e	F
VR530	tooth	R					e	F
VR530	tooth						e	F
VR530	tooth	R					e	F
VR529	jaw	L				e	e	F
HG29	jaw	R		e	g	f	e	F
VR532	jaw	R				g	e	F
HG29	jaw	R				g	e	F
VR532	jaw	L		g	g	g	e	F
HG29	jaw	R		g	g	g	e	F
HG29	jaw	R		g	g	g	e	F
VR532	jaw	R		g	g	g	e	F
HG29	jaw	L		g	g	g	e	F
VR532	jaw	R		h	g	g	e	F
VR530	jaw	R			g	g	e	F
HG29	jaw	L			g	g	e	F

Table A5.21 (*cont.*) All sites: sheep: eruption and wear of teeth (after Grant 1982: age classes follow Payne 1973)

Site and Phase	anatomy	side	DP4	P4	M1	M2	M3	Stage
VR532	jaw	L		f	g	g	e	F
HG29	jaw	L		f	g	g	e	F
VR530	jaw	L		g	h	g	e	F
VR532	jaw	L		g	h	g	e	F
VR530	jaw	L		g	h	g	f	F
VR530	jaw	R		g	k	g	f	F
HG29	jaw	R		g	g	g		F/G
VR530	jaw	R		f	h	g		F/G
VR530	jaw	R		g	g			F/G
VR530	jaw	L		f	k			G
VR529	jaw	L		h	k	g	g	G
VR532	jaw	R		j	k	g	g	G
VR529	jaw	R		g	k	g	g	G
VR530	jaw	R		f	k	g	g	G
VR529	jaw	L		g	k	g	g	G
HG29	jaw	L			l	g	g	G
VR532	jaw	L		h	m	g	g	G
VR530	jaw	L		h	m	h	g	H
VR530	jaw	L		h	m	h	g	H
VR532	jaw	L		h	m	h	g	H
VR530	jaw	L		h	m	h	g	H
VR532	jaw	L		h	m	h	g	H
13th–14th century: eastern suburb								
SJS30	jaw	L			h	g		
SJS16	jaw	R	a					A
SJS16	jaw	L	E					A
SJS16	jaw	R	a		V			A
CHR53	tooth	L	b					B
CHR53	tooth	L			f			C
SJS30	tooth	L				c		D
CHR53	tooth	R				c		D
SJS30	tooth	R				d		D
SJS16	tooth	R				f		D
CHR53	jaw	L			g	g		D
SJS30	jaw	L	g		g	d	V	D
SJS13	jaw	R		g		d	o	D
CHR53	tooth	R					c	E
CHR53	tooth	L					d	F
SJS30	jaw	L			h	g	f	F
SJS30	jaw	L					g	G
CHR53	tooth	R					g	G
CHR53	tooth	L					g	G
SJS30	tooth	R					g	G
CHR53	tooth	R					g	G
CHR53	tooth	L					g	G

Table A5.21 (*cont.*)   All sites: sheep: eruption and wear of teeth (after Grant 1982: age classes follow Payne 1973)

Site and Phase	anatomy	side	DP4	P4	M1	M2	M3	Stage
CHR53	jaw	L				g	g	G
CHR53	jaw	R			g	g	g	G
SJS16	jaw	R		h	h	g	g	G
CHR53	jaw	L		h	k	g	g	G
CHR53	jaw	L		h	m	h	g	G
SJS16	jaw	R		g	m	h	g	H
CHR53	jaw	R			m	l	g	H
13th–14th century: northern suburb								
VR635	jaw	L	a					A
VR743	jaw	R	l		g			C
VR616	jaw	R		d	g	g	b	E
VR616	jaw	R		f	k	g	d	F
VR635	jaw	L			g		e	F
VR616	jaw	R				g	f	F
VR637	jaw	R		h	g	g	g	G
VR635	jaw	R		h	k	g	g	G
VR635	jaw	L		j	m	h	g	G
14th–15th century: northern suburb								
VR700	tooth	L					b	E
VR700	jaw	L				g	e	F
VR792	jaw	R		g	h	g	f	F
VR792	jaw	R		g	j	g	f	F
VR700	tooth	L					g	G
VR700	jaw	L				g	g	G
VR700	jaw	R				g	g	G
VR700	jaw	R			h	g	g	G
VR792	jaw	L		h	k	g	g	G
16th century								
SJS49	jaw	L	f		E	C		B
SJS49	jaw	L			b	C		C
SJS49	jaw	R	h		d	V		C
SJS49	jaw	L				d	C	D
SJS49	tooth	R					e	F
VR763	jaw	L		f	g	g	e	F
SJS49	jaw	L		f	g	g	e	F
SJS49	tooth	L					f	F
VR763	jaw	L					f	F
SJS49	jaw	L					g	G
VR763	jaw	L					g	G
SJS49	jaw	R		g	h	-	g	G
SJS49	jaw	L		-	k	-	g	G
SJS49	jaw	R		h	h	g	g	G
SJS49	jaw	L			h	g	g	G
VR763	jaw	L		h	h	g	g	G
SJS49	jaw	L		h	j	g	g	G

Table A5.21 (*cont.*)   All sites: sheep: eruption and wear of teeth (after Grant 1982: age classes follow Payne 1973)

Site and Phase	anatomy	side	DP4	P4	M1	M2	M3	Stage
SJS49	jaw	L		h	j	g	g	G
VR763	jaw	R			k	g	g	G
SJS49	jaw	R			m	g	g	G
SJS49	jaw	L		a	m	g	g	G
VR763	jaw	R		h	m	g	g	G
SJS49	jaw	R		g	m	g	g	G
VR763	jaw	R		g	h			G/H
SJS49	jaw	R			m	h	g	H
SJS49	jaw	R		m	m	k	g	H
SJS49	jaw	L		m	m	k	g	H
SJS49	jaw	L			m	k		H/I
VR763	jaw	L					h	I
VR763	jaw	R			0	m	h	I
17th century eastern suburb								
CHR56	jaw	L		f	E			B
CHR56	tooth	R				f		D
CHR56	tooth	L					d	F
CHR56	tooth	L					d	F
CHR56	jaw	L		g	k	g	d	F
CHR56	tooth	L					g	G
CHR56	tooth	L					g	G
CHR56	jaw	R		-	k	g	g	G
CHR56	jaw	R		h	m	g	g	G
CHR56	tooth	R					g	G/H
CHR56	tooth	R					g	G/H
CHR56	tooth	R					g	G/H
CHR56	tooth	R					k	I

Table A5.22 Sheep and goat: fusion: Saxo-Norman northern suburb and city defences (VR529, VR530, VR532, HG29)

	vju	uf	fg	fus	% uf
VR529					
d humerus	1	1	0	5	28.6
p radius	0	2	0	7	22.2
acetabulum	0	2	0	0	100.0
glenoid	1	2	0	5	37.5
subtotal early	2	7	0	17	34.6
1st phalanx	0	0	0	2	0.0
d tibia	0	1	0	2	33.3
d metacarpal	0	2	0	4	33.3
d metatarsal	0	0	0	1	0.0
subtotal mid	0	3	0	9	25.0
calcaneum	0	0	0	1	0.0
p ulna	0	4	0	0	100.0
p femur	0	2	0	0	100.0
p humerus	1	1	0	0	100.0
p tibia	0	2	0	0	100.0
d radius	0	2	0	0	100.0
d femur	1	1	0	1	66.7
subtotal late	2	12	0	2	87.5
VR530					
d humerus	1	0	0	3	25.0
p radius	0	2	0	5	28.6
acetabulum	0	0	0	11	0.0
glenoid	2	2	0	2	66.7
subtotal early	3	4	0	21	25.0
1st phalanx	0	1	0	3	25.0
d tibia	0	3	0	16	15.8
d metacarpal	2	5	0	1	87.5
d metatarsal	3	2	0	1	83.3
subtotal mid	5	11	0	21	43.2
calcaneum	0	1	0	0	100.0
p ulna	0	1	0	1	50.0
p femur	0	1	0	1	50.0
p humerus	1	0	0	0	100.0
p tibia	0	2	0	1	66.7
d radius	0	0	0	1	0.0
d femur	0	1	0	0	100.0
subtotal late	1	6	0	4	63.6

	vju	uf	fg	fus	% uf
VR532					
d humerus	1	1			100.0
p radius	2	1		7	30.0
acetabulum		3	7		100.0
glenoid		4		3	57.1
subtotal early	3	9	7	10	65.5
1st phalanx		7	13		100.0
d tibia				7	0.0
d metacarpal	1	6		6	53.8
d metatarsal	1	2		5	37.5
subtotal mid	2	15	13	18	62.5
calcaneum				2	0.0
p ulna		5		1	83.3
p femur		3		1	75.0
p humerus	1	3			100.0
p tibia					
d radius	2			1	66.7
d femur		5		2	71.4
subtotal late	3	16	0	7	73.1
HG29					
d humerus	3			8	27.3
p radius	3			16	15.8
acetabulum				10	0.0
glenoid				4	0.0
subtotal early	6	0	0	38	13.6
1st phalanx				2	0.0
d tibia	1	3	2	9	40.0
d metacarpal	2	1	1	6	40.0
d metatarsal	2	4	1	4	63.6
subtotal mid	5	8	4	21	44.7
calcaneum				1	0.0
p ulna		2			100.0
p femur	2	1			100.0
p humerus	3	3		1	85.7
p tibia	1	2	1	1	80.0
d radius	4	1	1	4	60.0
d femur	2				100.0
subtotal late	12	9	2	7	76.7

Key: vju neonatal / very juvenile; uf unfused; fg fusing; fus fused; d distal; p proximal

Table A5.23 Sheep and goat: fusion: 13th–14th century: eastern suburb (SJS30, SJS16, CHR53)

	vju	uf	fg	fus	% uf
SJS30					
d humerus				3	0.0
p radius				8	0.0
acetabulum				6	0.0
glenoid	1				100.0
subtotal early	1	0	0	17	5.6
1st phalanx	1			2	33.3
d tibia				6	0.0
d metacarpal				4	0.0
d metatarsal	3			2	60.0
subtotal mid	4	0	0	14	22.2
calcaneum				2	0.0
p ulna				1	0.0
p femur					
p humerus					
p tibia				1	0.0
d radius					
d femur				3	0.0
subtotal late	0	0	0	7	0.0
SJS16					
d humerus	3			1	75.0
p radius	2				100.0
acetabulum		2		2	50.0
glenoid					
subtotal early	5	2	0	3	70.0
1st phalanx				7	0.0
d tibia	1			3	25.0
d metacarpal	3	1		2	66.7
d metatarsal	6	1	1		100.0
subtotal mid	10	2	1	12	52.0
calcaneum	2			1	66.7
p ulna				1	0.0
p femur	1	2			100.0
p humerus	1				100.0
p tibia	1				100.0
d radius	3			1	75.0
d femur	1		1		100.0
subtotal late	9	2	1	3	80.0
CHR53					
d humerus	2	1		13	18.8
p radius	1			4	20.0
acetabulum	1			5	16.7
glenoid	2			3	40.0
subtotal early	6	1	0	25	21.9
1st phalanx		1		12	7.7
d tibia				18	0.0
d metacarpal	1		1	6	25.0
d metatarsal		2		2	50.0
subtotal mid	1	3	1	38	11.6
calcaneum		1		2	33.3
p ulna		1	1	2	50.0
p femur	2	1		2	60.0
p humerus	1	1		1	66.7
p tibia		1	2		100.0
d radius	1	1		2	50.0
d femur	2		1	1	75.0
subtotal late	6	6	4	10	61.5

Key as Table A5.22

Table A5.24 Sheep and goat: fusion: 13th–14th century: northern suburb (VR637, VR975)

	vju	uf	fg	fus	% uf
VR637					
d humerus	0	2	0	4	33.3
p radius	1	0	0	3	25.0
acetabulum	0	1	0	2	33.3
glenoid	0	1	0	1	50.0
subtotal early	1	4	0	10	33.3
1st phalanx	0	0	0	4	0.0
d tibia	0	1	0	4	20.0
d metacarpal	0	4	0	1	80.0
d metatarsal	0	0	0	1	0.0
subtotal mid	0	5	0	10	33.3
calcaneum	0	0	0	0	0.0
p ulna	0	2	0	1	66.7
p femur	1	1	0	0	100.0
p humerus	0	1	0	1	50.0
p tibia	0	0	0	0	0.0
d radius	1	2	0	2	60.0
d femur	1	1	0	0	100.0
subtotal late	3	7	0	4	71.4
VR975					
d humerus				8	0.0
p radius				1	0.0
acetabulum				3	0.0
glenoid					
subtotal early	0	0	0	12	0.0
1st phalanx				3	0.0
d tibia				7	0.0
d metacarpal				2	0.0
d metatarsal		1			100.0
subtotal mid	0	1	0	12	7.7
calcaneum				1	0.0
p ulna				1	0.0
p femur		1			100.0
p humerus					
p tibia					
d radius				2	0.0
d femur				2	0.0
subtotal late	0	1	0	6	14.3

Key as Table A5.22

Table A5.25 Sheep and goat: fusion: 14th–15th century: northern suburb (VR700, VR792)

	vju	uf	fg	fus	% uf
VR700					
d humerus				3	0.0
p radius				4	0.0
acetabulum				2	0.0
glenoid				3	0.0
subtotal early	0	0	0	12	0.0
1st phalanx		1		8	11.1
d tibia				4	0.0
d metacarpal	1	5		3	66.7
d metatarsal				3	0.0
subtotal mid	1	6	0	18	28.0
calcaneum				1	0.0
p ulna				1	0.0
p femur		1		2	33.3
p humerus					
p tibia		1			100.0
d radius		1		5	16.7
d femur					
subtotal late	0	3	0	9	25.0
VR792					
d humerus		1		3	25.0
p radius	2				100.0
acetabulum		2		2	50.0
glenoid		2		1	66.7
subtotal early	2	5	0	6	53.8
1st phalanx		6		1	85.7
d tibia				2	0.0
d metacarpal		9		1	90.0
d metatarsal		6			100.0
subtotal mid	0	21	0	4	84.0
calcaneum					
p ulna		4			100.0
p femur		2			100.0
p humerus		1			100.0
p tibia		2			100.0
d radius		2		2	50.0
d femur		2			100.0
subtotal late	0	13	0	2	86.7

Key as Table A5.22

Table A5.26 Sheep and goat: fusion: 16th century (VR756, VR763, SJS49) (key as Table A5.22)

	vju	uf	fg	fus	% uf
VR756					
d humerus				5	0.0
p radius				4	0.0
acetabulum				3	0.0
glenoid				3	0.0
subtotal early	0	0	0	15	0.0
1st phalanx				1	0.0
d tibia				4	0.0
d metacarpal				2	0.0
d metatarsal		1		1	50.0
subtotal mid	0	1	0	8	11.1
calcaneum					
p ulna					
p femur					
p humerus					
p tibia				3	0.0
d radius				3	0.0
d femur				1	0.0
subtotal late	0	0	0	7	0.0
VR763					
d humerus				21	0.0
p radius	1			26	3.7
acetabulum		1		13	7.1
glenoid				22	0.0
subtotal early	1	1	0	82	2.4
1st phalanx		2		4	33.3
d tibia				13	0.0
d metacarpal		2		8	20.0
d metatarsal		1		7	12.5
subtotal mid	0	5	0	32	13.5
calcaneum				3	0.0
p ulna		1		1	50.0
p femur				2	0.0
p humerus		1	1	4	33.3
p tibia				6	0.0
d radius	1			12	7.7
d femur				9	0.0
subtotal late	1	2	1	37	9.8
SJS49					
d humerus	1			18	5.3
p radius	1			27	3.6
acetabulum					
glenoid					
subtotal early	2	0	0	45	4.3
1st phalanx				3	0.0
d tibia	2			17	10.5
d metacarpal				10	0.0
d metatarsal				7	0.0
subtotal mid	2	0	0	37	5.1
calcaneum				5	0.0
p ulna		1		4	20.0
p femur	4	4		4	66.7
p humerus	1	2		3	50.0
p tibia	3	1		9	30.8
d radius	1	4		15	25.0
d femur	4	2		10	37.5
subtotal late	13	14	0	50	35.1

Key as Table A5.22

Table A5.27   Sheep and goat: fusion:
17th century (CHR56)

CHR56	vju	uf	fg	fus	% uf
d humerus				21	0.0
p radius	1			11	8.3
acetabulum				19	0.0
glenoid				3	0.0
subtotal early	1	0	0	54	1.8
1st phalanx				3	0.0
d tibia				21	0.0
d metacarpal	1			9	10.0
d metatarsal	1			6	14.3
subtotal mid	2	0	0	39	4.9
calcaneum		1		3	25.0
p ulna					
p femur					
p humerus		1	1		100.0
p tibia			2	1	0.0
d radius		2		4	33.3
d femur				3	0.0
subtotal late	0	4	3	11	38.9

Key as Table A5.22

Table A5.28   **All sites: cattle: eruption and wear of teeth (after Grant 1982; see text for definition of age stages)**

Site and Phase	anatomy	side	DP4	P4	M1	M2	M3	Stage
Saxo-Norman								
HG29	jaw	L				h	g	3
VR529	jaw	R				k	h	4
VR530	jaw	L		f	k	k	h	4
VR530	jaw	R		f	k	k	h	4
13th–14th century: eastern suburb								
CHR53	jaw	R	b		E			1
CHR53	jaw	R	b					1
CHR53	tooth	L					c	2
SJS16	tooth	R					g	3
CHR53	tooth	R			l			3
CHR53	jaw	L	f		l	k		3
CHR53	tooth						g	3
SJS16	tooth	L					g	3
SJS16	tooth	L					j	4
SJS16	jaw	L				i	j	4
14th–15th century								
VR792	jaw	L	b		a			1
VR700	jaw	R	g		k	j		2
VR700	jaw	R			g			2
VR685	jaw	L	m					2
VR700	jaw	L		e	k	k	g	3
16th century								
SJS49	jaw	L	b					1
SJS49	jaw	L	b					1
SJS49	jaw	L	b		V			1
VR763	jaw	R	b		E			1
SJS49	jaw	R	f		l	k	k	4
17th century								
CHR56	tooth	R	c					1
CHR56	tooth	R					f	2
CHR56	tooth	L					c	2
CHR56	tooth	R					g	3
CHR56	jaw	L				k	g	3
CHR56	tooth	R					l	4

Table A5.29 Cattle: fusion: Saxo-Norman (VR530, HG29)

	vju	uf	fg	fus	% uf
VR530					
glenoid	0	0	0	4	0.0
acetabulum	0	0	0	3	0.0
subtotal < 1 yr	0	0	0	7	0.0
p radius	0	0	0	5	0.0
phalanx 2	0	0	0	2	0.0
d humerus	0	0	0	2	0.0
phalanx 1	0	0	0	4	0.0
subtotal < 2yr	0	0	0	13	0.0
d tibia	0	0	0	10	0.0
d metacarpal	0	1	0	2	33.3
d metatarsal	0	2	0	2	50.0
subtotal <3 yr	0	3	0	14	17.6
calcaneum	0	1	0	1	50.0
p ulna	0	0	0	0	
p femur	0	0	0	3	0.0
p humerus	0	0	0	0	
p tibia	0	1	0	1	50.0
d radius	0	1	0	1	50.0
d femur	0	0	0	1	0.0
subtotal < 5yr	0	3	0	7	30.0
HG29					
glenoid				3	0.0
acetabulum				11	0.0
subtotal < 1 yr	0	0	0	14	0.0
p radius	1			11	8.3
phalanx 2				3	0.0
d humerus				3	0.0
phalanx 1				7	0.0
subtotal < 2yr	1	0	0	24	4.0
d tibia		1			100.0
d metacarpal	1	3		9	30.8
d metatarsal	1	7		15	34.8
subtotal <3 yr	2	11	0	24	35.1
calcaneum					
p ulna				2	0.0
p femur		2	1	1	75.0
p humerus			1	1	50.0
p tibia					
d radius	1	2	1	1	80.0
d femur		1		1	50.0
subtotal < 5yr	1	5	3	6	60.0

Key as Table A5.22

Table A5.30 Cattle: fusion: 13th–14th century: eastern suburb (SJS30, CHR53))

	vju	uf	fg	fus	% uf
SJS30					
glenoid					
acetabulum				2	0.0
subtotal < 1 yr	0	0	0	2	0.0
p radius	1			4	20.0
phalanx 2				4	0.0
d humerus				3	0.0
phalanx 1		1		5	16.7
subtotal < 2yr	1	1	0	16	11.1
d tibia				1	0.0
d metacarpal				1	0.0
d metatarsal		1		3	25.0
subtotal <3 yr	0	1	0	5	16.7
calcaneum		1		1	50.0
p ulna				2	0.0
p femur				1	0.0
p humerus					
p tibia		1			100.0
d radius	1			1	50.0
d femur		1		1	50.0
subtotal < 5yr	1	3	0	6	40.0
CHR53					
glenoid				1	0.0
acetabulum				8	0.0
subtotal < 1 yr	0	0	0	9	0.0
p radius	1			10	9.1
phalanx 2				7	0.0
d humerus		2		5	28.6
phalanx 1	3	2		24	17.2
subtotal < 2 yr	4	4	0	46	14.8
d tibia	1	1	1	6	33.3
d metacarpal	1	1		7	22.2
d metatarsal				7	0.0
subtotal <3 yr	2	2	1	20	20.0
calcaneum	3	4		2	77.8
p ulna		2			100.0
p femur		1	2	2	60.0
p humerus					
p tibia		1		1	50.0
d radius	1	2			100.0
d femur		1		2	33.3
subtotal < 5yr	4	11	2	7	70.8

Key as Table A5.22

Table A5.31   Cattle: fusion : 13th–14th century: northern suburb (VR637, VR975)

	vju	uf	fg	fus	% uf
VR637					
glenoid				2	0.0
acetabulum				1	0.0
subtotal < 1 yr	0	0	0	3	0.0
p radius				3	0.0
phalanx 2					
d humerus				1	0.0
phalanx 1				2	0.0
subtotal < 2yr	0	0	0	6	0.0
d tibia				3	0.0
d metacarpal				2	0.0
d metatarsal				2	0.0
subtotal <3 yr	0	0	0	7	0.0
calcaneum		1			100.0
p ulna	1				100.0
p femur					
p humerus					
p tibia		1		3	25.0
d radius		1			100.0
d femur				1	0.0
subtotal < 5yr	1	3	0	4	50.0
VR975					
glenoid				2	0.0
acetabulum				4	0.0
subtotal < 1 yr	0	0	0	6	0.0
p radius				3	0.0
phalanx 2				4	0.0
d humerus				1	0.0
phalanx 1		1		5	16.7
subtotal < 2yr	0	1	0	13	7.1
d tibia				1	0.0
d metacarpal		1		5	16.7
d metatarsal		2			100.0
subtotal <3 yr	0	3	0	6	33.3
calcaneum		1			100.0
p ulna		1			100.0
p femur		2			100.0
p humerus				2	0.0
p tibia					
d radius		1			100.0
d femur		2		1	66.7
subtotal < 5yr	0	7	0	3	70.0

Key as Table A5.22

Table A5.32   Cattle: fusion: 14th–15th century: northern suburb (VR700)

VR700	vj	uf	fg	fus	%uf
glenoid					
acetabulum					
subtotal < 1yr				3	0.0
p radius	0	0	0	3	0.0
phalanx 2				2	0.0
d humerus				2	0.0
phalanx 1				2	0.0
subtotal < 2yr				5	0.0
d tibia	0	0	0	11	0.0
d metacarpal				1	0.0
d metatarsal		1		5	16.7
subtotal < 3yr				1	0.0
calcaneus	0	1	0	7	12.5
p femur	1			1	50.0
p ulna					
p humerus		1		1	50.0
p tibia					
d radius				4	0.0
d femur					
subtotal < 5yr		1	1	1	66.7

Key as Table A5.22

Table A5.33 Cattle: fusion: 16th century (VR756, VR 763, SJS49)

	vj	uf	fg	fus	%uf
VR756					
glenoid				2	0.0
acetabulum				1	0.0
subtotal < 1yr	0	0	0	3	0.0
p radius					
phalanx 2		1		1	50.0
d humerus		1		1	50.0
subtotal < 2yr	0	2	0	2	50.0
phalanx 1				4	0.0
d tibia					
d metacarpal					
d metatarsal				2	0.0
subtotal < 3yr	0	0	0	6	0.0
calcaneus					
p femur		1			100.0
p ulna					
p humerus				1	0.0
p tibia				1	0.0
d radius				1	0.0
d femur					
subtotal < 5yr	0	1	0	3	25.0
VR763					
glenoid	1	1		3	40.0
acetabulum				8	0.0
subtotal < 1yr	1	1	0	11	15.4
p radius	2			3	40.0
phalanx 2					
d humerus	1	1		5	28.6
subtotal < 2yr	5	3		30	21.1
phalanx 1				12	0.0
d tibia		3		2	60.0
d metacarpal				3	0.0
d metatarsal	1	1		5	28.6
subtotal < 3yr	1	4	0	22	18.5
calcaneus		3		3	50.0
p femur	2			2	50.0
p ulna				1	0.0
p humerus	1			2	33.3
p tibia				4	0.0
d radius	2	2		6	40.0
d femur	2	1		2	60.0
subtotal < 5yr	7	6	0	20	39.4

	vj	uf	fg	fus	%uf
SJS49					
glenoid					
acetabulum					
subtotal < 1yr	0	0	0	0	0.0
p radius	1	1		3	40.0
phalanx 2				12	0.0
d humerus	4			6	40.0
subtotal < 2yr	5	1	0	21	22.2
phalanx 1				29	0.0
d tibia	1	1		5	28.6
d metacarpal	1			7	12.5
d metatarsal	2			7	22.2
subtotal < 3yr	4	1	0	48	9.4
calcaneus	1			1	50.0
p femur	5	2		2	77.8
p ulna				2	0.0
p humerus	3			1	75.0
p tibia	1			3	25.0
d radius	4	1		5	50.0
d femur	4	1		3	62.5
subtotal < 5yr	18	4	0	17	56.4

Key as Table A5.22

Table A5.34 Cattle: fusion: 17th century (CHR56)

CHR56	vj	uf	fg	fus	%uf
glenoid	1			3	25.0
acetabulum				9	0.0
subtotal < 1yr					
p radius				4	0.0
phalanx 2				2	0.0
d humerus	2	1		3	50.0
subtotal < 2yr	3	1		21	16.0
phalanx 1	1	1		18	10.0
d tibia	1	1		1	66.7
d metacarpal	1			3	25.0
d metatarsal		1	2		100.0
subtotal < 3yr	3	3	2	22	26.7
calcaneus				2	0.0
p femur	2			4	33.3
p ulna	1				100.0
p humerus					
p tibia		2		1	66.7
d radius	1				100.0
d femur				1	0.0
subtotal < 5yr	4	2	0	8	42.9

Key as Table A5.22

Table A5.35   Cattle: measurements of 13th–14th-century horn cores from Victoria Road, Phase 783, c.1218, left-hand side. The table shows curvature, cross section, age class (after Armitage 1982) and measurements

curve	cross section	age class	basal circ	L outer curve (mm)	max dia	least dia
3	O	3	185	210	65.0	62.0
3	O	3	184	195	62.9	50.1
3	O	3	186	185	59.0	46.6
3	C	3	180		58.9	53.6
6	O	3	156		58.2	46.6
1	O	3	175		57.1	49.7
1	O	3	172	202	56.3	48.2
1	O	3	164	172	55.3	47.0
1	C	3	146		48.7	46.0
3	O	3	140	158	46.0	38.9
3	O	4	234		81.3	62.8
1	O	4	235		78.7	63.1
6	O	4	230		77.7	64.2
3	O	4	226		76.7	61.9
3	O	4	222	270	75.7	59.2
6	O	4	200		74.1	51.7
3	O	4	207		71.0	53.2
3	O	4	208		70.5	57.6
3	O	4	204		69.4	54.2
1	O	4	200		69.1	56.6
3	O	4	200	256	68.5	54.7
3	O	4	204		68.0	54.8
3	O	4	190	215	67.3	48.4
3	O	4	190		65.2	52.9
6	O	4	184		65.2	49.3
1	O	4	200		65.0	60.0
6	O	4	194	260	64.8	54.7
3	O	4	190	225	64.1	53.5
3	O	4	186		64.0	52.2
3	O	4	192	224	63.8	56.6
1	O	4	195		63.7	50.3
3	O	4	194		63.5	55.4
1	O	4	190		62.7	55.0
1	O	4	178		61.3	49.4
3	O	4	180		59.1	51.0
3	O	4	170		58.2	51.5
3	O	4	170		57.1	50.2
8	C	4	156	220	51.5	55.1
3	O	4				
3	O	5	224		78.8	56.6
1	O	5	234	340	78.0	65.5
3	O	5	218	224	77.6	58.7
8	C	5	202	307	76.5	57.0
3	O	5	218		76.3	59.1

Table A5.35 (*cont.*)   Cattle: measurements of 13th–14th-century horn cores from Victoria Road, Phase 783, c.1218, left-hand side. The table shows curvature, cross section, age class (after Armitage 1982) and measurements

curve	cross section	age class	basal circ	L outer curve (mm)	max dia	least dia
6	O	5	204	285	74.7	56.8
3	O	5	205		73.1	58.4
3	O	5	212		70.1	59.4
3	O	5	205		69.6	55.5
8	O	5	210	280	69.6	
6	O	5	186		65.1	50.0
3	O	5	195	258	64.4	56.4
3	O	5	190	288	63.8	58.9
3	O	5	190		62.7	53.2
3	O	5	190	214	62.1	51.7
3	O	5	204	250	60.2	53.4
3	O	5	180		59.4	48.4
1	O	5	175	205	59.2	51.0
8	O	5	175		58.0	51.1
3	O	5	160	200	56.7	43.6

key

age class (Armitage 1982)	curve	cross section	
0 infant	1 forward	o oval	basal circ — basal circumference
1 juvenile	2 forward tip down	c circular	L outer curve — length of outer curve
2 sub-adult	3 forward tip up		max dia — maximum diameter
3 young adult	4 backwards		least dia — least diameter
4 adult	5 backwards tip down		
5 old adult	6 backwards tip up		
	7 straight out		
	8 straight tip up		
	9 straight tip down		

Table A5.36 Cattle: measurements of horn cores from Victoria Road, Phase 783, c.1218, right-hand side

curve	cross section	age class	basal circ	L outer curve (mm)	max dia	least dia
3	O	3	190	215	68.7	49.8
3	O	3	184	225	63.2	52.4
3	O	3	180		63.0	50.2
1	O	3	176		62.3	47.4
3	O	3	175		62.0	48.5
3	O	3	175		55.4	47.1
1	O	3	155	177	54.7	42.0
3	O	3	160	185	52.2	48.6
3	O	3				
6	O	4	134	174	85.0	36.4
8	C	4	225		77.8	77.8
6	O	4	220		75.8	59.8
6	O	4	224	274	75.7	61.4
8	O	4	207		73.7	57.1
6	O	4	215		72.1	60.3
5	O	4	210	234	71.0	57.8
8	O	4	210		71.0	57.5
3	O	4	207		70.8	57.2
1	O	4	212		70.2	60.4
3	C	4	215	285	69.8	64.6
6	O	4	200		69.7	55.4
8	O	4	205	264	68.8	54.3
3	O	4	193	235	68.4	56.8
8	O	4	195	230	67.1	51.6
1	O	4			66.8	56.6
3	O	4	200		66.6	58.9
8	O	4	195		66.1	56.3
3	O	4	194	230	65.6	53.9
3	O	4	190	242	65.3	54.6
8	O	4	185		62.8	50.4
8	O	4	175		62.2	49.9
3	C	4	194	250	61.8	59.4
3	C	4	190	217	61.2	55.1
8	C	4	194		59.8	52.9
8	O	4	175	245	58.7	52.5
1	O	4	166		53.8	48.9
6	O	4	155	173	53.8	42.7
8	C	4	150	207	45.6	47.1
8	C	4				
8	C	4				
3	O	4				
		4				
8	O	5	195	230	89.8	53.0
8	O	5	240	285	83.6	61.8

Table A5.36 (*cont.*) Cattle: measurements of horn cores from Victoria Road, Phase 783, c.1218, right-hand side

curve	cross section	age class	basal circ	L outer curve (mm)	max dia	least dia
8	O	5	220		77.0	57.9
8	O	5	210	300	75.8	57.8
8	O	5	215	262	74.9	59.9
6	O	5	210	260	74.0	55.1
3	O	5	220		73.1	57.6
3	O	5	204		70.9	54.5
6	O	5	215		70.0	57.0
8	O	5	190	268	67.1	49.9
6	O	5	190	305	65.0	52.3
3	O	5	200	285	64.5	55.6
3	O	5	186	220	62.7	53.7
3	C	5	180		60.4	53.5
6	O	5	170	207	57.3	48.9
6	O	5				
3	O	5		250		

Key as Table A5.35

Table A5.37 Cattle: measurements of other bones (after Driesch 1976)

century	Site and Phase	c.	GL		Dp	Bp	SD	DD	Bd	WDA
Metacarpal										
10–11	VR532	3939	177.5		29.2	48.1	27.1	27.1	46.7	50.9
14	VR700	255	173.7		45.5	29.5	25.9	27.3	46.0	50.6
16	SJS49	330	198.0		40.3	62.0	33.7	33.8	56.4	63.8
16	VR763	3058	201.0		40.3	63.2	36.2	35.8	57.5	64.5
Metatarsal										
10–11	VR530	3136	191.5		40.1	41.2	24.3	27.2	44.4	47.3
13-14	VR637	4201	127.1		0.0	15.8	11.0	14.4	23.1	0.0
16	SJS49	337	244.0		52.2	52.4	28.2	35.8	57.1	61.4
16	VR763	3089	230.2		49.1	51.5	28.0	32.8	51.8	57.7
16	VR763	3025	198.5		36.5	40.7	20.7	27.9	42.0	46.6
16	VR763	3025	238.5		41.1	50.7	29.1	31.8	54.6	58.1
Astragalus			GLl	GLm	Bd					
10–11	VR529	3868	60.9	55.8	38.5					
10–11	VR532	3939	57.3	53.5	38.0					
13-14	VR635	3776	51.7	47.3	34.0					
16	SJS49	333	0.0	64.4	45.2					
Phalanx 1			GLpe	L2	Dp	Bp	SC	Bd		
10–11	HG29	827	52.1	52.9	34.5	27.4	22.2	25.5		
10–11	HG29	827	52.4	52.3	33.4	27.8	23.5	26.8		
10–11	HG29	827	48.1	46.2	28.2	26.7	21.9	26.1		
10–11	VR532	3939	52.0	50.0	0.0	25.2	20.6	24.2		
10–11	VR532	3939	50.1	48.5	0.0	23.0	20.1	22.6		
10–11	VR532	3939	51.5	50.0	0.0	22.7	20.6	23.8		
10–11	VR532	3939	51.7	49.5	0.0	24.8	20.1	23.5		
10–11	VR532	3939	52.5	51.5	0.0	25.0	21.0	22.7		
10–11	VR532	3939	54.5	52.7	0.0	29.0	24.3	27.9		
10–11	VR532	3939	51.6	49.5	0.0	23.2	19.9	23.0		
10–11	VR532	3939	50.7	48.1	0.0	25.5	21.1	23.4		
10–11	VR532	3939	50.7	50.2	0.0	23.6	20.5	22.5		
10–11	VR532	3939	58.9	57.8	0.0	27.7	22.1	23.8		
10–11	VR532	3939	50.8	49.5	0.0	22.8	19.7	21.8		
13-14	VR635	3886	50.2	48.8	0.0	25.4	21.3	24.3		
13-14	VR635	3776	50.0	49.0	0.0	21.6	19.2	22.2		
13-14	VR635	3886	53.6	53.5	0.0	23.3	19.3	22.1		
14	SJS30	290	58.1	54.8	0.0	30.6	28.9	31.0		
14	SJS30	290	59.3	59.8	0.0	30.8	26.8	31.8		
14	SJS30	349	57.9	56.8	0.0	77.9	22.8	24.8		
14	SJS30	290	48.7	48.1	24.2	21.2	19.6	21.0		
14	SJS30	290	48.0	49.0	26.1	26.2	22.8	24.2		
14	VR700	284	49.1	46.3	0.0	22.4	19.8	22.2		
14	VR700	255	50.5	52.1	0.0	28.1	23.0	27.3		
14	VR700	381	60.4	62.2	0.0	31.6	24.6	27.1		
14	VR700	284	59.6	56.6	0.0	30.8	26.7	28.0		
14	VR700	256	52.0	52.2	0.0	25.6	20.4	22.8		

Table A5.37 (*cont.*) Cattle: measurements of other bones (after Driesch 1976)

century	Site and Phase	c.	GLpe	L2	Dp	Bp	SC	Bd
14-15	VR792	312	48.3	46.3	0.0	24.8	20.8	23.9
14-15	VR685	135	58.8	54.6	0.0	28.8	25.0	29.0
16	SJS49	337	68.6	65.8	0.0	35.9	32.8	36.7
16	SJS49	333	58.5	58.2	0.0	33.2	27.2	29.5
16	SJS49	336	57.2	55.7	0.0	27.0	22.7	25.0
16	SJS49	337	55.0	54.5	0.0	25.5	21.2	23.3
16	SJS49	337	57.3	58.1	0.0	27.0	23.5	24.2
16	SJS49	337	58.1	58.9	0.0	32.6	27.2	33.2
16	SJS49	337	65.1	63.5	0.0	28.6	24.6	28.0
16	SJS49	336	66.0	62.5	0.0	34.4	28.5	32.6
16	SJS49	330	65.2	61.1	0.0	32.6	25.9	30.8
16	SJS49	330	51.2	49.5	0.0	24.7	21.7	23.3
16	SJS49	330	58.8	56.0	0.0	32.3	27.3	31.8
16	SJS49	334	64.1	61.7	0.0	29.4	25.3	29.5
16	SJS49	330	65.4	63.5	0.0	33.7	27.1	30.4
16	SJS49	330	59.5	60.8	0.0	0.0	30.2	28.6
16	SJS49	336	58.3	56.8	0.0	26.7	23.8	25.3
16	SJS49	330	61.3	62.3	0.0	30.9	24.8	27.4
16	SJS49	330	64.2	61.4	0.0	34.6	30.0	31.3
16	SJS49	337	50.7	49.6	0.0	26.8	21.9	23.4
16	SJS49	337	66.4	65.8	0.0	32.6	29.1	33.8
16	SJS49	316	67.9	62.1	0.0	36.6	31.9	35.3
16	SJS49	319	63.4	63.1	0.0	37.3	29.4	38.1
16	SJS49	319	57.2	54.8	0.0	28.0	23.0	25.4
16	SJS49	316	59.4	58.0	0.0	32.9	27.8	32.9
16	SJS49	353	61.9	59.6	0.0	34.9	30.4	33.4
16	VR763	3058	60.0	58.1	0.0	33.0	27.9	32.0
16	VR763	3089	53.9	53.1	0.0	27.8	24.4	26.6
16	VR763	3089	56.7	57.1	0.0	26.8	24.0	26.2
16	VR763	3058	56.7	56.6	0.0	34.4	27.6	31.6
16	VR763	3034	54.9	55.6	0.0	24.5	20.9	23.6
16	VR763	3058	53.5	50.8	0.0	27.8	21.0	25.0
16	VR763	3001	50.9	49.8	0.0	28.8	24.5	28.6
16	VR763	3001	54.2	51.9	0.0	26.1	22.6	26.0
16	VR763	3027	54.3	53.2	0.0	29.8	24.7	26.7
16	VR763	3027	60.7	57.8	0.0	34.8	29.0	33.3
10	VR529	3710	53.0	53.2	0.0	28.0	23.3	26.3
14	VR700	369	51.6	50.4	0.0	26.0	21.5	25.6

Key: WDA breadth of the distal articulation; L2 length of medial side

Table A5.38 Pig: eruption and wear of teeth (after Grant 1982: age stages after Maltby 1979, 55)

Site and Phase	c.	anatomy	side	DP4	P4	M1	M2	M3	Stage
Saxo-Norman									
VR532	4126	jaw	L	j		b		V	3
VR530	3136	jaw	L					E	3
VR532	3939	jaw	R	l					3/4
VR530	3030	jaw	R				c	a	4
VR532	3939	jaw	R				f	a	4
VR530	3225	jaw	R				e	c	5
VR532	4132	jaw	L		f	h	f		6
13th–14th century, eastern suburb									
SJS30	290	jaw	R	d		V	V		2
CHR53	116	tooth	L			d			3
CHR53	80	tooth	R			d			3
CHR53	61	tooth	L			e			3
CHR53	112	tooth	R			a			3
SJS29	407	jaw	R			d	V		3
SJS16	174	tooth				c			3
SJS16	199	jaw	R	k		d	V		3
SJS30	290	jaw	R	j		b	V		3
SJS30	290	jaw	R	m		d	V		3
CHR53	145	jaw	R	g		c	a		4
CHR53	145	jaw	R			f	c	V	5
CHR53	81	jaw	R		b	l	c		5
SJS30	290	jaw	L		a	k	b		5
SJS16	174	jaw	R					E	5
13th–14th century, northern suburb									
VR637	4534	jaw	R	a					1
VR616	522	jaw	L	E		V			1
VR637	4354	jaw	L	h		c			3
VR637	4354	jaw	R	h		c	E		3
VR637	3990	jaw	R		b	f	c	E	5
VR635	3886	jaw	L		e	d	c	a	6
Late 14th–15th century									
VR685	135	jaw	R	E					1
VR700	477	jaw	L	E		V			1
VR792	860	jaw	R	a					1
VR685	135	jaw	L	E					1
VR700	477	jaw	R	E					1
VR700	369	jaw	L	b					2
VR700	370	jaw	R			d	b	V	4/5
VR700	284	jaw	R		a	g	d	E	5
VR700	369	jaw	R		a	g	c	V	5
VR792	860	jaw	L		a	j	d	E	5
VR792	861	jaw	L		c	j	e	E	5
VR792	860	jaw	L		a	e	a		5
VR792	282	jaw	L		b	j	e	a	6

Table A5.38 (*cont.*) Pig: eruption and wear of teeth (after Grant 1982: age stages after Maltby 1979, 55)

Site and Phase	c.	anatomy	side	DP4	P4	M1	M2	M3	Stage
VR792	858	jaw	L				d	a	6
16th century									
SJS49	319	jaw	L	E					1
SJS49	330	jaw	L	a					1
SJS49	330	jaw	L	a					1
SJS49	337	jaw	L	a					1
SJS49	330	jaw	R	a					1
SJS49	337	jaw	L	a					1
SJS49	337	jaw	R	a					1
SJS49	336	jaw	L	a		V			1
SJS49	353	jaw	R	j		b			3
SJS49	334	jaw	R	d		f	E		3
SJS49	330	jaw	L				a		4
VR763	3058	jaw	R		E	d	b		4
SJS49	323	jaw	L				a	C	4/5
SJS49	323	jaw	L				a	C	4/5
SJS49	319	jaw	R		a	c	a		5
VR763	3025	jaw	R		b	g			5/6
VR763	3089	tooth	R					a	6
SJS49	334	jaw	R			g	c	a	6
SJS49	330	jaw	L				f	a	6
SJS49	336	jaw	R				f	a	6
SJS763	3089	tooth	R					d	6
17th century									
CHR56	19	jaw	R	a					1
CHR56	19	jaw	L	a					1
CHR56	19	jaw	R	l		c	V		3
CHR56	19	tooth		l					3/4
CHR56	19	jaw	R	m					3/4

Key: c. context

Table A5.39   Pig: fusion: Saxo-Norman (VR530, HG29)

	vju	uf	fg	fus	% uf
VR530					
d humerus			1		100.0
p radius	1			2	33.3
acetabulum				1	0.0
glenoid				4	0.0
subtotal 1 yr	1	0	1	7	22.2
1st phalanx				1	0.0
d tibia				2	0.0
d metacarpal		1		1	50.0
d metatarsal		1			100.0
subtotal 2 yr	0	2	0	4	33.3
calcaneum		2			100.0
p ulna					
p femur		1	1		100.0
p humerus					
p tibia					
d radius	1	1			100.0
d ulna					
d femur		1			100.0
subtotal late	1	5	1	0	100.0
HG29					
d humerus	1	1		1	66.7
p radius		1	0	5	16.7
acetabulum		1		2	33.3
glenoid				1	0.0
subtotal 1 yr	1	3	0	9	30.8
1st phalanx					
d tibia		1		2	33.3
d metacarpal		3			100.0
d metatarsal					
subtotal 2 yr	0	4	0	2	66.7
calcaneum				2	0.0
p ulna		2			100.0
p femur	1	1			100.0
p humerus		2			100.0
p tibia		2			100.0
d radius		2			100.0
d ulna					
d femur	1	3			100.0
subtotal late	2	12	0	2	87.5

Key as Table A5.22

Table A5.40   Pig: fusion: 13th–14th century: eastern suburb (SJS30, CHR53)

	vju	uf	fg	fus	% uf
SJS30					
d humerus			2	1	66.7
p radius	2			1	66.7
acetabulum				1	0.0
glenoid	1			1	50.0
subtotal 1 yr	3	0	2	4	55.6
1st phalanx					
d tibia	1	1			100.0
d metacarpal		1			100.0
d metatarsal		1			100.0
subtotal 2 yr	1	3	0	0	100.0
calcaneum		1			100.0
p ulna					
p femur		2			100.0
p humerus		1			100.0
p tibia	1				100.0
d radius	1				100.0
d ulna					
d femur		2			100.0
subtotal late	2	6	0	0	100.0
CHR53					
d humerus		2		4	33.3
p radius	1	2		7	30.0
acetabulum				2	0.0
glenoid	1				100.0
subtotal 1 yr	2	4	0	13	31.6
1st phalanx		3		3	50.0
d tibia			4	1	80.0
d metacarpal	1	4			100.0
d metatarsal	1	1		1	66.7
subtotal 2 yr	2	8	4	5	73.7
calcaneum		2		1	66.7
p ulna		1		1	50.0
p femur	1	1			100.0
p humerus		2			100.0
p tibia		1			100.0
d radius		2			100.0
d ulna					
d femur	1	3		1	80.0
subtotal late	2	12	0	3	82.4

Key as Table A5.22

**Table A5.41 Pig: fusion:
13th–14th century: northern suburb (VR975)**

VR975	vju	uf	fg	fus	% uf
d humerus		1		1	50.0
p radius		1	1	2	50.0
acetabulum			1		100.0
glenoid		2		3	40.0
subtotal 1 yr	0	4	2	6	50.0
1st phalanx		1			100.0
d tibia		2			100.0
d metacarpal					
d metatarsal					
subtotal 2 yr	0	3	0	0	100.0
calcaneum		3			100.0
p ulna		2			100.0
p femur		1			100.0
p humerus					
p tibia					
d radius		3			100.0
d ulna		1			100.0
d femur		1			100.0
subtotal late	0	11	0	0	100.0

Key as Table A5.22

**Table A5.42 Pig: fusion: 14th–15th century:
northern suburbs (VR700) (key as Table A5.22)**

VR700	vju	uf	fg	fus	% uf
d humerus	1	5		1	85.7
p radius		2		5	28.6
acetabulum					
glenoid				5	0.0
subtotal 1 yr	1	7	0	11	42.1
1st phalanx					
d tibia		4			100.0
d metacarpal		5		2	71.4
d metatarsal				1	0.0
subtotal 2 yr	0	9	0	3	75.0
calcaneum		2			100.0
p ulna		4			100.0
p femur	1	1			100.0
p humerus		6			100.0
p tibia		4			100.0
d radius		3			100.0
d ulna		2			100.0
d femur	1	2		1	75.0
subtotal late	2	24	0	1	96.3
n	3	40	0	15	58

Key as Table A5.22

Table A5.43   Pig: fusion: 16th century (VR756, VR763, SJS49)

	vju	uf	fg	fus	% uf
VR756					
d humerus		1		2	33.3
p radius		1		2	33.3
acetabulum				2	0.0
glenoid					
subtotal 1 yr	0	2	0	6	25.0
1st phalanx		1			100.0
d tibia		2			100.0
d metacarpal				1	0.0
d metatarsal					
subtotal 2 yr	0	3	0	1	75.0
calcaneum		4			100.0
p ulna		1			100.0
p femur					
p humerus		1			100.0
p tibia		1			100.0
d radius		1			100.0
d ulna		1			100.0
d femur					
subtotal late	0	9	0	0	100.0
VR763					
d humerus		4	1	3	62.5
p radius	1	2		5	37.5
acetabulum		1		1	50.0
glenoid	1	1		1	66.7
subtotal 1 yr	2	8	1	10	52.4
1st phalanx		1		1	50.0
d tibia	3	1		1	80.0
d metacarpal			1		100.0
d metatarsal		3		2	60.0
subtotal 2 yr	3	5	1	4	69.2
calcaneum		1			100.0
p ulna		2			100.0
p femur	2	1			100.0
p humerus	1				100.0
p tibia	3	2			100.0
d radius	1	7			100.0
d ulna					
d femur	2	3			100.0
subtotal late	9	16	0	0	100.0

	vju	uf	fg	fus	% uf
SJS49					
d humerus	3	1		2	66.7
p radius	5	2		3	70.0
acetabulum		1			100.0
glenoid					
subtotal 1 yr	8	4	0	5	70.6
1st phalanx	1	1		2	50.0
d tibia	3	1			100.0
d metacarpal					
d metatarsal					
subtotal 2 yr	4	2	0	2	75.0
calcaneum		2			100.0
p ulna					
p femur	1				100.0
p humerus	3	3			100.0
p tibia	3	1			100.0
d radius	6	3			100.0
d ulna		1			100.0
d femur	1				100.0
subtotal late	14	10	0	0	100.0

Key as Table A5.22

Table A5.44 Pig: fusion: 17th century (CHR56)

CHR56	vju	uf	fg	fus	% uf
d humerus		2		4	33.3
p radius				4	0.0
acetabulum				6	0.0
glenoid		1		1	50.0
subtotal 1 yr	0	3	0	15	16.7
1st phalanx		2			100.0
d tibia	1	5		1	85.7
d metacarpal	1	1		1	66.7
d metatarsal					
subtotal 2 yr	2	8	0	2	83.3
calcaneum		3			100.0
p ulna		2			100.0
p femur					
p humerus		1			100.0
p tibia	1	1			100.0
d radius				1	0.0
d ulna					
d femur					
subtotal late	1	7	0	1	88.9

Key as Table A5.22

Table A5.45 Domestic fowl: humerus measurements (after Driesch 1976)

century	Site and Phase	c.	GL	SC
10–11	VR530	3174	61.4	6.5
10–11	VR530	3174	60.5	6.6
10–11	VR530	3174	61.5	6.4
10–11	VR530	3174	60.8	6.4
10–11	VR532	3939	64.5	6.7
10–11	VR530	3174	74.3	7.3
10–11	VR532	3939	65.3	7.1
10–11	VR532	4126	67.2	0.0
10–11	VR532	3973	75.0	7.8
10–11	VR532	3973	74.5	7.4
10–11	VR532	3973	59.3	5.9
10–11	VR532	3973	59.1	6.4
10–11	VR530	3174	67.2	6.8
10–11	VR532	4132	0.0	7.1
13	SJS13	198	72.6	7.1
13	SJS16	174	65.4	6.4
13	SJS13	198	71.6	6.5
13–14	CHR53	63	71.0	6.6
13–14	VR635	3886	48.9	0.0
13–14	VR637	4189	64.9	5.6
13–14	VR635	3886	45.8	0.0
13–14	VR635	3788	0.0	5.9
13–14	VR637	4189	64.9	5.5
13–14	VR635	3886	49.9	0.0
13–14	VR635	3886	48.6	0.0
13–14	VR635	3886	45.6	0.0
13–14	VR635	3886	49.2	0.0
13–14	VR975	137	0.0	5.7
13–14	VR975	137	68.3	6.7
13–14	VR975	137	74.6	7.9
13–14	VR975	137	0.0	6.7
13–14	VR975	137	0.0	6.0
14	SJS30	500	59.8	5.5
14	SJS30	500	63.4	6.4
14	SJS30	500	59.9	5.5
14	SJS30	290	76.2	7.8
14	VR700	483	49.0	0.0
14	VR700	483	49.1	0.0
14	VR700	483	48.2	0.0
14	VR700	483	52.4	0.0
14	VR700	483	63.9	6.1
14	VR700	375	64.5	6.3
14	VR700	483	64.0	6.0
14	VR700	369	71.2	7.1
14–15	VR792	861	63.5	5.9
15–16	VR756	952	0.0	8.3
15–16	VR756	952	0.0	7.6
15–16	VR756	952	79.7	8.4
16	SJS49	336	75.0	8.0
16	SJS49	333	0.0	6.6
16	SJS49	337	0.0	7.7

century	Site and Phase	c.	GL
10–11	HG29	908	63.3
10–11	VR530	3174	59.7
10–11	VR530	3174	59.4
10–11	VR530	3174	59.5
10–11	VR530	3174	72.7
10–11	VR530	3174	64.2
10–11	VR530	3174	59.0
10–11	VR532	3979	60.9
10–11	VR532	4132	62.5
10–11	VR532	3973	58.2
10–11	VR532	3973	74.4
10–11	VR532	3973	58.2
10–11	VR532	3939	66.7
13	SJS13	198	70.9
13	SJS13	198	72.2
13–14	CHR53	63	63.6
13–14	CHR53	69	47.6
13–14	HG20	1052	69.4
13–14	VR637	4189	61.2
13–14	VR783	1228	72.2
13–14	VR635	3886	43.9
13–14	VR635	3886	49.3
13–14	VR635	3886	47.8
13–14	VR975	137	58.7
13–14	VR975	137	47.6
13–14	VR635	3886	48.3
13–14	VR637	4189	62.3
14	SJS30	290	68.3
14	SJS30	500	53.8
14	SJS30	290	59.7
14	SJS30	500	57.3
14	SJS30	500	57.4
14	SJS30	500	61.8
14	SJS30	500	61.8
14	VR700	477	54.8
14	VR700	483	47.5
14	VR700	375	62.8
14	VR700	483	62.6
14	VR700	483	52.2
14	VR700	483	62.4
15–16	VR756	952	63.0
15–16	VR756	952	73.5
15–16	VR756	952	70.1
15–16	VR756	952	61.8
15–16	VR756	952	77.1
15–16	VR756	952	62.4
16	SJS49	336	67.7
16	SJS49	319	73.7
16	SJS49	316	79.3
16	SJS49	316	68.8
17	CHR56	19	77.3

Table A5.46 Domestic fowl: ulna measurements (after Driesch 1976)

century	Site and Phase	c.	GL	Bd
10–11	HG 29	831	74.0	6.3
10–11	HG 29	976	68.9	6.1
10–11	HG 29	976	70.7	5.7
10–11	HG 29	908	73.2	6.1
10–11	HG 29	908	76.3	6.1
10–11	VR 530	3016	69.5	6.2
10–11	VR 530	3174	72.7	6.4
10–11	VR 530	3174	72.5	6.4
10–11	VR 530	3174	67.5	6.5
10–11	VR 530	3174	67.0	6.0
10–11	VR 530	3174	60.8	5.7
10–11	VR 532	3939	69.0	6.5
10–11	VR 530	3174	67.2	6.5
10–11	VR 532	3973	81.8	7.9
10–11	VR 532	3973	81.0	7.7
10–11	VR 532	4132	71.8	6.4
10–11	VR 532	3978	65.3	6.6
13	SJS 16	174	77.6	6.2
13	SJS 13	198	78.9	7.7
13–14	CHR 53	67	70.8	6.4
13–14	CHR 53	59	52.5	0.0
13–14	VR 635	3886	48.7	0.0
13–14	VR 635	3886	49.1	0.0
13–14	VR 635	3886	53.8	0.0
13–14	VR 635	3806	71.8	6.0
13–14	VR 637	4189	65.7	0.0
13–14	VR 783	1228	71.9	6.6
13–14	VR 635	3886	46.2	0.0
13–14	VR 635	3886	46.0	0.0
13–14	VR 975	137	65.3	6.0
13–14	VR 637	4189	65.7	0.0
13–14	VR 975	137	0.0	6.6
14	SJS 30	500	70.6	5.9
14	SJS 30	290	79.0	6.8
14	SJS 30	500	63.4	0.0
14	VR 700	382	71.1	6.2
14	VR 700	483	70.3	6.3
14	VR 700	483	66.1	6.0
14	VR 700	483	70.6	6.3
14–15	VR 792	861	69.9	5.6
14–15	VR 792	279	70.0	0.0
15–16	VR 756	952	83.7	7.6
15–16	VR 756	952	53.7	0.0
15–16	VR 756	952	74.2	6.7
16	SJS 49	336	92.1	7.9
16	SJS 49	340	76.2	7.0
16	SJS 49	336	75.2	6.7
16	SJS 49	319	75.7	7.3
16	SJS 49	319	75.2	7.0

Table A5.47 Domestic fowl: femur measurements (after Driesch 1976)

Table A5.48   Domestic fowl: tibiotarsus measurements (after Driesch 1976)

century	Site and Phase	c.	GL	La	Bd
10–11	HG29	930	0.0	88.3	5.3
10–11	HG29	930	0.0	96.3	5.8
10–11	VR532	3978	83.5	80.9	5.8
10–11	VR530	3136	93.6	0.0	5.8
10–11	VR529	3868	0.0	96.5	6.1
10–11	VR532	3973	96.1	93.5	5.4
10–11	VR532	4132	97.5	94.3	0.0
10–11	VR532	4132	0.0	0.0	6.0
10–11	VR532	3973	116.9	111.4	7.8
10–11	VR532	3939	0.0	109.6	6.9
10–11	VR532	4126	93.8	0.0	0.0
10–11	VR532	3973	116.8	112.0	7.6
10–11	VR530	3174	0.0	92.7	5.4
10–11	VR532	3973	91.1	88.5	5.6
10–11	VR530	3174	0.0	92.5	5.6
10–11	VR530	3174		90.7	5.7
10–11	VR530	3174	0.0	90.2	0.0
13	SJS13	198	0.0	107.9	6.4
13	SJS13	198	0.0	108.5	6.0
13	SJS13	198	0.0	0.0	6.8
13–14	CHR53	105	46.8	0.0	0.0
13–14	CHR53	101	0.0	0.0	6.4
13–14	VR635	3886	62.5	0.0	0.0
13–14	VR635	3886	64.0	0.0	0.0
13–14	VR783	1228	100.0	97.0	6.0
13–14	VR637	4189	88.7	0.0	0.0
13–14	VR635	3886	63.4	0.0	0.0
13–14	VR637	4189	88.7	0.0	0.0
13–14	VR635	3886	84.3	0.0	0.0
14	SJS30	500	82.7	0.0	0.0
14	SJS30	500	82.9	0.0	0.0
14	SJS30	500	0.0	93.9	5.3
14	SJS30	500	93.4	0.0	5.3
14	VR700	477	0.0	98.2	5.4
14	VR700	477	0.0	79.2	0.0
14	VR700	483	0.0	98.2	5.2
14	VR700	483	98.5	98.5	5.1
14	VR700	483	0.0	89.5	5.0
14	VR700	483	0.0	69.9	0.0
14	VR700	370	94.7	0.0	5.9
14	VR700	483		64.0	0.0
14	VR700	483	0.0	69.7	0.0
14–15	VR792	861	0.0	90.6	5.0
14–15	VR792	861	0.0	90.3	5.0
15–16	VR756	952	0.0	0.0	6.9
16	SJS49	323	0.0	0.0	6.9
16	SJS49	334	0.0	0.0	5.5
16	SJS49	340	0.0	90.2	5.4
16	SJS49	336	0.0	114.0	5.8
16	SJS49	334	0.0	125.8	7.2
16	SJS49	336		105.9	6.1
16	SJS49	336		130.6	7.6
16	SJS49	336	0.0	0.0	5.2

Table A5.49 Domestic fowl: tarsometatarsus measurements (after Driesch 1976)

century	Site and Phase	c.	GL	SC	century	Site and Phase	c.	GL	SC
10–11	HG29	930	65.0	5.5	13–14	VR635	3886	44.7	0.0
10–11	VR532	4126	64.5	5.3	13–14	VR635	3886	40.6	0.0
10–11	VR530	3173	60.7	5.3	13–14	VR637	4189	59.7	0.0
10–11	VR532	4126	68.1	5.9	13–14	VR635	3886	45.3	0.0
10–11	VR530	3174	65.9	5.6	13–14	VR635	3886	43.7	0.0
10–11	VR532	3973	80.4	7.7	13–14	VR635	3886	46.6	0.0
10–11	VR530	3174	64.5	5.8	14	SJS30	500	53.9	0.0
10–11	VR532	4132	63.4	0.0	14	SJS30	500	63.8	5.6
10–11	VR532	4132	61.8	0.0	14	SJS30	500	63.9	5.6
10–11	VR532	4132	68.2	5.8	14	SJS30	290	46.3	0.0
10–11	VR529	3868	66.4	5.5	14	SJS30	500	67.2	6.3
10–11	VR532	3973	62.4	5.9	14	SJS30	290	65.7	5.9
10–11	VR530	3174	65.2	5.6	14	VR700	369	78.8	7.2
10–11	VR530	3174	64.4	5.8	14	VR700	369	53.3	0.0
10–11	VR532	3973	80.4	7.6	14	VR700	483	49.7	0.0
13–14	CHR53	59	82.0	7.8	14	VR700	183	71.0	5.9
13–14	SJS29	416	60.4	5.9	14	VR700	483	61.3	5.3
13–14	VR783	1228	69.7	6.8	14	VR700	370	79.0	7.1
13–14	VR975	137	44.0	5.3	14–15	VR792	861	60.6	5.2
13–14	VR635	3788	55.3	0.0	14–15	VR685	136	62.4	5.4
13–14	VR975	137	0.0	5.4	14–15	VR685	136	62.0	5.2
13–14	VR637	4189	60.1	0.0	14–15	VR792	363	77.4	6.8
13–14	VR783	1228	68.4	6.6	15–16	VR756	952	88.9	0.0
13–14	VR635	3886	77.7	6.4	16	SJS49	336	71.4	6.3
13–14	VR635	3886	53.1	0.0	16	SJS49	336	0.0	9.6
13–14	VR635	3788	49.4	0.0	16	SJS49	336	103.8	8.5
13–14	VR635	3886	50.4	0.0	16	SJS49	337	0.0	8.6

Table A5.50 Goose: measurements (after Driesch 1976)

century	Site and Phase	c.			
humerus			**GL**		**SC**
13–14	VR635	3788	159.0		11.1
16	SJS49	330	91.7		0.0
radius					
13–14	VR635	3788	15.3		
13–14	VR635	3788	14.2		
14–15	VR792	861	14.4		
16	SJS49	316	15.2		
coracoid			**GL**	**Lm**	
13–14	VR635	3788	72.4	62.3	
13–14	VR975	137	73.3	0.0	
15–16	VR756	952	72.4	63.0	
16	SJS49	330	75.5	67.1	
16	SJS49	330	80.1	69.8	
femur			**GL**		**SC**
10–11	VR529	3868	80.7		9.1
13–14	CHR53	116	75.5		8.9
13–14	CHR53	61	83.2		8.9
13–14	VR975	137	75.1		8.9
13–14	VR635	3788	78.3		8.5
13–14	VR635	3788	79.4		8.3
13–14	VR637	4189	79.4		9.3
14	SJS30	290	80.2		10.2
14	SJS30	290	0.0		8.9
tibiotarsus			**GL**	**La**	**SC**
13–14	VR635	3788	0.0	128.7	7.7
13–14	VR975	137	0.0	0.0	0.0
13–14	VR975	137	136.2	132.4	7.7
13–14	VR616	500	135.9	0.0	8.6
13–14	VR635	3776	0.0	0.0	8.1
16	SJS49	323	0.0	125.0	7.7
16	SJS49	323	0.0	0.0	9.1
16	SJS49	336	0.0	0.0	8.5
tarsometatarsus			**GL**		**SC**
10–11	VR529	3868	87.7		8.3
13	SJS16	174	82.1		7.9
13–14	VR975	137	0.0		8.5
13–14	VR635	3788	82.7		8.2
13–14	VR635	3788	81.2		8.4
13–14	VR635	3788	790.0		78.0
13–14	VR635	3788	79.6		7.7
14	VR700	256	92.4		7.6
14	VR700	370	78.3		7.9
16	SJS49	323	84.8		8.4

century	Site and Phase	c.		
carpometacarpus			**GL**	**Bp**
10	VR532	3939	98.0	0.0
10	VR529	3868	88.0	0.0
10	VR529	3868	83.2	0.0
10	VR529	3868	88.8	0.0
13	SJS16	174	86.0	0.0
13–14	VR635	3886	82.9	0.0
13–14	VR635	3788	89.3	0.0
13–14	VR635	3886	90.6	0.0
13–14	VR783	1228	88.7	0.0
13–14	VR635	3886	88.6	0.0
13–14	VR635	3886	86.1	0.0
13–14	VR635	3886	92.4	0.0
13–14	VR635	3886	92.1	0.0
13–14	VR637	4345	92.2	7.2
13–14	VR616	499	87.9	7.4
13–14	VR616	864	91.2	7.3
13–14	VR616	864	88.9	7.4
13–14	VR975	137	81.4	0.0
13–14	VR975	137	81.5	0.0
13–14	VR616	804	77.5	6.8
13–14	VR616	804	90.9	7.7
13–14	VR616	804	89.1	7.9
13–14	VR616	804	85.9	7.3
13–14	VR616	804	94.6	7.8
13–14	VR616	868	91.3	7.5
13–14	VR616	868	76.5	7.1
13–14	VR616	868	92.8	7.3
13–14	VR616	866	85.8	7.7
13–14	VR616	868	87.0	7.7
14	SJS30	500	92.5	0.0
14	VR700	256	84.4	6.5
14–15	VR792	364	85.2	7.2
14–15	VR792	280	95.0	7.6
16	SJS49	340	84.7	0.0
16	SJS49	340	80.0	0.0
16	SJS49	337	94.5	0.0
16	SJS49	336	85.9	0.0
17	CHR56	19	95.9	0.0

Table A5.51 Duck: measurements (after Driesch 1976)

taxon	Site and Phase	element	side	GL	Bp	SC	Bd
Anas platyrhynchos ?domestic	VR532	humerus	L	95.7	24.4	8.4	16.0
Anas sp.	HG29	humerus	L	82.0	19.1	6.8	13.3
Anas sp.	VR635	ulna	L	72.2	9.0	0.0	10.1
Anas platyrhynchos	VR49	coracoid	R	57.1			
Anas platyrhynchos	VR532	coracoid	R	55.2			
Anas platyrhynchos	VR792	femur	R	52.7	12.5	5.2	13.3
Anas platyrhynchos	SJS49	femur	R	52.5	12.3	5.4	12.5
Anas cf *platyrhynchos*	VR532	femur	L	50.1	11.0	4.8	11.4
Anas sp.	VR532	femur	L	45.0			
Anas sp.	VR685	femur	R	44.0			
Anas platyrhynchos ?domestic	VR532	carpometacarpus	L	60.2			
Anas cf *platyrhynchos*	VR532	carpometacarpus	L	55.6			
Anas sp.	VR530	carpometacarpus	R	50.0			
Anas platyrhynchos ?domestic	VR700	tarsometatarsus	L	49.2	10.8	5.5	11.2

**Table A5.52 Horse:
crown heights of molar teeth (after Levine 1982)**

Victoria Road: Phase 743	mandible R	mandible L
P2	37.2	
P3	59.7	59.3
P4	65	64
M1	55.4	55.3
M2	59.6	58.2
M3	62.1	
		maxilla L
P2		54.7
P3		59.4
P4		52.8
M1		57.6
M2		53.3
M3		41.8
Age = 7–8 yr		

Victoria Road: Phase 763	maxilla R	maxilla L
P2		19.7
P3	27.8	25.8
P4	36.8	
M1	22.6	
M2	33.2	32.6
M3	32.5	32.4
Age = 13–15 yr		

Bibliography

Addyman, P V, 1976 Archaeology and Anglo-Saxon Society, in G de G Sieveking, I M Longworth & K E Wilson (eds), *Problems in Economic and Social Archaeology*. London, Duckworth, 309–22

Albarella, U, 1995 Depressions on sheep horn cores, *J Archaeol Sci*, **22**, 699–704

Albarella, U, 1997 Size, power, wool and veal: zooarchaeological evidence for late medieval innovations, in G D Boe, F Verhaeghe, and I A P Zellik (eds), *Environment and Subsistence in Medieval Europe. Papers of the 'Medieval Europe Brugge 1997' conference, Vol 9*, 19–30

Albarella, U, Beech, M, & Mulville, J, 1997 *The Saxon, Medieval and Post-Medieval Mammal and Bird Bones Excavated 1989–91 from Castle Mall, Norwich, Norfolk*. London, Ancient Monuments Laboratory Report 72/97. London: English Heritage

Albarella, U, & Davis, S, 1994 *The Saxon & Medieval Animal Bones excavated 1985–1989 from West Cotton, Northamptonshire*, Ancient Monuments Laboratory Report 17/94. London

Albarella, U, & Davis, S, 1996 Mammals and birds from Launceston Castle, Cornwall: decline in status and the rise of agriculture, *Circaea* **12 (1)** (1996 for 1994), 1–156

Armitage, P L, 1980 A preliminary description of British cattle from the late twelfth to the early sixteenth century, *The Ark*, **7**, 405–13

Armitage, P, 1982 A system for ageing and sexing the horn cores of cattle from British post medieval sites (with special reference to unimproved British longhorn cattle), in Wilson *et al*, 37–54

Armitage, P L, 1982 Studies on the remains of domestic livestock from Roman, medieval, and early modern London: objectives and methods, in Hall & Kenward, 94–106

Armitage P L, & Clutton-Brock J, 1976 A system for the classification and description of the horn cores of cattle from archaeological sites, *J Archaeol Sci*, **3**, 329–48

Audouin-Rouzeau, F, 1987 Medieval and early modern butchery: evidence from the monastery of La Charité-sur-Loire (Nievre), in *Food and Foodways*, Vol 2, 31–48

Audouin-Rouzeau, F, 1991a La taille du mouton en Europe de l'antiquité aux temps modernes. Fiches d'Osteologie Animale pour l'Archaeologie Series B: Mammiferes no 3. CNRS APDCA: St Juan les Pins

Audouin-Rouzeau, F, 1991b La taille du boeuf domestique en Europe de l'Atlantique aux temps modernes. Fiches d'Osteologie Animale pour l'Archaeologie Series B: Mammiferes no 2. CNRS APDCA: St Juan les Pins

Ayres, K, Locker, A, & Serjeantson, D, 2003 Mammal, bird, and fish remains and oysters. Phases 2f–4a: The Medieval Abbey: Food consumption and production, in A Hardy, A Dodd, & G Keevill (eds), *Aelfric's Abbey: Excavations at Eynsham Abbey, Oxfordshire, 1989–1992*, Thames Valley Landscapes Vol **16**. Oxford: Oxford University School of Archaeology / Oxford Archaeology, 360–406

Bacher, A, 1967 Vergleichend morphologische Untersuchungen and Einzelknochen des postkranialen Skeletts in Mitteleuropa vorkommender Schwane und Gänse. Unpublished thesis. Munich

Baker, J, & Brothwell, D, 1980 *Animal Diseases in Archaeology*. London: Academic Press

Balaam, N D, Levitan, B, & Straker, V, 1987 *Studies in Palaeoeconomy and Environment in South West England*, BAR Brit Ser **181**. Oxford: British Archaeological Reports

Barrett, J H, Nicholson, R A, & Ceron-Carrasco, R, 1999 Archaeo-ichthyological evidence for long-term Socioeconomic Trends in Northern Scotland: 3500 BC to AD 1500, *J Archaeol Sci*, **26**, 353–388

Beveridge, W, 1939 *Prices and Wages in England from the Twelfth to the Nineteenth Century*. London: Longmans

Biddick, K, 1989 *The Other Economy: Pastoral Husbandry on a Medieval Estate*. Berkeley: University of California Press

Biddle, M, 1975 Excavations at Winchester, 1971. Tenth and final interim report: part 1, *Antiq J*, **55**, 96–126.

Biddle, M, 1976 *Winchester in the Early Middle Ages: an Edition and Discussion of the Winton Domesday*. Winchester Studies **1**.

Biddle, M, 1983 The study of Winchester: archaeology and history in a British town. *Proc of the British Academy*, **69**, 93–135

Biddle, M, 1990 Bone, antler, ivory and horn working. 2. The nature and chronology of bone, antler, and horn working in Winchester, in M Biddle (ed), 252–64

Biddle, M (ed), 1990 *Artefacts from Medieval Winchester. II. Object and Economy in Medieval Winchester*. Oxford: Clarendon Press

Biddle, M, & Brown, D, 1990 Writing equipment, in M Biddle (ed), 729–54

Biddle, M, & Smith, D, 1990 The querns, in M Biddle (ed), 881–90

Binford, L R, 1978. *Nunamuit Ethnoarchaeology*. New York: New York Academic Press

Bobis, L., 1987, Le chat au Moyen Age, *Ethnozootechnie*, **No 40** – Le Chat. Paris: Societé d'ethnozootechnie, 39 – 44

Boer, H de, Heuvel, W van den, & Krauwer, M, 1994 Het dierlijk bot. In M. Krauwer & F Snieder (eds.) *Nering en vermaar. De opgravning van een veertiende eenwse markt in Amersfoort*. Utrecht: Matrijs

Boessneck, J, Müller, H-H, & Teichert, M, 1964 Osteologische Unterschiede zwischen Schäf und Ziege, *Kuhn-Archiv*, **78**

Boessneck, J, Driesch, A von den, Meyer-Lemppenau, U, Ohlen, E, & von Wechsler, 1971 Die Tierknochenfunde aus dem Keltischen Oppidum von Manching, *Die Ausgrabungen in Manching*, **6**. Wiesbaden

Bond, J M, & O'Connor, T P, 1999 *Bones from Medieval Deposits at 16–22 Coppergate and Other Sites in York*, The Archaeology of York 15/5. York: Council for British Archaeology

Bourdillon, J, 1978 The animal bone, in J S F Walker, Excavations in Medieval Tenements on the Quilter's Vault site in Southampton, *Proc of the Hampshire Field Club & Archaeol Soc*, **35** (1979), 207–12

Bourdillon, J, 1980a Town life and animal husbandry in the Southampton area, as suggested by the excavated bones, *Proc of the Hampshire Field Club and Archaeol Soc*, **36** (1980), 181–91

Bourdillon, J, 1980b The animal bone of Hamwih – some comparisons, in M Kubasiewicz (ed), *Archaeozoology 1*. Szczecin

Bourdillon, J, 1983 Animals in an urban environment, M Phil thesis, University of Southampton

Bourdillon, J, 1984 *Animal Bones from Middle Saxon Southampton: the Six Dials Variability Study*, Ancient Monuments Laboratory Report, No 4580. London

Bourdillon, J, 1985 *Animal bone from Late Saxon contexts in Southampton*, Ancient Monuments Laboratory Report, No 4926. London

Bourdillon, J, 1988 Countryside and town: the animal resources of Saxon Southampton, in D Hooke (ed), *Anglo Saxon Settlements*. Oxford: Blackwell, 177–95

Bourdillon, J, 1993 Animal bones, in A H Graham and S M Davies (eds), *Excavations in the Town Centre of Trowbridge*, **2**, 134–43

Bourdillon, J, 1998 The faunal remains, in R Poulton (ed), *The Lost Manor of Hextalls, Little Pickle, Bletchingley*. Kingston: Surrey County Archaeological Unit, 139–74

Bourdillon, J, & Coy, J, 1980 The Animal Bones, in P Holdsworth (ed), *Excavations at Melbourne Street, Southampton*, CBA Res Rep 33. London: Council for British Archaeology, 79–121

Brain, C K, 1976 Some principles in the interpretation of bone accumulations associated with man, in G Isaac & E McCown (eds), *Human Origins*. New York, 76–111

Bramwell, D, 1975 The bird bones, in C Platt and R Coleman-Smith (eds), *Excavations in Medieval Southampton 1953–1969. The excavation reports, I*. Leicester: Leicester University Press, 40–1.

Bridbury, A R, 1955 *England and the Salt Trade in the Later Middle Ages*. Oxford: Clarendon Press. Connecticut: Greenwood Press, reprinted 1973.

Brothwell, D, 1981 Disease as an environmental parameter, in Jones & Dimbleby, 231–247

Bull, G, & Payne, S, 1982 Tooth eruption and epiphyseal fusion in pigs and wild boar, in Wilson *et al*, 55–71

Campbell, B M S, Galloway, J A, Keene D, & Murphy, M, 1993 A Medieval capital and its grain supply: agrarian production and distribution in the London region *c* 1300. *Historical Geography Research Series*, **30**. Institute of British Geographers

Carpenter Turner, B, 1992 *A History of Winchester*. Chichester: Phillimore & Co

Clapham, A R, Tutin, T G, and Warburg, E F, 1962. *Flora of the British Isles*. Cambridge University Press

Clason, A T, 1977 Pre- and Protohistoric Sheep in the Netherlands. *Ethnozootechnie*, **No 21**, 87–94

Clutton-Brock, J, Dennis-Bryan, K, Armitage, P L, & Jewell, P A, 1990 Osteology of the Soay Sheep, *Bulletin of the British Museum of Natural History (Zoology)*, **56 1**, 1–91

Colley, S M, Todd, S J P, & Campling, N R, 1988. Three-dimensional computer graphics for archaeological data exploration an example from Saxon Southampton, *J of Archaeol Sci*, **15**, 99–106

Cowles, G, 1979 The bird bones, in J H Williams, *St. Peter's Street, Northampton: Excavations 1973–1976*. Northampton: Northampton Development Corporation, 333–4

Coy, J, 1982 The role of wild fauna in urban economies in Wessex, in Hall & Kenward, 107–16

Coy, J, 1983 Birds as food in prehistoric and historic Wessex, in C Grigson & J Clutton-Brock (eds), *Animals and Archaeology 2: Shell middens, fishes and birds*, BAR Int Ser 183. Oxford, British Archaeological Reports, 181–95

Coy, J, 1984 *Animal bones from Saxon, Medieval and Post Medieval phases (10–18) of Winchester Western Suburbs*, Ancient Monuments Laboratory Report No 4910. London

Coy, J, 1985a Assessing the role of pigs from faunal debris on archaeological settlements, in N Fieller, D Gilbertson, & N Ralph (eds), *Palaeobiological Investigations: Research Design, Methods and Data Analysis*, BAR British Series, Report 266. Oxford: British Archaeological Reports, 55–64

Coy, J, 1985b Fish bones, in Cunliffe & Munby, 256–261

Coy, J, 1989 The provision of fowls and fish for towns, in Serjeantson & Waldron, 25–40

Coy, J, 1995 Animal bones, in Fasham & Keevill, 132–9

Coy, J, 1997 Animal remains, in Hawkes, J W, Cross, J, Fasham, P J, Carruthers, W, 1997 *Excavations on Reading Waterfront Sites 1979–1988*. Salisbury: Wessex Archeology

Coy, J, & Maltby, M, 1987. Archaeozoology in Wessex: vertebrate remains and marine molluscs and their relevance to archaeology, in H Keeley (ed), *Environmental Archaeology: a regional review*, **Vol II**, 204–51

Coy, J, & Maltby, M, 1991 The animal bone analyses on the M3 project – A review, in P J Fasham & R J B Whinney (eds), *Archaeology and the M3*, Hampshire Field Club Archaeol Soc Monogr **7**. Hampshire Field Club, 97–104

Cummins, J G, 1988 *The Hound and the Hawk: the Medieval Art of Hunting*. London: Weidenfeld & Nicholson

Cunliffe, B (ed), 1975 *Excavations at Portchester Castle Volume 1: Roman*, Report of the Research Committee of the Soc of Antiq of London, **XXXII.** London

Cunliffe, B (ed), 1976 *Excavations at Portchester Castle, Vol II: Saxon*, Report of the Research Committee of the Soc of Antiq of London, **XXXIII.** London

Cunliffe, B, & Munby, J (eds), 1985 *Excavations at Portchester Castle: Vol IV: Medieval: The Inner Bailey*. London: Society of Antiquaries/Thames & Hudson

Cutting, C L, 1955 *Fish Saving*. London: Leonard Hill

Darby, H C, 1976 *A New Historical Geography of England before 1600*. Cambridge: Cambridge University Press

Davis, S J M, 1992 *A rapid method for recording information about mammal bones from archaeological sites*, Ancient Monuments Laboratory Report 19/92. London

Davis, S J M, 1991 *Faunal remains from the Late Saxon – Medieval farmstead at Eckweek in Avon, 1988–1989 excavations*, Ancient Monuments Laboratory Report 35/91. London

Dobney, K, Jaques, D, & Irving, B, 1996 *Of Butchers and Breeds: Report on vertebrate remains from various sites in the City of Lincoln*, Lincoln Archaeological Studies 5. Lincoln: City of Lincoln Archaeology Unit

Driesch, A von den, 1976 *A Guide to the Measurement of Animal Bones from Archaeological Sites* (Peabody Museum Bulletin 1). Harvard: Peabody Museum

Driesch, A von den, & Boessneck, J, 1974 Kritische Anmerkungen zür Wideristhohen-Berechnung aus Längermassen vor- und frügeschichtlicher Tierknochen. *Saugetierkundliche Mitteilungen*, **22, 4**, 325–48

Dyer, C, 1988 Changes in diet in the later middle ages: the case of the harvest workers, *Agric History Review*, **36** (1988), 21–37

Dyer, C, 1989a The consumption of freshwater fish in medieval England, in M Aston (ed), *Medieval fish, fisheries and fish ponds in England*. Oxford: British Archaeological Report, 27–38

Dyer, C, 1989b, *Standards of living in the later Middle Ages: Social change in England c 1200–1520*. Cambridge: Cambridge Medieval Textbooks

Eastham, A, 1976 The bird bones, in Cunliffe, 287–96

Eastham, A, 1985 The bird bones, in Cunliffe, 233–9

English Heritage, 1992 *Management of Archaeological Projects*. London

Erbersdobler, K, 1968 *Vergleichend morphologische Untersuchungen an Einzelknochen des postcranialen Skeletts in Mitteleuropa vorkommender mittelgrosser Huhnervogel*. Unpublished thesis. Munich.

Evans-Pritchard, E E, 1940 *The Nuer*. Oxford: Clarendon Press

Ewbank, J M, Phillipson, D W, & Whitehouse, R D, 1964 Sheep in the Iron Age: a method of study. *Proc Prehist Soc* **17**, 423–6

Fasham, P J, & Keevill, G (eds), 1995 *Brighton Hill South (Hatch Warren): an Iron Age farmstead and deserted medieval village in Hampshire*. Salisbury: Wessex Archaeology

Flandrin, J, 1990 Fats in French cooking from the 14th to the 18th centuries, in G Ziant (ed), *Lipids and Health*. Amsterdam: Elsevier

Gerrard, C M, 1987 A regional approach to faunal data, in Balaam, Levitan, & Straker (eds), 81–88

Getty, R, 1975 *Sisson & Grossman's The Anatomy of the Domestic Animals*. London: Saunders

Gidney, L J, 1991 *Leicester, The Shires, 1988 excavations: The animal bones from the Medieval deposits at Little Lane (Interim report)*, Ancient Monuments Laboratory Report **57/91.** London

Gomersall, M, & Whinney, R, 2007 The Hospital of St John the Baptist, Winchester, *Hampshire Studies* **62**, 83–108

Grant, A, 1975 Appendix B: the use of toothwear as a guide to the age of domestic animals, in Cunliffe (ed), 437–50

Grant, A, 1976 The animal bones, in Cunliffe (ed), 262–87

Grant, A, 1982 The use of tooth wear as a guide to the age of domestic ungulates, in Wilson *et al*, 91–108

Grant, A., 1985 The animal bones, in Cunliffe & Munby (eds), 244–55

Grant, R, 1991 *The Royal Forests of England*. Stroud: Sutton Publishing

Green, F J, 1979a *Medieval Plant Remains: Methods and Results of Archaeobotanical Analysis from Excavation in Southern England, with Especial Reference to Winchester and Urban Settlements of the 10th–15th Centuries*, M Phil Thesis. University of Southampton

Green, F J, 1979b The plant remains, in C M Heighwey, A P Garrod, & A G Vince (eds), Excavations at 1 Westgate Street, Gloucester, *Medieval Archaeology* **23**, 86–190

Green, F J, 1982 Problems of interpreting differentially preserved plant remains from excavations of medieval urban sites, in Hall & Kenward (eds), 40–6

Green, F J, 1984 The archaeological and documentary evidence for plants from the medieval period in England, in Zeist & Casparie (eds), 99–114

Green, F J, 1991 Landscape archaeology in Hampshire: The Saxon plant remains, in J M Renfrew (ed), *New Light on Early Farming*, Proceedings of the 7th Symposium of the International Work Group for Palaeoethnobotany 1986, 363–77

Green, F J, 1994 Cereals and plant foods: a reassessment of the Saxon economic evidence from Wessex, in Rackham (ed), 83–8

Green, F J, 1996 Mesolithic or later houses at Bowmans Farm, Romsey Extra, Hampshire, England, in T Darvill & J Thomas (eds), *Neolithic Houses in Northwest Europe and Beyond*, Oxbow Monograph **57**. Oxford: Oxbow, 113–22

Green, F J, & Lockyear, K, 1992 Plant remains from buried soils, Romsey, Hants, *Review of Palaeoethnobotany and Palynology* **73**, 57–70

Green, F J, & Lockyear, K, 1994 Seeds, sherds and samples: site formation processes at the Waitrose

Site, Romsey, in R Luff & P Rowley-Conwy (eds), *Whither Environmental Archaeology ?* Oxbow Monograph **38**. Oxford: Oxbow, 91–104

Greenfield, H J, 1988 Bone consumption by pigs in a contemporary Serbian village: implications for the interpretation of prehistoric faunal assemblages, *J of Field Arch* **15**, 473–9

Gomersall, M, & Scobie, G, in prep *The Saxon and Medieval Suburbs of Winchester. Excavations 1971–1986*

Habermehl, K-H, 1975 *Die Alterbeststimmung bei Haus- und Labortieren.* Hamburg: Paul Parey

Hall, A R, & Kenward, H, (eds) 1982 *Environmental Archaeology in the Urban Context.* CBA Res Rep **3**. London: Council for British Archaeology

Harcourt, R, 1974. The dog in prehistoric and early historic Britain, *J Archaeol Sci* **1**, 151–76

Harting, J E, 1864 *The Ornithology of Shakespeare.* Old Woking: Gresham Books, reprinted 1978

Harvey, B, 1993 *Living and Dying in England 1100–1540: the Monastic Experience.* Oxford: Clarendon Press

Hatting, T, 1975 The influence of castration on sheep horns, in A T Clason (ed), *Archaeozoological Studies.* North Holland, 345–51

Helbaek, H, 1971 The origin and migration of rye, *Secale Cereale* L; a palaeoethnobotanical study, in P H Davis, P C Harper, & I C Hedge (eds), *Plant Life of South-West Asia.* Edinburgh, Botanical Society of Edinburgh

Higham, C, & Message, M, 1969 An assessment of a prehistoric technique of bovine husbandry, in D Brothwell & E S Higgs (eds), *Science in Archaeology.* London: Thames & Hudson, 315–30

Hillman, G, 1984 Interpretation of archaeological plant remains: The application of ethnographic models from Turkey, in Zeist & Casparie (eds), 1- 41

Hinton, D A, Keene, S, & Qualmann, K, 1981 'The Winchester Reliquary', *Medieval Archaeology* **25**, 45–77

Hodgson, G W I, (nd) Report on the animal remains excavated during 1975–76 from the mediaeval levels at the High Street Site, Perth. Duncan of Jordanstone College of Art

Hoffman, R, 1987 Introduction. An Annotated Bibliography of the Pike *Esox lucius*: the proto-history of pike in western culture, in E J Crossman & J M Casselman (eds), *The Pike.* Toronto: Royal Ontario Museum, vii-xvii

Holmes, J M, 1981 Report on the animal bones from the resonance chambers of the Whitefriars Church, Coventry, *Post Medieval Archaeology* **15**, 126–53

James, T B, 1997 *Winchester.* London: English Heritage

Johansson, F, & Hüster, H, 1987 *Untersuchungen an Skelettresten von Katzen aus Haithabu (Ausgrabung 1966–1969),* Berichte über die Ausgrabungen in Haithabu, **24**. Neumunster: Wachholz

Jones, A G, 1976 The fish bones, in G Black (ed), Excavations in the sub-vault of the Misericorde of Westminster Abbey, February to May, 1975, *Trans of the London & Middlesex Arch Soc* **27** (1976), 170–6

Jones, G E M, 1984 Interpretation of archaeological plant remains: Ethnographic models from Greece, in Zeist & Casparie (eds), 43–61

Jones, G, & Halstead, P, 1995 Maslins, mixtures and monocrops: on the interpretation of archaoebotanical crops samples of heterogonous composition, *J Archaeol Sci* **22**,103–14

Jones, M, 1978 The plant remains, in M Parrington (ed), *The Excavation of an Iron Age Settlement, Bronze Age Ring Ditch and Roman Features at Ashville Trading Estate, Abingdon (Oxfordshire) 1974–78.* Oxford Arch Unit Report 1, CBA Res Rep **28**. London: Council for British Archaeology

Jones, M, & Dimbleby, G (eds), 1981 *The Environment of Man: the Iron Age to the Anglo-Saxon period*, BAR Brit Ser **87**. Oxford: British Archaeological Reports

Jones, R T, Wall, S M, Locker, A M, Coy, J, & Maltby, M, 1981 *Computer Based Osteometry: Data Capture User Manual*, Ancient Monuments Laboratory Report **3342**. London: English Heritage

Keene, D, 1985 *Survey of Medieval Winchester*, Winchester Studies Vol 2. Oxford: Oxford University Press

Laird, M, 1986 *English Misericords.* London, John Murray

Langdon, J, 1986 *Horses, Oxen and Technological Innovation.* Cambridge: Cambridge University Press.

Lange, E, 1975, The development of agriculture during the first millennium AD, *Geologiska Foreningens Stockholm Forhandlingak* **97**, 115–24

Levine, M, 1982 The use of crown height measurements and eruption-wear sequences to age horse teeth, in Wilson *et al*, 223–50

Levitan, B, 1982 The faunal remains, in P Leach (ed), *Ilchester Volume 1. Excavations 1974–1975*, Western Archaeological Trust, 269–85

Locker, A., forthcoming The fish bones, in *The Abbey of St Mary Graces; excavations at the Royal Mint 1984– 88.* London: Museum of London

Lucas, A T, 1982 *Cattle in Ancient and Medieval Irish Society.* Dublin: reprinted from O' Connell School Union Record 1937–1958

MacGregor, A, 1985 *Bone, Antler, Ivory & Horn.* London: Croom Helm

Maltby, M, 1979 *Faunal Studies on Urban Sites: The Animal Bones from Exeter 1971–1975.* Huddersfield: Charlesworth

Maltby, M, 1981 Iron Age, Romano-British and Anglo-Saxon animal husbandry – a review of the faunal evidence, in Jones & Dimbleby (eds), 155–204

Maltby, J M, 1985 Patterns in faunal assemblage variability, in G Barker & C Gamble (eds), *Beyond Domestication in Prehistoric Europe.* London: Academic Press, 33–74

Maltby, M, 1989 Urban-rural variations in the butchering of cattle in Romano-British Hampshire, in Serjeantson & Waldron (eds), 75–106

Maltby, M, 1993 Animal bones, in P J Woodward, S M Davies, & A H Graham (eds), *Excavations at the Old Methodist Chapel and Greyhound Yard, Dorchester.* Dorchester: Dorset Natural History & Archaeological Society, 315–40

Maltby, M, (nd) *The animal bones from the later Roman phases from Winchester northern suburbs: 1: The unsieved samples from Victoria Road trenches X-XVI*, Ancient Monuments Laboratory Report, **125/87**. London: English Heritage

Maltby, M, in press *Feeding a Roman Town. Environmental evidence from excavations in Winchester, 1972–1985.* Winchester Museums

Maltby, M, & Bourdillon, J, (nd) Assessment of the animal bones from the Winchester suburbs. Unpublished archive report, Winchester Museums, 1989

Markham, G, 1986 *The English Housewife,* in M R Best (ed). Kingston: McGill-Queen's University Press

McCormick, F, 1988 The domesticated cat in Early Christian and Medieval Ireland, in G Mac Niocaill & P F Wallace (eds), *Keimelia: Studies in Medieval Archaeology and History in memory of Tom Delaney.* Galway: Galway University Press, 218–28

Matolcsi, J, 1970 Historische Erforschung der Korpergrosse des Rindes aufgrund von ungarischen Knochenmaterial, *Zeitschrift für Tierzuchtung und Zuchtungsbiologie* **87**, 89–137

Montanari, M, 1994 *The Culture of Food.* Oxford: Blackwell

Murphy P L, & Wiltshire P E J, 1994 A proposed scheme for evaluating plant macrofossil preservation in some archaeological deposits, *Circaea* **11,1**, 1–6

Noddle, B, 1975. The animal bones, in C Platt & R Coleman-Smith (eds) *Excavations in Medieval Southampton 1953–1969, Vol 1. The excavation reports.* Leicester, Leicester University Press, 332–41

Noddle, B, 1977 Mammal bone, in H Clarke & A Carter (eds), *Excavations in Kings Lynn 1963–70.* Society for Medieval Archaeology, 378–98

Noddle, B, 1980. Identification and interpretation of the mammal bones, in P Wade-Martins (ed) *North Elmham Park Vol II,* East Anglian Archaeology **9**, 377–409

O'Connor, T P, 1982 *Animal Bones from Flaxengate, Lincoln c 870–1500,* The Archaeology of Lincoln **18, 1**. London: Council for British Archaeology / Lincoln Archaeological Trust

O'Connor, T, 1984 *Selected Groups of Bones from Skeldergate and Walmgate,* Archaeology of York **15/1**. London: Council for British Archaeology for York Archaeological Trust

O'Connor, T, 1989 What shall we have for dinner? Food remains from urban sites, in Serjeantson & Waldron 1989, 13–24

O'Connor, T P, 1991. *Bones from 46–54 Fishergate,* Archaeology of York **15/4**. London: Council for British Archaeology for York Archaeological Trust

O'Connor, T P, 1992 Provisioning urban communities: a topic in search of a model, *Anthropzoologica* **16**, 101–06

Oschinsky, D (ed), 1971 *Walter of Henley.* Oxford: Clarendon Press

Payne, S, 1973 Kill-off patterns in sheep and goats: the mandibles from Asvan Kale, *Anatolian Studies* **23**, 281–303

Payne, S, 1985 Morphological distinctions between the mandibular teeth of young sheep, *Ovis,* and goats, *Capra, J of Archaeol Sci* **12**, 139–47

Penn, J, Field, D, & Serjeantson, D, 1984 Evidence of Neolithic occupation in Kingston: excavations at Eden Walk, 1965: with notes on medieval animal bone and ground axes from Kingston, *Surrey Archaeological Collections* **75**, 207 – 24

Phoebus, Gaston, 1984 *The Hunting Book* (text by Gabriel Bise, trans J P Tallon). Geneva: Liber

Polloth, K, 1959 *Die Schäfe und Ziegen des Latene-Oppidums Manching.* Studien an vor- und fruhgeschichtlichen Tierresten Bayerns **VI**. University of Munich

Postan, M M, 1972 *The Medieval Economy and Society. An Economic History of Britain 1100 – 1500.* London: Weidenfeld & Nicholson

Prummel, W, & Frisch, H-J, 1986 A guide for the distinction of species, sex and body side in bones of sheep and goat, *J of Archaeol Sci* **13**, 567–77

Qualmann, K E, Rees, H, Scobie, G D, and Whinney, R, 2004 *Oram's Arbour. The Iron Age enclosure at Winchester. Volume 1: Investigations 1950–1999.* Winchester: Winchester Museums Service

Rackham, J, 1994 Economy and environment in Saxon London, in Rackham 1994, 126–136

Rackham, J (ed.), 1994 *Economy and environment in Anglo-Saxon England,* CBA Res Rep 89. York: Council for British Archaeology

Rees, H, Crummy, N, Ottaway, P, and Dunn, G, 2008 *Artefacts and Society in Roman and Medieval Winchester. Small finds from the suburbs and defences, 1971–1986.* Winchester: Winchester Museums

Robertson, J C, 1989 Counting London's horn cores: sampling what? *Post-med Arch*, **23** (1989), 1–10

Rossiaud, J, 1990 The city-dweller and life in cities and towns, in J Le Goff (ed), *The Medieval World* (trans L G Cochrane). London: Collins & Brown, 139–80

Sadler, P, 1990 Faunal Remains, in J R Fairbrother (ed), *Faccombe Netherton: Excavation of a Saxon and Medieval Manorial Complex* II, British Museum Occasional Paper no 74, 462–508

Serjeantson, D, 1988 Archaeological evidence for the antiquity of seabird fowling in the Western and Northern Isles of Scotland, *ArchaeoZoologia* **II (1.2)**, 209–24

Serjeantson, D, 1989a Introduction, in Serjeantson & Waldron, 1–12

Serjeantson, D, 1989b Animal remains and the tanning trade, in Serjeantson & Waldron, 129–146

Serjeantson, D, 1991 Diet at St Albans Abbey, *The Journal of the International Wine & Food Society,* 16, 46–50

Serjeantson, D, 1996 The animal bones, in *Runnymede Bridge Research Excavations, Volume 2: Refuse and Disposal at Area 16 East, Runnymede,* in S Needham & T Spence (eds). London: British Museum Press, 2, 194–223

Serjeantson, D, 2000 Good to eat *and* good to think with: classifying animals from complex sites, in P Rowley-Conwy (ed), *Animal Bones, Human Societies.* Oxford: Oxbow, 179–89

Serjeantson, D, 2005 Science is Measurement. ABMAP, a database of domestic animal bone measurements, *Environ Archaeol* **10**(1).

Serjeantson, D, & Waldron, T, (eds), 1989. *Diet and Crafts in Towns: the Evidence of Animal Remains from*

the Roman to the Post Medieval Periods, BAR Brit Ser
199. Oxford: British Archaeological Reports

Serjeantson, D, Waldron, T, & Bracegirdle, M, 1992
Medieval horses from Kingston-upon-Thames,
London Archaeologist, **7 (1)**, 9–13

Serjeantson, D, Waldron, T, & McCracken, S, 1986 Veal
and calfskin in eighteenth century Kingston?,
London Archaeologist **5**, 9, 227–32

Serjeantson, D, and Woolgar, C M, 2006 Chapter 8:
Fish consumption in medieval England, in C M
Woolgar, D Serjeantson & T Waldron (eds), *Food in
Medieval England: Diet and nutrition,* Oxford Studies
in History and Archaeology. Oxford: Oxford Uni-
versity Press

Smith, P L, 1994 *The early Norman animal bone from Carisbrooke Castle, the Isle of Wight,* Ancient Monuments
Laboratory Report. London: English Heritage

Smith, P L, 1995 *The fish remains from Launceston Castle,
Cornwall.* Ancient Monuments Laboratory Report
56/95. London: English Heritage

Spahn, N, 1986 *Untersuchungen an Skelettresten von
Hunden und Katzen aus dem mittelalterlichen
Schleswig,* Ausgrabung Schild 1971–1975, 5

Sykes, N, 2004 The introduction of fallow deer to
Britain: a zooarchaeological perspective, *Environmental Archaeology* 9, 75–83

Teichert, M, 1975 Osteometric studies on the cal-
culation of the withers height of sheep, in A T
Clason (ed), *Archaeozoological Studies.* Amsterdam:
Elsevier, 51–69

Thomas, K, 1983 *Man and the Natural World.* London:
Allen Lane

Tubbs, C R, 1986 *The New Forest.* London

Usher, G, 1974 *A Dictionary of Plants Used by Man.*
London: Constable

Veale, E M, 1966 *The English Fur Trade in the Later Middle
Ages.* Oxford: Clarendon Press

Victoria County History, 1912 Hampshire, Volume 1.
London

Victoria County History, 1912 Hampshire, Volume 5.
London

Wenham, L P, 1964 Hornpot Lane and the horners of
York, *Annual Report of the Yorkshire Philosophical
Society*, 25–36

West, B, 1982 Spur development: recognising caponised
fowl in archaeological material, in Wilson *et al*,
255–61

West, B, 1985 Chicken legs revisited, *Circaea* **3, 1**,
11–14

Wheeler, A, & Jones, A K G, 1989 *Fishes,* Cambridge
Manuals in Archaeology. Cambridge: Cambridge
University Press

Wilkinson, M, 1979 The fish remains, in Maltby, 74–81

Williams, D, 1977 The plant macrofossil contents of
medieval pits at Sewer Lane, Hull, in P Armstrong
(ed), *Excavations in Sewer Lane, Hull, 1974,* East
Riding Archaeologist 3, Report Series No 1

Wilson, B, Grigson, C, & Payne, S, 1982 *Ageing and
Sexing Animal Bones from Archaeological Sites,*
BAR Brit Ser **109**. Oxford: British Archaeological
Reports

Woelfle, E, 1967 Vergleichend morphologische Untersuchungen an Einzelknochen des postkranialen
Skeletts in Mitteleuropa verkommender Enten,
Halbgänse, und Sager. Munich: Unpublished
thesis

Woolgar, C, 1995 Diet and consumption in gentry and
noble households: a case study from around the
Wash, in R E Archer and S Walker (eds), *Rulers and
Ruled in Late Medieval England. Essays presented to
Gerald Harriss.* London: Hambledon Press, 17–31

Woolgar, C, 1999 *The Great Household in Late Medieval
England.* New Haven: Yale University Press

Woolgar, C M, 2000 'Take this penance now, and
afterwards the fare will improve': Seafood and
late medieval diet, in D J Starkey, C Reid, and N
Ashcroft (eds), *England's Sea Fisheries: the commercial sea fisheries of England and Wales since 1300.*
London: Chatham, 36–44

Zant, J M, 1993 *The Brooks, Winchester, 1987–88. The
Roman structural remains,* Winchester Museums
Service Archaeology Report **2**. Winchester: Win-
chester Museums

Zeist, W van, & Casparie, W A, 1984 *Plants and Ancient
Man, Proceedings of the sixth symposium of the Inter-
national Work Group for Palaeoethnobotany, 1983.*
Rotterdam: Balkema

Index *by Sue Vaughan*

Page numbers in *italics* denote illustrations. Colour plates between pages 76 and 77 are indicated by *f76*. All street names and locations are in Winchester unless specified otherwise.